Elementary Microbiology

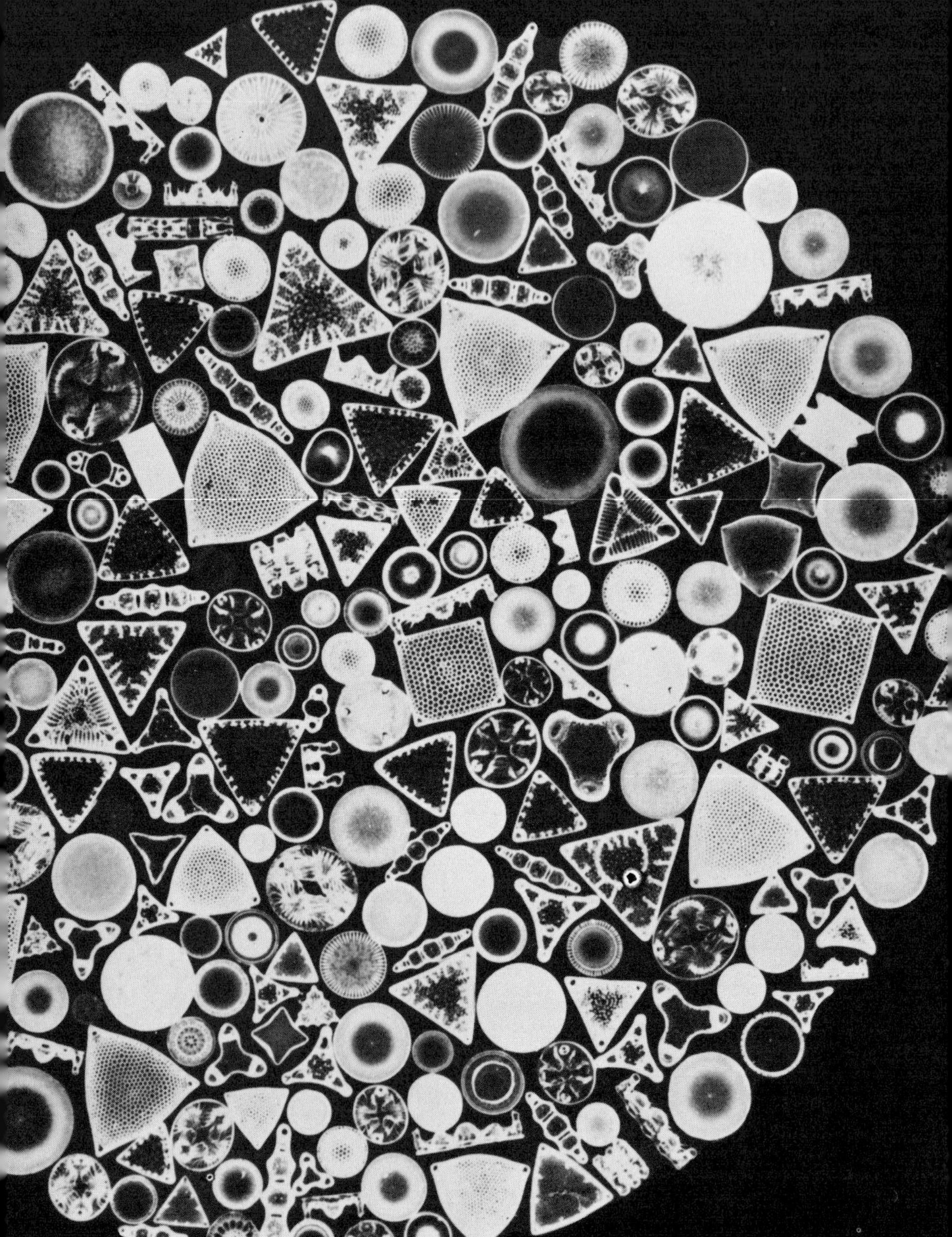

ELEMENTARY MICROBIOLOGY

Orville Wyss

Professor of Microbiology, University of Texas

O. B. Williams

Late Professor of Microbiology, University of Texas

Earl W. Gardner, Jr.

Associate Professor of Biology, Texas Christian University

John Wiley and Sons, Inc.

New York and London

Library of Congress Catalog Card Number: 63-12293
Printed in the United States of America

Preface

This book developed out of an association with the late Dr. O. B. Williams, a scientist who was devoted to students and teaching. Our objective was to present a textbook for a course given for nonmajors in microbiology. This course has a threefold purpose.

(1) We present a selected portion of the subject matter to give such students a view of the scope of the science and the procedures employed to obtain information in this field. Our experience has taught us that this does not mean each subdivision of microbiology must be accorded equal treatment to obtain balance; rather, we have given our students a clearer picture of our science by purposely dealing with certain subjects in depth, which, of course, necessitates dealing with other subjects in a more cursory manner. The selection is probably not important as long as the student is aware of the approach.

(2) From this first contact with microbiology, we expect to interest good students who have, for the first time, an exposure to the tremendous appeal of our science. This might be a delayed reaction. Some of our best graduate majors have been students who, after receiving a Bachelor of Arts degree with emphasis in other sciences or in mathematics, enrolled for graduate work in microbiology because of their experience in the elementary microbiology course.

(3) For students who change to a microbiology major after taking this course, the presentation is such that the apt students can, with additional reading and study, proceed successfully in the advanced courses of microbiology.

Methods of testing have not been available to measure the relative effectiveness of this book. We offer no special defense for our emphasis or our approach other than that we have used this material in a mimeographed form, and we were pleased with the results. It has been rewritten and illustrated and is presented not as a compendium of microbiology, but as a text for an elementary course to be used in conjunction with the traditional lecture, laboratory, and library reading assignments.

April 1963

ORVILLE WYSS
EARL W. GARDNER

Pronunciation Guide to Names of Frequently Mentioned Microbes

Actinomyces bovis	Ăk tĭ nō̇ mī′ sēz bō′ vĭs
Azotobacter vinelandii	Ȧ zō tō̇ băk′ tẽ r vĭn lăn′ dē ē
Bacillus anthracis	Bȧ sĭl′ ŭs an thrā′ sĭs
Clostridium botulinum	Klŏs trĭd′ ĭ ŭm bŏt ū̇ lī′ nŭm
Diplococcus pneumoniae	Dĭp lō kŏk′ ŭs nū mō′ nĭ ē
Escherichia coli	Ĕsh ẽr ēk′ ĭ ȧ kō′ lī
Fungi imperfecti	Fŭn′ jī ĭm pẽr fĕk′ tī
Lactobacillus acidophilus	Lăk tō bȧ sĭl′ ŭs ăs ĭ dŏf′ ĭ lŭs
Mycobacterium tuberculosis	Mī′ kō băk tē′ rĭ ŭm tū bûr′ kū lō′ sĭs
Paramecium	Păr ȧ mē sĭ ŭm
Penicillium chrysogenum	Pĕn ĭ sĭl′ ĭ ŭm krīs o jĕn′ ŭm
Salmonella typhosa	Săl mō nĕl′ ȧ tī fōs′ ȧ
Staphylococcus aureus	Stăf′ ĭ lō kŏk′ ŭs ô′ rē ŭs
Streptococcus pyogenes	Strĕp′ tō kŏk′ ŭs pī ŏj′ ĕn ēz
Treponema pallidum	Trĕp ō̇ nē′ mȧ păl′ ĭ dŭm
Vibrio comma	Vĭb′ rĭ ō̇ kŏm′ ȧ

Contents

1

The Nature and Scope of Microbiology

The science of microbiology studies those plant and animal forms not visible to the naked eye. These forms, called microorganisms or microbes, include viruses, rickettsiae, bacteria, yeasts, molds, algae, and protozoa. The term **bacteriology** is often used as a synonym for **microbiology** because the laboratory tools and techniques as well as the theoretical approaches in the study of the **bacteria** have been useful in studying other microbes.

In the strict sense bacteriology is a subdivision of microbiology (Fig. 1.1). Other subdivisions include **mycology,** the study of yeasts and molds; **virology,** the study of viruses and rickettsiae; and **immunology,** the study of those chemical modifications in the blood and tissues which are involved in immunity to disease. Often included are **fermentations,** which concern the chemical reactions brought about by microbes yielding such useful products as beer, vinegar, and antibiotics. This diverse subject matter is limited and unified by the use of certain basic procedures for securing information which were originally devised by bacteriologists. With the exception of certain protozoa, the study of microscopic forms of the animal kingdom is usually excluded from microbiology since laboratory facilities and the background training of the scientist in that field are generally that of a specialist in animal biology (zoology). Similarly much of the study of algae—and even a part

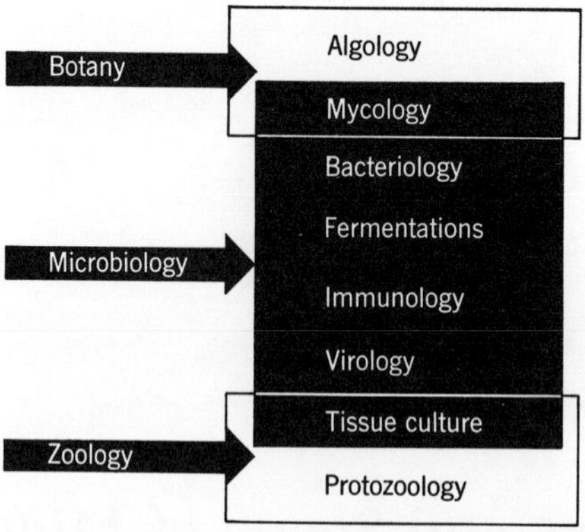

Fig. 1.1. Microbiology includes those disciplines where the methods for getting new information are similar. The tools of the microbiology laboratory have been borrowed by zoologists and botanists for some of their problems, and biological science departments are often organized as indicated.

of that field of knowledge dealing with molds—requires an educational background in botany. But in recent years, botanists and zoologists dealing with the problems of microorganisms have found it often more convenient to group their studies under a single designation, microbiology.

The nonscientist tends to think of microbiologists as men bending over microscopes, scanning glass slides for germs. But the nature and scope of the subject can be appreciated by considering what microbiologists actually do for a living.

Medicine. Many microbiologists are employed in jobs that are allied to the practice of medicine; technologists are employed in hospitals, in laboratories, and in doctors' offices. Assisting in diagnosis of infectious disease is among their more demanding activities. In modern medicine many ailments of which people complain are easily recognizable by clinical symptoms. Situations do occur, however, in which the physician is unable to determine the nature of the ailment. In such instances it may be necessary for the microbiologist to aid the physician by carrying out certain tests. These may involve relatively easy procedures, or they may be difficult and time-consuming. In the diagnosis of gonorrhea, pus from the inflamed area of the genitals is smeared on a glass slide and stained by a special dye. Microscopic examination usually reveals whether the inflammation is a result of the activities of the bacteria causing gonorrhea or the presence of some other agent. Similarly, microscopic examination of smears, which are made from lesions of the skin, from the lungs, from intestinal discharges, from the throat, or from the ear canals may produce sufficient information for the physician to make the necessary diagnosis and institute proper treatment.

In some situations the organism causing the difficulty cannot be identified by microscopic observation. In such cases, the microbiologist often attempts to grow the organism from the diseased tissue. The physician can usually diagnose whooping cough by observing the behavior of the patient, but occasionally symptoms appear which are not characteristic of the disease, and the physician requires laboratory aid. Since the whooping cough microbe looks like thousands of other organisms when observed under the microscope, it is necessary to grow the organism which is secured from the patient. The patient is asked to cough against the surface of a jelly, made according to a special nutrient formula. The culture is then placed in an incubator overnight. If the whooping cough organism is present, characteristic masses of cells will develop which the bacteriologist can recognize as this particular organism and, following confirmatory tests of it, he can advise the physician accordingly (Fig. 1.2).

The blood stream of a healthy individual is ordinarily free from any living microorganisms which would grow in the test tubes of the microbiologist. Therefore, when a patient exhibits symptoms which are not typical of a disease easily identified by the physician, the bacteriologist may be asked to place blood, freshly drawn from the patient, in a test tube containing the proper food material for growing microorganisms. After a waiting period of about 24 hours to permit growth of any bacteria that might be present, the test tube contents are observed under the microscope. The presence of bacteria in the blood stream indicates the source of the patient's disorder. The type of microorganism present may easily lead to identification of the disease and efficacious treatment.

Some organisms, such as the viruses, do not grow in the test tubes of the bacteriologist. In such cases laboratory animals are inoculated with materials taken from the patient. By inoculating mice, rats, guinea pigs, hamsters, or rabbits, it is often possible to obtain a clear-cut diagnosis for a disease, such as an atypical encephalitis. But, by and large, the great majority of diseases can be determined by the well-trained and practiced physician from his bedside observation. The laboratory work of the bacteriologist is designed to aid in cases where the symptoms are unusual and beyond the experience of the physician, or when he wishes to confirm his judgment by bringing in additional evidence from laboratory work.

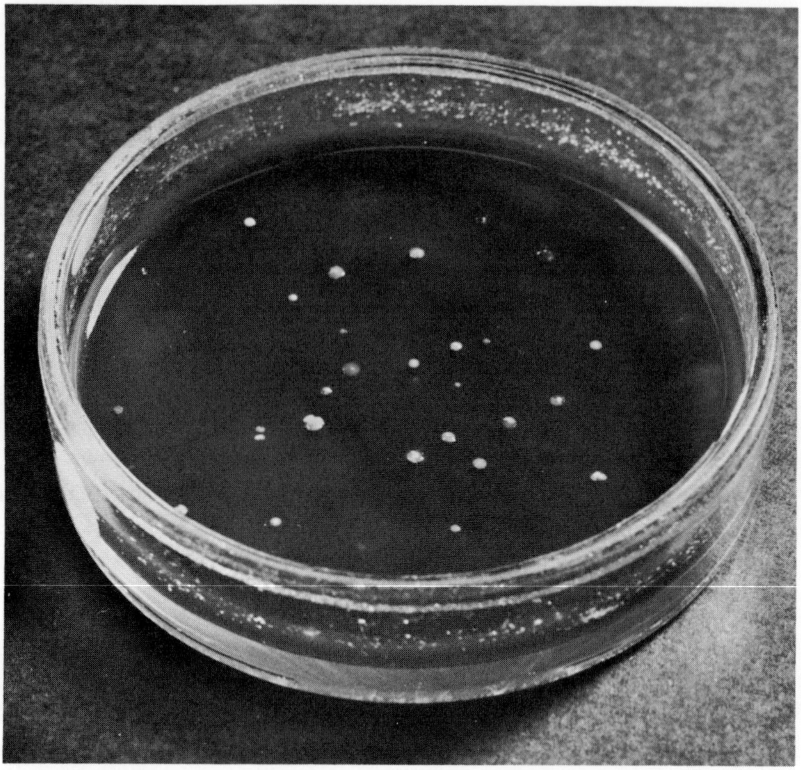

Fig. 1.2. This petri plate has been exposed to a child's cough. The bacteria expelled by the cough impinged on the blood agar and grew during incubation at 37°C to form the distinctive piles or colonies. The pearly, glistening colonies are those of the whooping cough organism, which the skilled microbiologist can distinguish from those of the other harmless bacteria.

The study of blood serum from the patient often aids in diagnosis of disease. Relatively soon after the onset of a disease the patient produces in his blood serum chemical substances called antibodies, which are characteristic of the disease and which can be detected and measured in the microbiological laboratory. For example, a blood test is required for a marriage license, for employment as a food handler, upon application for life insurance, or upon entrance into the military service of the United States. The blood test involves examination for the chemical substances which result from infection with syphilis. In this way an infection may be detected in a person who is unaware of the illness, and treatment can be instituted for the protection of the person and those he contacts.

The microbiologist's work does not end with assisting in diagnosis; he may be asked to study the nature of the organisms and the probable response of the patient's disorder to one or another drug. The physician then may be advised, for example, that the organism found in the bloodstream of the patient is not sensitive to penicillin, but that streptomycin worked remarkably well in bringing about destruction of the organism in the test tube, and thus will likely be useful to the patient. Medical microbiologists also follow the progress of the patient during treatment: for example, in a tuberculosis sanatorium it is necessary to determine when patients cease to cough up the tubercle bacillus in their sputum in order that patients may not be released from treatment too early.

Public Health. The public health microbiologist who works for state and nationally supported agencies on public health and sanitation problems is closely allied to the medical microbiologist. In the United States the public health is served at several levels. At the federal level are those workers at the National Institutes of Health and regional laboratories who carry out research on unsolved problems of microbiology. All the states have health departments with a centrally located laboratory and many branch laboratories for studying public health problems, encompassing such widespread activities as production of vaccines, the investigation of unusual outbreaks or epidemics of disease, supervision of health tests for food handlers, recommendations for the best practices in the handling of sewage or water and food, and advisory service to the state legislature on laws for the protection of the health of the citizen and his livestock. The public health microbiologist also supervises private medical laboratories, gathers statistics on diseases occurring within the state, and publishes these statistics together with bulletins on public health problems. County health officers work on local problems and may supervise institutions for indigent patients.

Industry. A large number of microbiologists find employment in industry. At the present time one of the major microbiological activities is the manufacture of antibiotic substances. These are chemicals which are produced by certain microorganisms and are used in the treatment of diseases caused by other microorganisms. More than half of the dollar volume of the drugs sold in drugstores are antibiotics which, prior to 1940, were unknown to the druggist. The aggregate selling price of these drugs approaches one billion dollars per year, constituting the volume of a major industry. The chemical industry produces antibiotics from huge tanks in which these microorganisms are grown (Fig. 1.3). The microbiologist supervises the tanks and

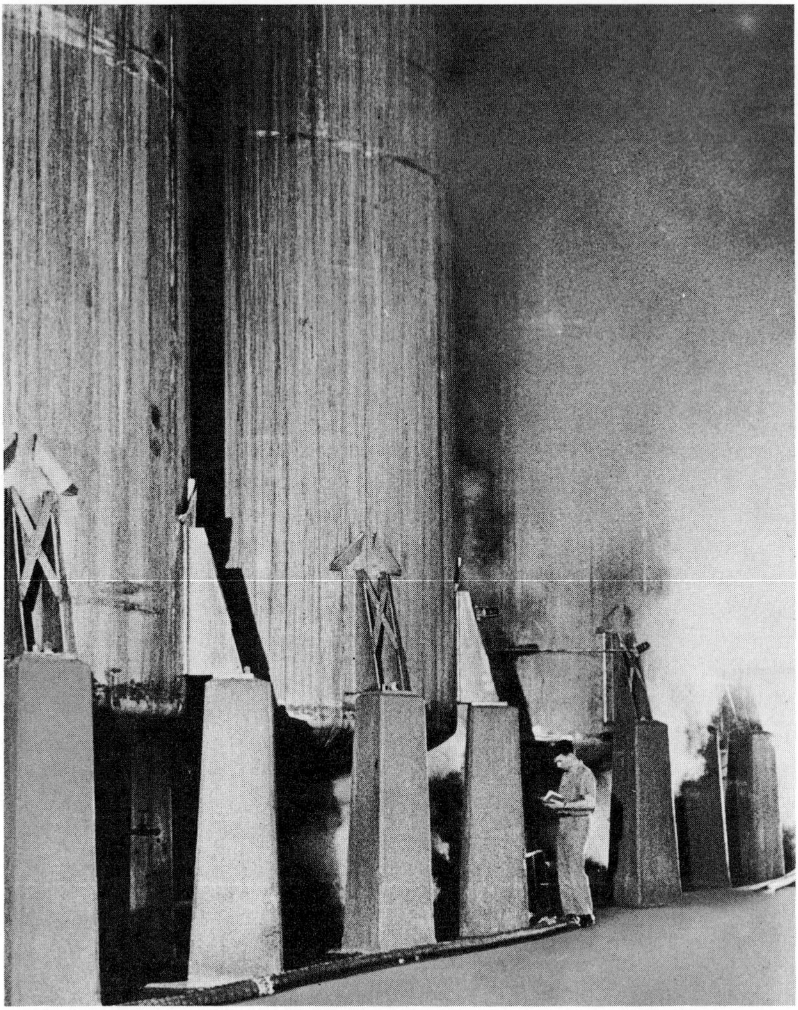

Fig. 1.3. Production Fermentors. These huge fermentation tanks, filled with sterile nutrient medium, are inoculated with the high-yielding culture grown in seed tanks. Sterile air is forced through the inoculated mash, and temperature and pH are controlled throughout the fermentation. After the fermentation is completed, the contents of the tanks are filtered and processed further before a final product is obtained. *Photo courtesy Chas. Pfizer & Co.*

fermentation, maintains and preserves the stock cultures, builds up seed inoculum for the large tanks from his test tube cultures, continually tests his strains, and selects those that are the highest and most efficient producers of the materials which he desires (Fig. 1.4). He must

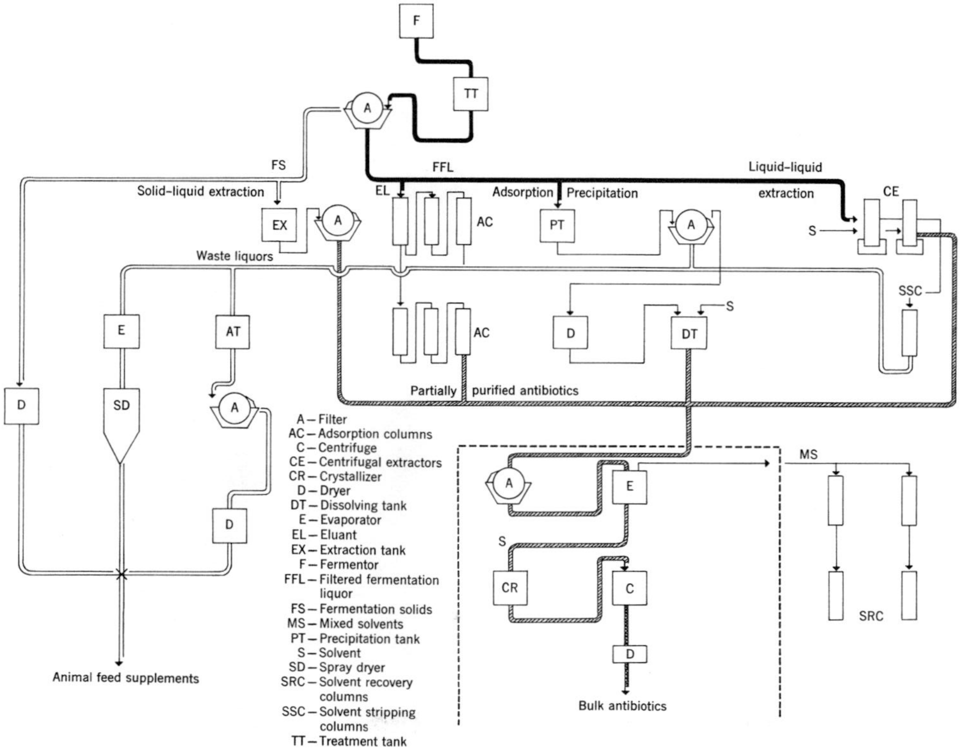

Fig. 1.4. Antibiotic Process. The flow diagram shows the antibiotic recovery process used by Chas. Pfizer and Co. All fermentation-produced antibiotics follow the general recovery scheme shown here. *Diagram courtesy Chas. Pfizer & Co.*

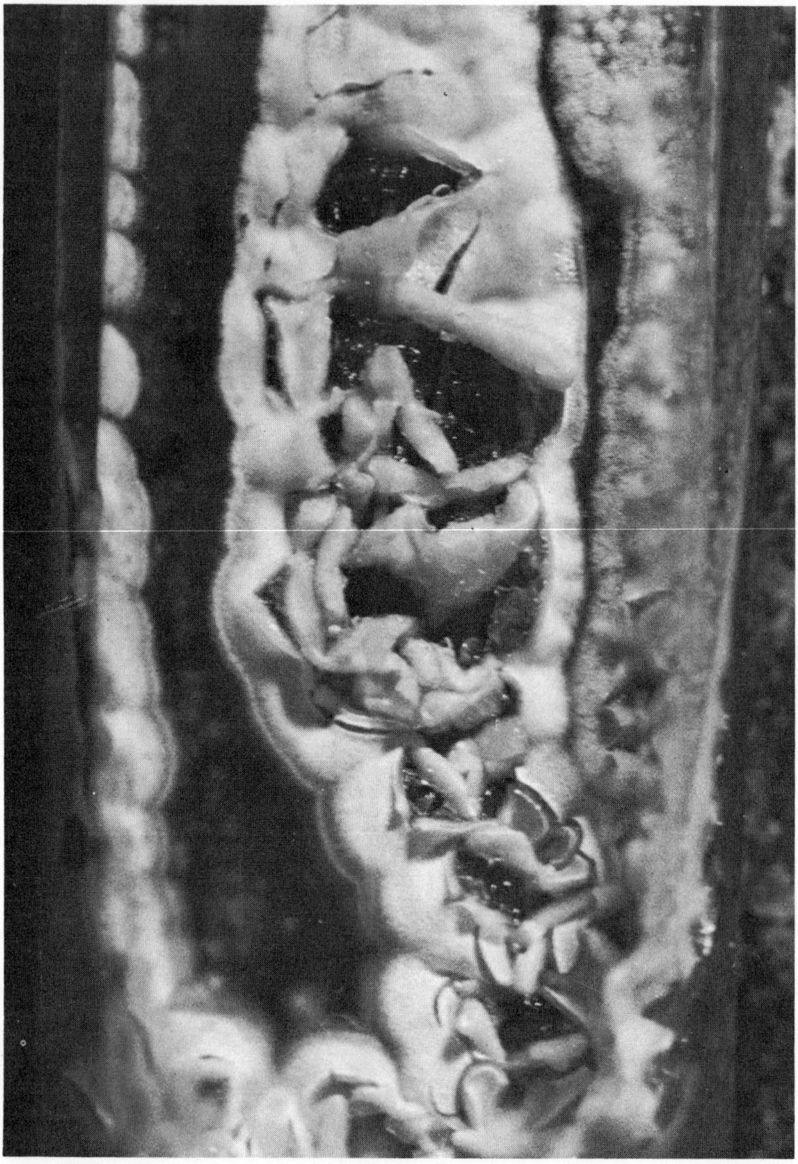

Fig. 1.5. Mold growth—a close-up view. Growing in this test tube is the mold *Streptomyces rimosus,* which is used in the production of terramycin. This antibiotic was discovered in 1949 and is effective in the treatment of over 100 diseases. *Photo courtesy Chas. Pfizer & Co.*

supervise the extraction of the antibiotics from the broth in which they are produced and test the potency, purity, and safety of the product (Fig. 1.5). This testing guarantees that the individual vials of antibiotics possess the activity stated on the label and that the products are free from any other microorganism or chemical which would make the use of these substances dangerous.

Another activity of microbiologists in the industrial field is the production of vaccines for the purpose of giving immunity against the diseases for which such a procedure has been found workable. The preparation of most vaccines requires the production of large amounts of the specified microorganism, which has either been modified or killed, so that it will not produce a serious case of the disease and yet, upon injection into the body, will give rise to an immunity which will protect the person against infection. In the production of the vaccine against whooping cough, the organisms are grown in broth and then harvested and killed by the addition of chemicals. Each batch must be tested to insure that there are no living organisms present and that vaccinated animals, when subjected to a challenge dose of the living organisms, are protected and will not succumb to the disease. The smallpox vaccine is raised on the embryos of chicks, developing in eggs (Fig. 1.6) or on the skin of a calf. This vaccine is a living organism but has been so selected and treated that it will cause only an isolated lesion at the point of inoculation and at the same time will confer immunity. Some vaccines are produced in the rabbit or in other animals. Polio vaccine is grown on monkey kidney tissue which is cultured in flasks and tubes.

The vaccines are referred to as **biologicals.** This term also includes immune serum which is still occasionally used for the treatment of certain diseases. These serums are nothing more than the liquid part of the blood of previously vaccinated humans or animals which contains the chemical substances providing immediate protection against a developing case of a disease.

The industrial microbiologist is concerned with the testing of other chemicals and equipment used in the control of microbiological activity in widely diverse environments: treatment of water and sewage, air purification, disinfection of dishwashing rinse water, or of the skin of a patient about to undergo surgery.

Much of the work of microbiologists in industry has nothing to do with the production of substances to be used in medicine. Microbiological products are used widely in the chemical industry. Solvents, such as ethyl, propyl, and butyl alcohol, and citric, gluconic, lactic, and acetic acids are produced by growing microorganisms on starches and sugars in large scale processes. At the present time many of these

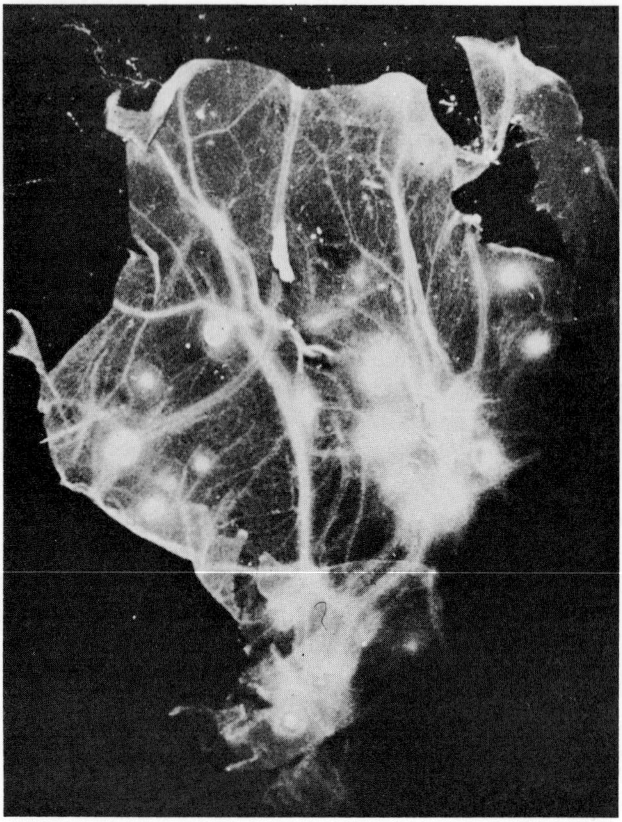

Fig. 1.6. Colonies of virus grow as small white patches on a membrane of a developing chick embryo. Here the membrane has been removed from the shell of the incubating egg and spread out to show the lesions produced when vaccinia virus (that used to vaccinate humans against smallpox) is grown in embryonated eggs. *Photo from Scientific American, courtesy Chas. Pfizer & Co.*

substances can be produced somewhat more cheaply by chemical procedures using byproducts of the petroleum industry as starting materials. However, the limited amount of petroleum on this earth will eventually lead to higher prices, whereas the materials used in microbial fermentation are renewable every year through the growing of crops. Fermentation products will become cheaper as agriculturists employ new methods, improved plant fertilizers, and insecticides. Therefore, future development along microbiological lines appears certain, since industrial microbiology may potentially be applied in the synthesis of many other useful products when the price structure renders this profitable.

Some industrial processes employ microorganisms in modifying chemicals to yield some substance more valuable than the starting material. For example, certain sugar factories are prohibited by law from disposing of waste molasses by dumping it into streams or rivers. It is more economical to ferment the molasses to produce solvents—even at a loss—in order to eliminate the waste product. In European countries where petroleum is scarce, even such raw materials as sawdust and waste wood products are converted into sugar by treatment with acid, and the sugar is then fermented by microbes yielding useful chemicals such as alcohols and acetone.

A number of the vitamins are produced more cheaply by microorganisms than by chemical synthesis. The vitamin, riboflavin, which is extensively used in chicken feed, is produced to a large extent by a fermentation process. Under this process riboflavin accumulates in the broth in which certain microorganisms are grown. In the manufacture of vitamin C, one step in the process is more easily accomplished by microorganisms than by a standard chemical manipulation in the laboratory. The same is true in the production of the hormone, cortisone. The chemist carrying out the multiple steps in synthesis finds it difficult to introduce a hydroxy group into the proper position on the cortisone molecule, but this step is readily accomplished by the inoculation of the proper microorganism into the material. Then the chemist can proceed with further manipulations which lead to the final active cortisone product. Folic acid and vitamin B_{12} are produced largely through fermentation. They may be isolated from the waste liquor of antibiotic-producing industries but are also produced through specific fermentation processes designed especially to yield the vitamin in question.

Some of the earliest manufacturing processes employed microorganisms. Microbes have long been used to release the fibers from the stem of the flax plant, allowing them to be separated and spun into linen thread. Crude microbial processes have long been used to carry out one or more steps in the manufacture of leather. Very fine leathers are now produced only under careful supervision of the activities of bacteria which modify the animal hides in preparation for tanning.

The microbiologist's attention is required on problems of microbial deterioration of any industrial material that remains sufficiently moist to support microbial growth—from fence posts to steel pipe, and from pup tents to the drilling muds used in oil wells.

Food. Bacteriologists working in the dairy industry have a threefold problem. In the first place, several diseases of the cow are transmissible to man by means of milk. Proper control procedures are required to insure that milk is free of these disease-producing organisms as well as possible infectious agents from milk handlers. Second, the quality of milk is measured in part by the number of organisms in it. The presence of a large number of bacteria indicates careless methods of production and also seriously affects the shelf life of the milk in food stores or in the home. Continued growth of the medically harmless bacteria in milk will soon produce off-flavors, making the milk unacceptable to the consumer. Estimation of the number of bacteria in milk is necessary to determine how much the farmer should be paid, since this is the basis for classifying milk as Grade A or B or C. Finally, in the manufacture of numerous dairy products such as cheese and butter, the activity of microbes is of paramount importance in determining the flavor and texture of the product and must be carefully controlled during the manufacturing process.

Food is a vehicle capable of carrying disease-producing organisms from a food handler to the consumer. Certain microorganisms which grow in food may cause food poisoning or food infection. Whenever a food is produced, a race begins between man and microbe to see which shall consume it. The microbiologist resorts to many artifices to limit the microbe to as little as possible.

Microorganisms are used in the production of a number of food materials such as sauerkraut and soya sauce; yeasts are used in the production of bread and various fermented beverages. Many of these materials were produced long before the existence of microbiology; even today, in some breweries, the brewmaster is regarded as an artist who acquires his knowledge through an apprenticeship. However, most large breweries employ formally trained microbiologists to culture and control the yeast and to examine the microbiological aspects of the various processes in manufacture. In areas of high wine production, like California, special laboratories have been equipped to deal with the microbiological problems peculiar to the wine industry.

Microbiologists are employed by water plants to determine whether the water is safe for drinking. In the disposition of the used water supply (i.e., the sewage) of cities, microbiologists concern themselves with the action of the bacteria useful to the disposition process. Also of concern are the potential dangers of disposing of sewage into recreation areas or where shellfish abound, because of the possibility of introducing infectious disease through shellfish consumption.

Agriculture. At agricultural colleges and experiment stations, bacteriologists are interested in problems of soil. The soil abounds with microorganisms of many types, and their activities have an effect upon the fertility of the soil, as measured by its ability to produce useful crops. In a few instances, as in the growth of legumes, efficient strains of microorganisms are inoculated into the soil with the seed in order to improve the growth of these plants (Fig. 1.7). We may speculate that in the not too distant future the farmer will no more think of farming with the ordinary natural microorganisms in his soil than he would consider using the wild grasses for pasture and hay, wild plants for grains or fruits, or wild animals as the producers of edible flesh. Microbiologists determine which activities of the microorganisms are desirable in the soil and how these activities can be encouraged. They also study the problem of using chemical substances to destroy microorganisms whose activities may be undesirable in the soil. The production of composts and organic manures is a microbiological problem.

Assays. Microbes are useful in certain assay or measurement procedures. For example, it is easy to find a microbe whose growth is determined by the amount of a certain vitamin present in the food material. The amount of growth which the microbe makes on the food being assayed can be compared with the amount of growth made under

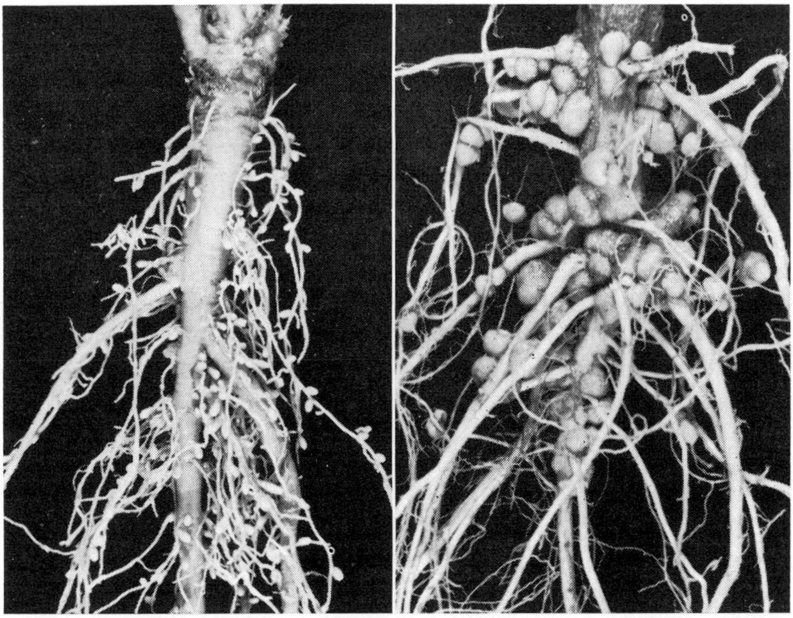

Fig. 1.7. Root nodules are small tumors that develop on the roots of legume plants when invaded by the proper strain of root nodule bacteria. While possibly originating as a plant disease, this has evolved as a symbiosis, where plants growing on nitrogen-poor soil benefit from the ability to fix atmospheric nitrogen in the nodules. *Photo courtesy J. C. Burton.*

the same conditions on a growth medium containing measured amounts of the pure vitamin. Vitamin assay procedures have been standardized so that they are routine for practically all of the water-soluble vitamins. The usefulness of such procedures was illustrated in the development of vitamin B_{12}, the anti-anemia vitamin. The amount of vitamin B_{12} in rich natural sources, such as liver, is so small that the substance cannot be measured there by any known chemical procedure. When the only method of analysis was its administration to humans with anemia, progress in research was exceedingly slow. When B_{12} was purified by extracting it from liver, it was necessary at each step to determine whether the vitamin was in the extract or remained in the residue. Analytical procedures required the participation of a number of anemic patients who would consent to live on a diet low in the vitamin until illness became severe, and then to take either one or the other of the two fractions to determine which contained the active substance. Since many purification steps were required, many patients were needed, and progress in purification was thus almost impossible. However, when it was discovered that certain strains of microorganisms could be obtained that would fail to grow in a medium containing all the other food they needed, with the exception of the anti-anemia substance, experiments could be done rapidly, and pure crystalline vitamin B_{12} was soon isolated.

Microorganisms are used for the assay of many other chemicals which either stimulate or inhibit their growth or development. These chemicals include not only the organic compounds but also trace amounts of certain minerals. Such tests may be used as an index of soil fertility, since the chemical substances in the soil which are available to the green plant will also be available to the microorganism. Surveys of the microbial population of the soil have been used as aids in prospecting for petroleum. Where the soil microbes can utilize volatile petroleum products rapidly, it is suspected that seepage of such materials is occurring from an underground pool, and oil or gas may be found in the area.

Biological Warfare. History records successful use of biological warfare by the Conquistadores, who disseminated the white man's diseases by artfully distributing to the Indians garments from infected persons.

A considerable number of microbiologists work on the production of microbes which might render an enemy less effective by producing infections in him, in his animals, and in his plant crops. The ability of the initial infection to multiply itself is an aggressive feature in biological warfare not present in other weapons. Biological-warfare research reverses the usual objectives of microbiology in medicine. Rather than

Table 1.1. Nobel Prize Winners Whose Work Relates to Microbiology

Year	Name	Dates	Nationality	Citation
1901	Emil von Behring	1854–1917	German	Serum therapeutics
1902	Sir Ronald Ross	1857–1932	English	Transmission of malaria from mosquito to human
1905	Robert Koch	1843–1910	German	Founded scientific bacteriology and bacterial culture
1907	Charles Louis Alphonse Laveran	1845–1922	French	Protozoans as irritants of disease (trypanosomes, etc.)
1908	Paul Ehrlich Elie Metchnikoff	1854–1915 1845–1916	German Russian	Immunity
1913	Charles Richet	1850–1935	French	Anaphylactic test
1919	Jules Bordet	1870–	Belgian	Discoveries in the realm of immunity
1927	Julius Wagner-Jauregg	1857–1940	Austrian	Therapeutic importance of malaria vaccination in Dementia paralytica
1928	Charles Nicolle	1866–1936	French	Typhus exanthematicus
1930	Karl Landsteiner	1868–1943	American	Human blood groups
1939	Gerhard Domagk	1895–	German	Antibacterial effect of prontosil (sulfonamide chemotherapy)
1945	Sir Alexander Fleming	1881–1955	English	Discovery of penicillin
	Ernst Boris Chain Sir Howard Florey	1906– 1898–	Brit. citizen English	Development of penicillin
1946	Wendell M. Stanley John H. Northrop	1904– 1891–	American American	Production of purified enzymes and virus products
1951	Max Theiler	1899–	S. African	Discoveries concerning yellow fever
1952	Selman A. Waksman	1888–	American	Co-discovery of Streptomycin
1953	Fritz Albert Lipman	1899–	Ger.-Am.	Discovery of Coenzyme A

Table 1.1. (Continued)

Year	Name	Dates	Nationality	Citation
1954	John F. Enders Thomas H. Weller Frederich C. Robbins	1897– 1915– 1916–	American American American	Discovery that poliomyelitis viruses multiply in tissue cultures
1958	George Wells Beadle Joshua Lederberg Edward Lawrie Tatum	1903– 1925– 1909–	American American American	Discovery that genes act by regulating chemical processes
1959	Severo Ochoa Arthur Kornberg	1905– 1918–	American American	Discoveries of the mechanism in the biological synthesis of ribonucleic and deoxyribonucleic acids
1960	Sir Frank MacFarland Burnet Peter Brian Medawar	1899– 1915–	Australian British	Discovery of acquired immunological tolerance to tissue transplants
1962	James Watson	1928–	American	DNA Structure

destroying and limiting the spread of microbes, biological warfare seeks to produce large quantities of the infectious agent, to keep it alive and vigorous, and to seek out methods of effective spreading. At the same time a large program involves working out defensive methods of detecting and dealing with an enemy attack with biological weapons.

While the value of biological weapons in modern warfare will be uncertain unless actual tests are carried out under war conditions, our nation has had no prudent alternative but to make both offensive and defensive preparations.

Tools in Research. Perhaps the most interesting and, in the long run, most profitable efforts of microbiologists are those concerning uses of microorganisms in research. The microbe is now used so widely as a research tool that in large universities we can rarely find a department in the natural sciences where one or another of the research workers is not using microorganisms. Numerous examples could be cited. The Department of Psychology may use microbes to assay for the presence of certain amino acids and vitamins in the excretions of psychotic individuals.

The Department of Aeronautics may employ microbes for measuring the effect of cosmic rays on living things. Engineers are interested in the microbial decomposition of petroleum wastes, while students of home economics study the control of microbial spoilage in refrigerators. The similarities among the fundamental processes of living things lead many research workers to employ the microbe as a convenient tool for fruitful basic studies on problems ranging from photosynthesis to cancer. An astonishingly large proportion of the modern biological research programs, which have led to recognition and fame (e. g., Nobel prizes and other national and international awards), have been conducted using microorganisms as research tools (Table 1.1). Finally, many students of microbiology desire to understand the microbe for its own sake, that is, to know what it is and how it functions.

SUMMARY. Microbiology deals with the less complicated living creatures and especially with what they are and what they do. It concerns itself with the destructive and constructive activities of microorganisms. The microbiologist is employed by federal and state public health departments, by the drug industry, by milk and other food manufacturers, by agricultural experiment stations, and by any number of unrelated fields in which microbes are used as research tools. The successful practice of microbiology is based on developing procedures rendering those microorganisms which hurt us less harmful, and making those which help us more useful.

2

How It Began

Organisms which we would consider "alive" have perhaps existed for three billion years, half of the more than six billion years (approximate age) of the earth. Fossil records of blue-green algae estimated to be almost a billion years old have been studied (Fig. 2.1). In spite of the fact that many of the microorganisms are composed of substances which are too soft to leave fossil records, many authorities believe that living forms similar to the bacteria may have been among the early types of life on earth. Billions of years of evolution and development occurred between the emergence of microorganisms and man's recognition of their significance.

In contrast, the recorded history of microbiology is measured in terms of mere hundreds of years. Just as political history was studied as a chronological record of the rise of statesmen and nations, so scientific history has been studied as the consecutive biographies of scientists and their achievements (Table 2.1). The biographical approach greatly oversimplifies the development of the biologic sciences. Many of our "great" discoveries were made and publicized several times before they gained common acceptance. The qualifications of those whom we elect to "greatness" are extremely uneven. Sometimes we honor those who put the keystones in the arches of discoveries. At other times we select those who made an initial con-

Fig. 2.1. A fossil record of blue-green algae that lived a billion years ago. *Photo courtesy American Museum of Natural History.*

tribution upon which the later discovery rested. Occasionally attention is focused upon an early scientist who made essentially no contribution to the main stream of development, but was important when a renewal of interest caused others to rediscover his contribution in ancient scientific writings.

The development of science is regarded by some as similar to a project in map-making. History records only the names of those whose portion of the map contains the great rivers or mountain peaks. Very often it is not until later that we discover that the true wealth of the land lies under the drab, flat areas.

Table 2.1. Some Reference Points in Microbiological History

1546—Fracastorius suggests living agents as cause of disease
1590—Janssen perfects a compound microscope
1676—Leeuwenhoek reports first observations of microorganisms
1762—von Plenciz suggests that each disease is caused by a different subvisible organism
1796—Jenner introduces smallpox vaccination
1810—Appert wins Napoleon's prize for food canning
1839—Schönlein suggests the relation of fungus to skin disease in man
1853—De Bary demonstrates that molds may cause plant disease
1857—Pasteur reports microbial origin of fermentation
1864—Pasteur resolves the problem of spontaneous generation
1870—Lister uses antiseptics in surgery
1876—Koch grows pure cultures of the anthrax organism
1882—Burrill discovers that plant disease can be caused by bacteria
1884—Metchnikoff reports the phenomenon of phagocytosis
1885—Pasteur produces vaccines for rabies and anthrax
1890—Winogradsky isolates nitrifying bacteria from soil
1892—Iwanowski shows the viral nature of tobacco mosaic disease
1895—Ehrlich introduces the antigen-antibody theory of immunity
1898—Löffler and Frosch prove the viral nature of hoof and mouth disease
1906—Ehrlich produces the chemotherapeutic agent "606"
1915—Twort and d'Herelle (1917) discover viruses which attack bacteria
1928—Fleming recognizes potential medical usefulness of penicillin
1931—Goodpasture uses embryonated eggs for virus culture
1935—Domagk presents the first sulfonamide
1944—Electron microscopes are made available
1949—Enders develops tissue-culture methods for viruses

The First View of Microorganisms. Fossil records indicate that disease-producing microorganisms have plagued man from the time of his early appearance on earth. Roman and Arabic writers speculated on the existence of nonvisible forms of life. Some early philosophers even suggested that "germs" of contagion passed from one person to another causing disease. Needless to say, all of these theories remained mere speculation until man devised instruments for the observation of subvisible organisms.

A study of the origin of the microscope leads us through the development of spectacles, the improvement of glass, and the consequent general interest in lenses. The fine art of lens grinding apparently occupied the attention of many artisians in Holland and the low countries around the turn of the sixteenth century. Zacharias Janssen had produced a compound microscope by 1590, but his lenses were too imperfect and his perserverance insufficient to permit him to see the microbes.

Anton van Leeuwenhoek, a linen draper of Delft, Holland, is credited with the first recorded observation of the world of subvisible life. During his leisure hours, this successful Dutch merchant produced simple microscopes consisting of home-ground convex lenses mounted in brass and silver. His lenses were so perfect that when Leeuwenhoek coupled them with keen eyesight and extreme patience he was able to observe the larger microorganisms for the first time. He communicated the descriptions of his microscopical discoveries in a series of letters to the Royal Society of London from about 1676 until his death in 1723. Although these letters served as the first record of investigations in microbiology, few of Leeuwenhoek's contemporaries could repeat his studies with the instruments available at the time. During the two centuries which followed, those interested in microscopy were forced to confine their attention to larger forms of life. Meanwhile, rapidly developing technology led to the production of better and cheaper glass, which, in turn, resulted in the production of excellent lenses and the ultimate emergence of the modern compound microscope.

Disproof of Spontaneous Generation. The first observation of microorganisms revived speculation concerning the origin of living things. Although the concept of the voluntary generation of higher plants and animals from nonliving materials had been largely abandoned by the time of Leeuwenhoek, it was a far more difficult task to prove that microbes were not produced spontaneously. Some of the first true experimentation with these newly discovered microbes was directed toward an explanation of their mysterious appearance in organic infusions.

Early in the eighteenth century an Italian priest named Spallanzani boiled beef broth in containers and then sealed them against air. Since no growth appeared in his airtight containers, the critics of the period claimed that the absence of spontaneous generation in this case merely resulted from the exclusion of air which was vital for the process. Nearly 100 years later, a retired French confectioner named Appert made practical use of Spallanzani's experiment by devising a method for preserving food. He boiled airtight containers of food and upon opening the containers later found the food well preserved.

Toward the end of the eighteenth century it became apparent that oxygen was essential for the life of higher animals. At this time it seemed possible that the airtight seal of Spallanzani and Appert prevented growth because it excluded oxygen, rather than microbial precursors. A series of ingenious studies were then initiated which strongly suggested that growth of microbes would not occur in properly heated infusions which, though exposed to air, had been treated to remove or destroy all microbial life. In 1837, Schwann passed air into boiled infusions through red-hot tubes, and thirteen years later Schroeder and von Dusch performed more decisive experiments by filtering air through cotton into the boiled flasks.

In 1864, the brilliant French chemist, Louis Pasteur, reported his investigations which conclusively demonstrated the faulty logic of the investigators who defended spontaneous generation. He simply boiled infusions in flasks with long, narrow, gooseneck openings (Fig. 2.2). Untreated air passed freely in and out, but microbes settled in the gooseneck and no microbial growth developed in the broth. Certainly Pasteur's true genius lay at least in part in his ability to devise and carry through the convincing crucial experiment.

By 1851, previous to the above studies, Pasteur had established a name for himself by other experimentation in the field of microbial decomposition. He had observed that, unlike other living things, some microorganisms preferred to live in the absence of oxygen. He called these organisms **anaerobes,** and he named the anaerobic decomposition of sugars **fermentation.** His work on fermentations led him to an investiga-

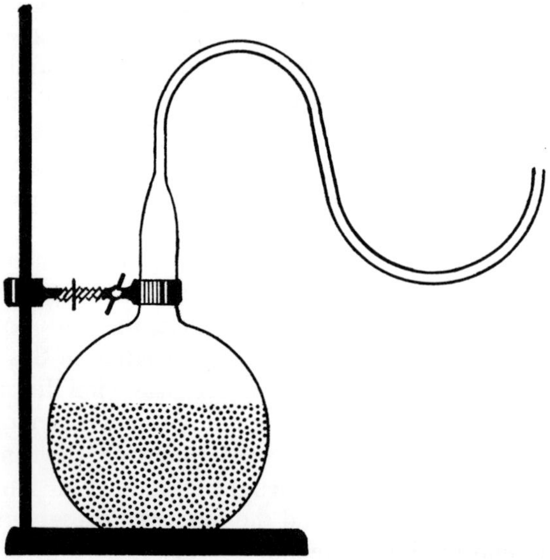

Fig. 2.2. The famous swan-neck flask used by Pasteur during his studies on spontaneous generation. The construction of the neck permitted free access of air to the flask contents, but prevented entry of microorganisms present in the air.

tion of the "sick" wines of France. The inferior flavors of these beverages rendered them unsuitable for competition with the better wines produced in the cooler regions of Germany. He showed that "sickness" was due to the growth of flavor-destroying bacteria. He devised a heating process which is now called **pasteurization** by which the harmful bacteria were destroyed, but the flavor of the wine preserved. He thus guided the French vintner to domination of the wine industry of the world.

The Growth of Medical Microbiology. Although disease epidemics have been witnessed during all periods of recorded history, it was not until the middle of the eighteenth century that man began to comprehend the true nature of their cause. The idea of communication of disease by contact was expressed many times by early thinkers, but, since these suppositions could not be founded upon direct observation of the disease producers, they did not greatly influence the train of thought of the times. For example, in 1546 Fracastorius theorized that disease was the result of "infection" passing from one individual to another in the form of "seeds" or "germs." In 1762, von Plenciz further insisted that each disease was due to a different kind of invisible, living thing.

In 1839, the German physician Johann Schönlein discovered the parasitic fungus which caused the skin infection known as **favus.** Thus, for the first time, the relationship between a microorganism and a human disease was brought to light. In 1853, Anton De Bary demonstrated that certain molds caused the smuts and rusts of a number of food plants.

For the master scientist, Pasteur, it was only a transitional step from "sick" wines to "sick" silkworms. After five years of exhaustive study, he was able to prove that **pebrine,** a disease of silkworms which threatened to destroy the silk industry, was due to a microscopic protozoan. He devised methods for its prevention, rescued the industry, and saved for France several million dollars yearly.

Another great figure, contemporary to Pasteur, was the German physician, Robert Koch (Fig. 2.3). His great successes stemmed from the techniques he devised. He developed a liquefiable, solid culture medium and worked out methods for isolating pure strains of disease-producing microbes free from contamination by ordinary organisms of the dust and air. His investigations of single kinds of organisms in test tubes were free from the confusion that results from studying mixtures. He was the first to prove unequivocally the cause and effect relationship of bacteria to disease. This feat was accomplished in 1876 with the disease anthrax.

Koch's techniques were so useful that students from all parts of the world flocked to his laboratory to learn methods. The decade and a half following 1878 is commonly called the Golden Age of Bacteriology. In

Fig. 2.3. Dr. Robert Koch (1843–1910) in search of the rinderpest microbe. The elaborate laboratory equipment which was so useful to Koch in developing methods for solving many problems in microbiology will not aid him here; rinderpest is caused by a virus which is invisible under the light microscope and which fails to grow outside of animal cells. *Photo courtesy The Bettmann Archive.*

the words of Koch, "New discoveries come like apples falling from a tree." During this period, most of the bacteria which cause disease were isolated, described, and studied in the test tubes of the bacteriologist or in his laboratory animals. Koch himself isolated the tubercle bacillus and published a classical monograph on this work, which served as a model for his students and later investigators.

Although certain fungi had already been reported as plant-disease producers, it was not until 1882 that the American scientist Burrill discovered that fire blight in pears was caused by bacteria. This finding stimulated the development of plant pathology to which other Americans, including Erwin F. Smith, made significant contributions.

In 1892, Iwanowski reported the first experiments which led to knowledge of the viruses. In an attempt to isolate the causative agent for the tobacco mosaic disease, he found that Koch's methods failed to reveal an organism that could be viewed under the microscope. He passed the juice from an infected area of a plant through a filter with a pore-size small enough to hold back bacteria. Since the filtered juice still retained its disease-producing capacity, Iwanowski concluded that he was working with organisms too small to be observed by the microscopes of that time. He named the newly discovered microbe the **filtrable virus.**

In 1898, Löffler and Frosch demonstrated that hoof and mouth disease of cattle was caused by a virus-like agent. During the decade following 1900, the virus nature of a variety of common diseases was demonstrated. In 1915, Twort and, in 1917, d'Herelle created a furor when they announced the discovery of viruses that could attack bacteria. These investigators found that broth cultures of certain bacteria could be dissolved by the addition of a bacteria-free filtrate from sewage. The name **bacteriophage** was proposed by d'Herelle because he considered the filtrable agent to be a living microbe which "ate" bacteria.

The Development of Immunology. One of the greatest contributions to preventive medicine was made in 1796 when Edward Jenner transferred material from a human cowpox pustule to the arm of a healthy boy. A few weeks later the boy was inoculated with infectious matter from a smallpox patient; he failed to develop the disease. By 1800, several thousand persons had been similarly inoculated to prevent smallpox and the science of immunology was born (Fig. 2.4).

By 1880, Pasteur had isolated a microorganism which he considered the cause of a disease known as fowl cholera. By accident, he discovered that chickens would not die of the disease when they were inoculated with the organisms that had been standing in his laboratory test tubes for several weeks. Furthermore, when the same chickens were reinoculated with fresh vigorous cultures, they were resistant to the disease. It was evident to Pasteur that he had in his hands a procedure for extending to other diseases a vaccination process similar to the one which had been outlined by Jenner years before. Pasteur then subjected other disease-producing organisms to altered environmental conditions such as aging, drying, growth at abnormal temperatures, and treatment with chemicals. By 1885, he had developed methods for the production of successful vaccines for anthrax in cattle and sheep, and for rabies in humans and dogs.

Fig. 2.4. Tiny virus. These four ovals are air-dried vaccinia virus particles magnified many times by an electron microscope at the Virus Laboratory of the University of California (Berkeley). Vaccinia, or cowpox, is the material used in vaccinations to immunize against smallpox. *Photo courtesy Chas. Pfizer & Co.*

The work with vaccines led to extensive research and speculation on the whole problem of immunity. In 1884, Élie Metchnikoff demonstrated the role of white blood cells as destroyers of disease-producing bacteria. He named these special blood cells **phagocytes** and advanced the theory that they were the agents which produced immunity. A few years later, Paul Ehrlich presented a theoretical explanation of immunity based on the concept of chemical changes in certain soluble substances in blood serum. Our present knowledge suggests that both mechanisms play roles in the immune response, but the arguments which arose between the followers of the two theories did much to ground immunology on a scientific basis.

The Development of Chemotherapy. By 1870, the English physician Joseph Lister had shown that wound infections caused by microorganisms could often be prevented by using dressings saturated with a solution of carbolic acid. Together with Koch, he devised ingenious tests for determining the necessary strengths of chemical substances used to destroy microorganisms outside the body.

Meanwhile, Ehrlich turned his attention to the possibility of using chemical substances to destroy microorganisms within the body. However, the search for materials that could be introduced into an animal to destroy specific microbes without poisoning the animal tissues proved to be a particularly difficult one. His study led him to the investigation of chemicals that were particularly successful in the treatment of syphilis. In 1906, after 606 trials, he discovered an arsenic compound that would destroy the syphilis microbe and yet not cause particular harm to the

Fig. 2.5. Penicillin mold. This symmetrical colony of green mold is *Penicillium chrysogenum*, a mutant form of which now produces almost all of the world's commercial penicillin. *Photo courtesy Chas. Pfizer & Co.*

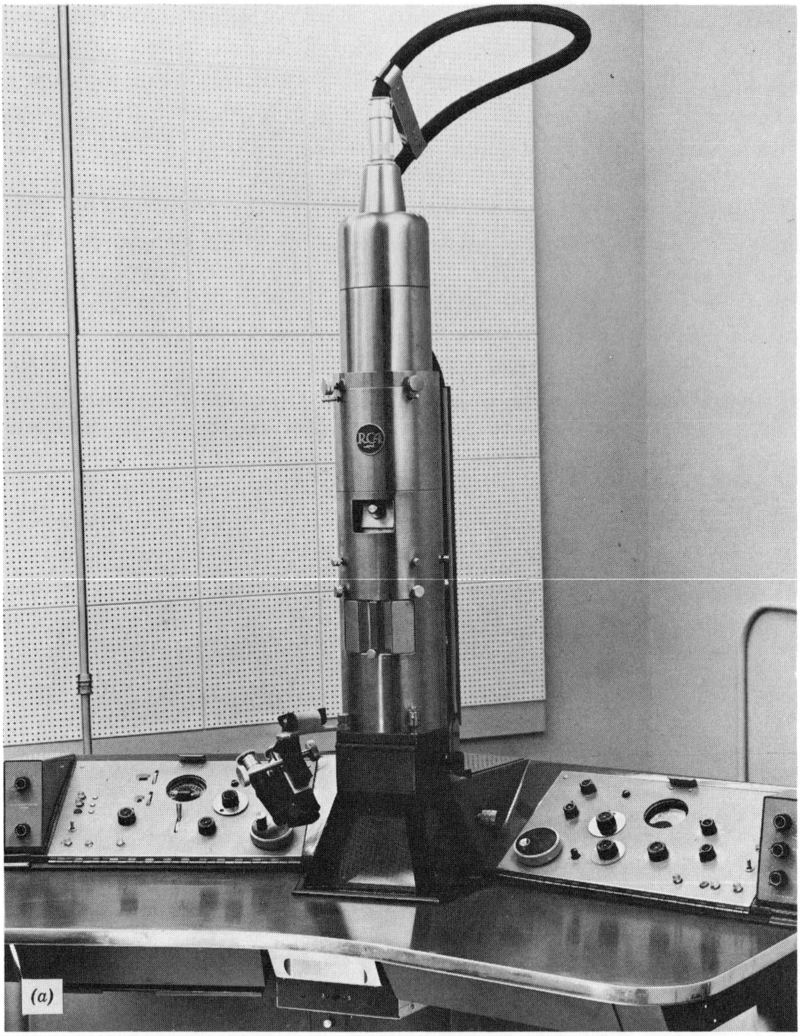

Fig. 2.6. (*a*) Modern RCA electron microscope. (*b*) Details that can be seen in bacteria examined with it. These are pictures of ultrathin slices of bacteria showing some cells cut lengthwise and some crosswise. *Photo (a) courtesy RCA.*

patient. His failure to produce compounds effective against other microbial disease-producers did not discourage other investigators from continuing the search.

Over 25 years later, Gerhard Domagk discovered that a red azo-dye compound named **prontosil** was active in curing a number of bacterial

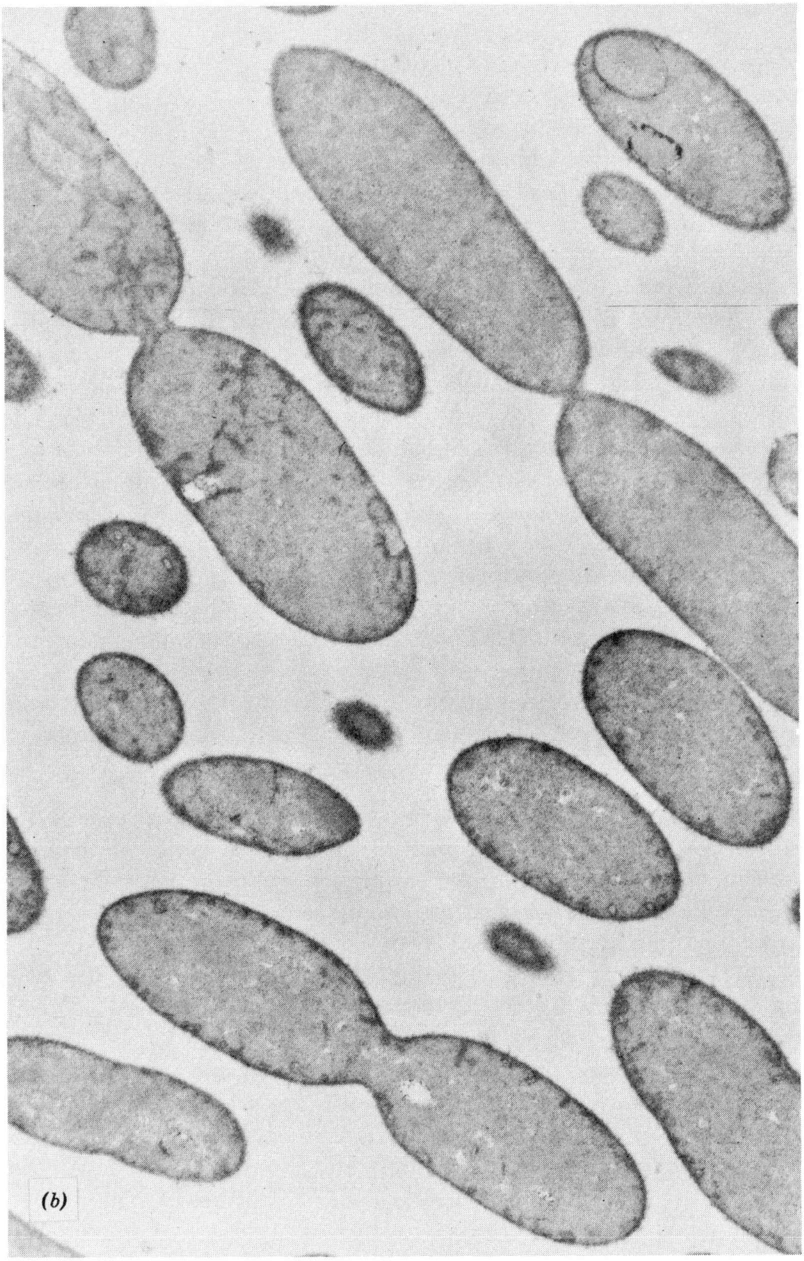
(b)

infections. Later experiments showed that the antibacterial properties of the dye resided in the colorless sulfanilamide portion of the compound. The successful **sulfonamides** that followed demonstrated clearly that it was possible to obtain chemical agents against a wide variety of microbial infections, and that these chemicals could be introduced into the body without producing serious toxic symptoms.

In 1929, Alexander Fleming reported that the mold *Penicillium notatum* produced a substance which prevented the growth of certain bacteria on laboratory culture media. He named the antibacterial substance **penicillin** (Fig. 2.5) and suggested that it could be useful in medicine. His discovery went unnoticed until technology had developed sufficiently to perceive the true value of the antibiotic. As the development of the microscope awaited the technology of glass making, so the production of penicillin awaited the development of a chemical technology for its isolation from natural material; it awaited the stimulus following the successful development of sulfonamide chemotherapy; it awaited a knowledge of procedures in genetics for the development of mutant strains of *Penicillium*, yields of which were high enough for economic production; and it awaited a political climate in sympathy with subsidizing the construction of facilities for such a speculative venture.

As soon as the success of penicillin was assured, great numbers of scientists began searching among the microorganisms for strains and cultures that would produce antibacterial chemicals. In the decade beginning in 1940, a great number of such cultures were discovered. Some have proved to be so useful in medicine that many of the problems of bacterial infections are now successfully controlled.

Recent Advances in Virus Research. In spite of the success of the vaccination program in which smallpox vaccine was grown on the belly of a calf, the lack of methods for culturing other viruses thwarted progress in this field. In 1931, Goodpasture and his associates discovered that the developing chick embryo was an excellent medium for growth of a number of viruses. The use of the embryonated hen's egg was soon standard procedure for the detection, isolation, and study of many common viruses.

Meanwhile, workers in the field of botany and zoology had perfected methods for growing bits of tissue in test tubes. The procedures were patterned after the culture of bacteria and nutritional studies of microorganisms. In 1949, J. F. Enders and his co-workers developed methods for growing viruses on such test-tube cultures of living tissues. This new technique permitted cultivation of those viruses which failed to develop in chick embryos, selection of tissues for optimum virus growth, and large-scale propagation of viruses. A widely publicized result was the development of a vaccine for poliomyelitis.

With the development of the electron microscope (Fig. 2.6), man was able to view the virus for the first time. In addition, he was permitted to study, in much greater detail, the **cytology** of the larger microbial forms. However, in spite of this tremendous advance in the field of microscopy, the interpretation of structural details is still difficult.

SUMMARY. The history of microbiology, probably as much as any other science, emphasizes the dependence of each scientist upon his predecessors. No great discovery is made without previous discovery, and, in this science especially, technical developments almost always precede waves of advance. The development of the microscope stimulated a wave of scientific attention to microscopic observation. The early workers, Koch and Pasteur, provoked waves of discovery as a result of their work on methods and theory. The rise of biochemistry, the creation of the first synthetic antibacterial agent, the development of antibiotics, the use of the chick embryo, and the procedures for tissue culture are all interrelated in the complex of techniques which make up modern science. Even now the fundamental research of today's scientists, which often seems unlikely to benefit mankind, will furnish the basis for the practical applications (useful discoveries) of the future. Conversely, men whose contributions receive great current attention may, a few generations from now, appear as obscure as the inventor of the spermaceti candle.

3

What Are Bacteria?

Historical development of microbiology centers around the laboratories of Koch and Pasteur who studied those microbes which are classified as bacteria. While the problem of classification will be dealt with in detail in later chapters, it is necessary here to consider briefly how bacteria fit into the world of living things.

Microbiologists deal primarily with organisms from the plant kingdom. However, in the animal kingdom the phylum Protozoa contains the single-celled animals whose microscopic nature and relationship to the bacteria make them suitable objects for study in the bacteriology laboratory. Animals and plants have been differentiated by a series of characteristics. Most importantly, first, plants generally take their food in solution, while the animals take their food in particulate form; and, second, plants generally have rigid cell walls, while animal cell boundaries are flexible and soft. According to those bases, the protozoa are classified with animals and the bacteria are classified with plants (Table 3.1).

In the plant kingdom the division Protophyta contains bacteria, rickettsiae, viruses, and blue-green algae, while the second division, Thallophyta, includes other plants that are not differentiated into tissues such as leaves, roots, and stems. Those thallophytes having green pigment are called **algae**, and those without green pigment are referred to

Table 3.1. Classification of Living Forms *

I. Animal Kingdom
- Phylum 1. **Protozoa**
- Phyla 2–11. Other animals

II. Plant Kingdom
- Phylum 1. **Protophyta**—primitive plants without intracellular membranes.
  - Class 1. **Schizophyceae**—the blue-green algae
  - Class 2. **Schizomycetes**—the bacteria, actinomycetes and related forms.
  - Class 3. **Microtatobiotes**—the rickettsiae and viruses
- Phylum 2. **Thallophyta**—primitive plants with intracellular membranes
  - Subphylum 1. **Algae**—the green, red, and brown algae and the diatoms
  - Subphylum 2. **Fungi**—the molds and yeasts
- Phyla 3–5. Other plants

* Those of interest to the microbiologist are in heavy print.

as **fungi**. The fungi include the yeasts and the molds and are subdivided further as are the algae (See Chapters 7 and 8). The bacteria constitute the Schizomycetes, a class of organisms that divide by fission or splitting. Under the Schizomycetes a number of further subdivisions include (1) the true bacteria, which are typical of the commonly held concepts of bacteria—probably because members of this group were the first studied seriously by Koch and Pasteur; (2) the actinomycetes, which are mold-like bacteria; (3) the spirochaetes, which are the spiral-shaped bacteria with soft, flexible cell walls, a feature which makes them similar to animal organisms such as the protozoa; (4) the sheathed bacteria, which are related to the green algae; and (5) the slime bacteria.

In the class Microtatobiotes, the rickettsiae are smaller organisms classified between the true bacteria and the other group of this class, the viruses, the smallest of living things. Most microbiologists regard viruses as "living organisms" by defining "living" as those things which, under proper conditions, have the ability to reproduce and to mutate. Since no clear-cut borderlines exist between one group of living things and another, classification systems are devised to aid the human mind in considering wider groups of organisms having similar characteristics (Fig. 3.1). This device, though intellectually useful, can be misleading unless it is recognized that between every pair of related groups are transitional forms that might be placed in either.

A descriptive definition of bacteria must be sufficiently inclusive to fit the majority of those organisms encountered; however, any description will probably fail to fit those specimens with unusual features

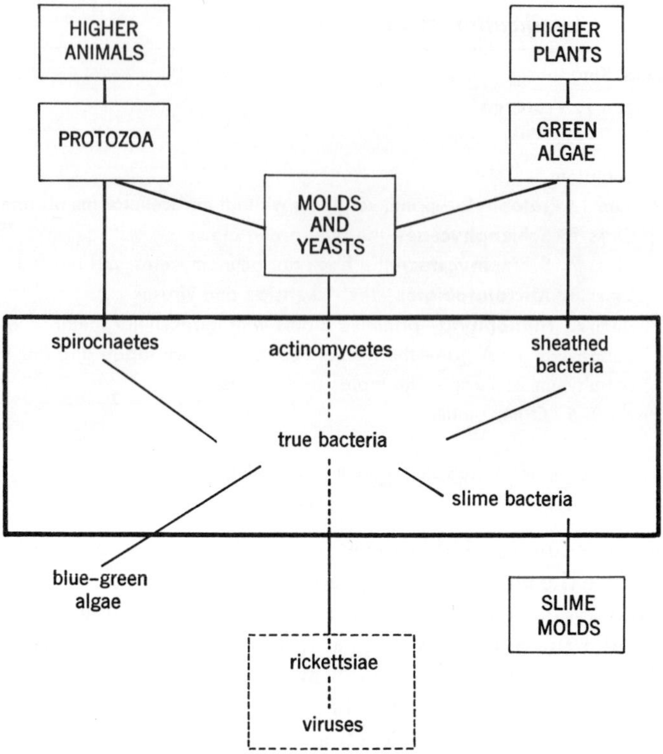

Fig. 3.1. Apparent relationships between biological forms. Those not in capital letters are protophyta (primitive plants). In the dotted line box are the Microtatobiotes. In the heavy line box are the Schizomycetes (fission fungi or bacteria).

which relegate them to the outer edges of the group. The simplest dictionary definition states that bacteria are microscopic, unicellular, primitive plants of the class Schizomycetes, widely distributed in nature and existing as rods, spheres, or spirals. Such a definition requires elaboration.

Microscopic Size. Everyone recognizes that bacteria are extremely small, but just how small is often difficult to comprehend. The best light microscopes magnify about 1000 times, and, if a round object which is about the size of a bacterium is magnified 1000 times, it would then appear as big as a period on the printed page. A man magnified a thousand times would appear more than a mile high and about a quarter of a mile broad (Fig. 3.2).

In order to deal with microbic size, a new measure of length, the micron, was introduced. The micron, equal to 0.001 millimeter, is written as the Greek letter μ. Though the range of the bacteria is between 0.2 μ and 2.0 μ, the average bacterium is about one micron in thickness, which means that if a thousand of them were lined up side by side, they would just reach across a period on a printed page. One trillion (10^{12}) bacteria of average size could be packed into a 1 milliliter (ml) pipette, and, since a teaspoon is about 5 ml, five times that number would fill a teaspoon. Since there are about 2,500,000,000 (2½ billion) people in the world, we find that a teaspoon full of packed bacteria represents 2000 times as many organisms as there are people on the earth.

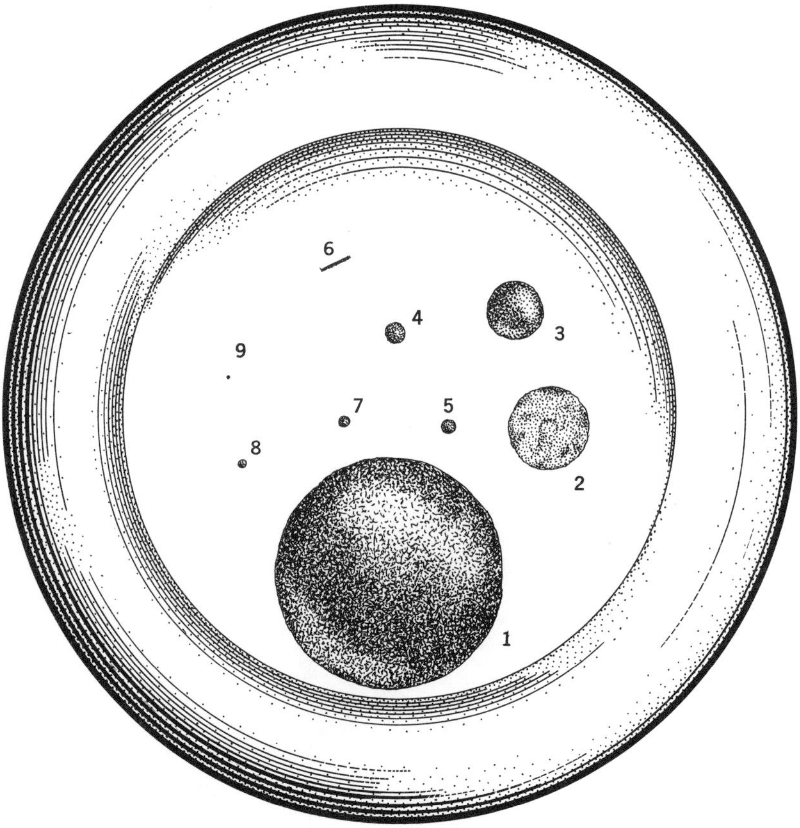

Fig. 3.2. Relative sizes are shown by superimposing microbial forms on a red blood cell: (1) Mold spore, (2) Ordinary bacterium, (3) Small bacterium, (4) Rickettsia, (5) Psittacosis virus, (6) Tobacco mosaic virus, (7) Bacteriophage, (8) Yellow fever virus, (9) Polio virus.

Cellular Characteristics. The second word in our definition, "unicellular," indicates that each living organism consists of a single cell having the general cellular structure that is observed in higher animals and plants. The **protoplast** consists of organized **protoplasm** enclosed by a membrane and surrounded by a cell wall. The protoplasm consists of **cytoplasm, a nucleus,** and **inclusion granules** (Fig. 3.3). In the cells of Protophyta (bacteria, blue-green algae, etc.), no distinguishable membranes separate the nucleus or other organelles from the cytoplasm. Streaming of the granules in the cytoplasm can not be observed. Unusual chemicals are found in the bacterial cell wall, and unusual storage products occur in the bacterial cytoplasm. Nuclear division in bacteria does not involve mitosis. Mitochondria and plastids are absent. With these exceptions the bacterial cell may be regarded as a plant cell in miniature.

Often in typical bacteria several cells are connected, but the important characteristic, "unicellular," indicates the lack of active association among these cells. Each cell is capable of independent life, and each carries out its life processes, growth, multiplication, and death without depending on the others, which may be attached to it in chains or in clumps. A single cell detached from a mold and placed in a proper situation for growth will yield a new mold, but, in many of the molds, the cell groups show a definite specialization of function. Certain of the cells serve for attachment to the food material; others, for securing moisture and oxygen from the air; others, for bearing the fruiting bodies. However, such specialization is not generally found in

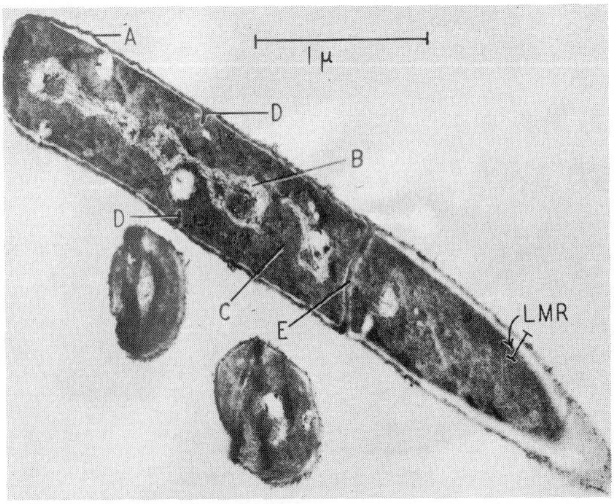

Fig. 3.3. Electron micrograph of thin section through bacterium showing: LMR-limit of light microscope resolution, (A) cell wall, (B) nuclear material, (C) cytoplasmic granules, (D) beginning of a new cross wall, (E) cross wall. *Photo by G. B. Chapman and J. Hillier: J. Bact., LXVI, 362–373, Sept. 1953, courtesy S.A.B., LS-325.*

bacteria. At the other extreme, the viruses appear to be something less than a complete cell and thus are not considered bacteria.

Primitive Plants of the Class Schizomycetes. The third descriptive term in our definition is "primitive plants" Protophyta. As demonstrated in Table 3.1, this is a division of the plant kingdom. Since they have no stalks and roots they are primitive. The bacteria are not included in the Thallophyta since they have neither the green pigment of the algae nor the complex branching of the fungi. The class Schizomycetes means "fission fungi" and implies multiplication by splitting in half rather than by budding (as is seen in the yeasts) or by developing masses of spores or by combining sexually.

Ubiquitous Distribution. Bacteria are found almost everywhere in nature. They are absent in the healthy tissues of living plants and animals, although they occur in great numbers on the external and internal surfaces of living things. Presumably living bacteria are absent from the depths of the earth and from the sterilized equipment of the microbiology laboratory. They occur most abundantly where there is food, moisture, and a suitable temperature for growth. From such places as the soil, surface waters, and animals and plants, bacteria spread by air, water, or living carriers. Without adequate growth conditions they eventually die, but the effectiveness of their spread insures that survivors can always be recovered from the upper atmosphere, the arctic snows, or the ocean depths. Concern has been expressed that space travel will carry bacteria to the planets and confuse scientists who will later attempt to study the development of life there.

Shapes and Arrangement of Bacteria. Under the thousandfold magnification of modern light microscopes the shape of the bacterial cell can be distinguished. Its most common shape is that of a cylinder, and such organisms are referred to as bacilli (singular = bacillus). In some bacillus forms the length of the cell is only slightly greater than the diameter; in others the cell may be up to ten times as long as it is thick. The ends of the cell may be square-cut or rounded. Some bacilli tend to remain stuck together after division and thus produce long chains of cells, while others break apart rather easily and appear as individual cells. Some cells tend to bulge in the middle, while others may bulge on one end, appearing definitely club-shaped. All these minor differences aid the trained bacteriologist in identifying the microorganism being studied.

A spherically shaped cell is referred to as a **coccus** (plural = cocci). Certain cocci appear as perfect little balls, while others have shapes ranging from cylinders to forms like beans, arrowheads, or even cones. When the length and the width of the cell are about equal and there

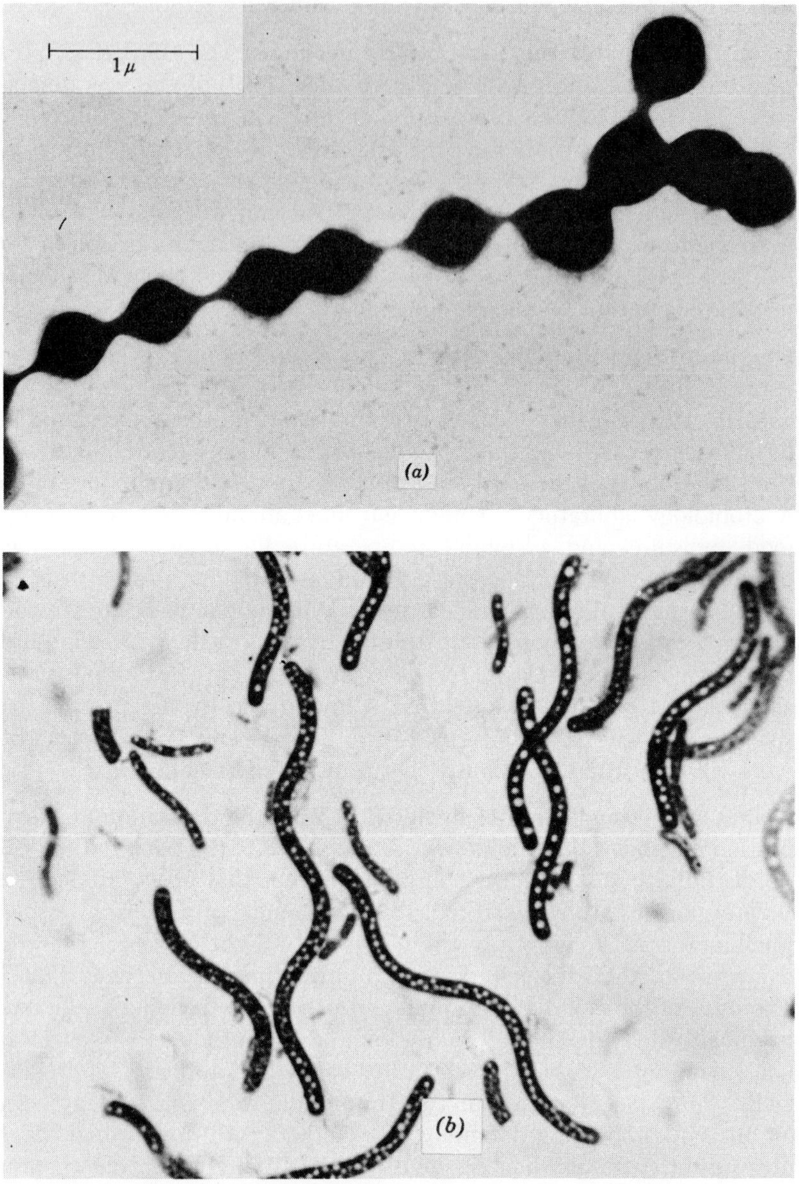

Fig. 3.4. (*a*) Streptococci showing plasmodesms, the thin cytoplasmic strands connecting divided cells. *Photo by Stuart Mudd and D. B. Lackman: J. Bact., XLI; 416, 1941, courtesy S.A.B. LS-71.* (*b*) Light microscope picture of *Spirillum serpens* stained to show fat globules.

is no evidence of a definite cylindrical shape, the cells are "true" cocci. The arrangement of the various cocci is distinctive. For example, the organisms causing the most common type of pneumonia frequently are observed as two attached cocci. Such a pair is referred to as **diplococcus.** When cocci divide in one plane and all progeny continue to divide in a parallel plane, chains are formed; this group is referred to as **streptococcus** (Fig. 3.4). Sometimes the organisms divide in three planes and adhere together in packets making a cube of eight cells: this is termed a **sarcina.** If cocci divide in different planes so that the spherical cells adhere together like bunches of grapes, the arrangement is called **staphylococcus.** When cells separate after division and are found singly, they are called **micrococcus.**

Most bacilli are slightly curved rather than perfectly straight, but, if the curvature is definite, the organisms are referred to as **spirilla** (singular = spirillum). Many of the spirilla are only slightly curved or comma-shaped, while others are coiled up like a corkscrew. The

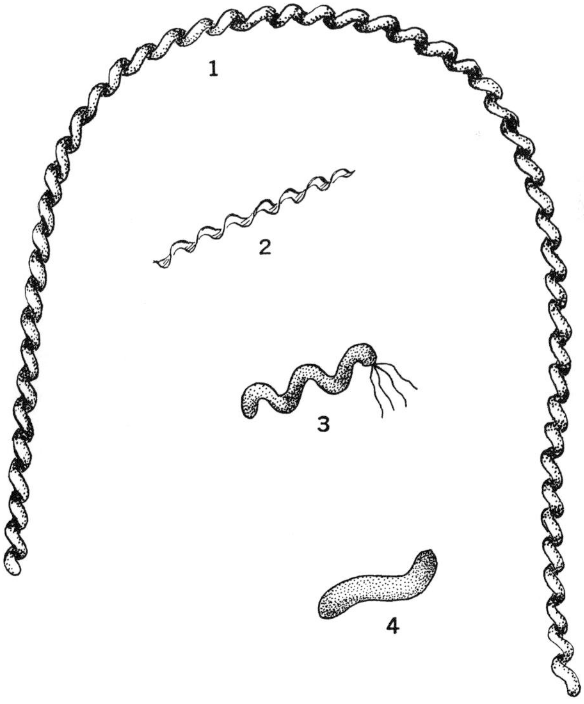

Fig. 3.5. Examples of spiral shaped organisms include the flexible walled spirochetes: (1) *Spirochaeta plictatus* and (2) *Treponema pallidum.* Two rigid walled spirilla are pictured: (3) *Spirillum minus* and (4) *Spirillum undula.*

spirillum differs from the spirochete (Fig. 3.5) in that spirilla are rigid, and the cell wall does not flex or bend when the cell is in motion. Often the details of cell structure, cell shape, and cell grouping are important in indicating the identity of the organism.

Almost 2000 different species of bacteria are recognized by bacteriologists and have been given identifying names. Each bacterial name consists of two Latin words, italicized when printed and underlined when written in script or type. In order to prevent confusion, this binomial system of nomenclature long used by botanists follows well-defined international codes. The initial letter of the name is capitalized. Often one or both of the names describe the organism, but they may be derived from the Latinized name of a person. Bacteria that are well known often acquire a common name also.

Common Name	*Scientific Name**	*Meaning of Scientific Name*
tubercle bacillus	*Mycobacterium tuberculosis*	the moldlike bacterium causing tuberculosis
pneumococcus	*Diplococcus pneumoniae*	the coccus occurring in pairs that causes pneumonia
milk-souring bacteria	*Streptococcus lactis*	the coccus occurring in chains that is found in milk
colon bacillus	*Escherichia coli*	an organism from the bowel: named after Escherich
plague bacillus	*Pasteurella pestis*	the organism named in honor of Pasteur: causes plague, a disease formerly called "the pest"

*The two words make up the species name. The first word is the genus name and the second is the specific epithet.

SUMMARY. Bacteria are those microbes belonging to the plant kingdom which were first studied by the early microbiologists. They are microscopic, unicellular, primitive plants which may range in form from a simple cylinder to a long spiralling thread. They may be found in any environment which provides food, moisture, and a suitable temperature for growth. Their variety of form and function is most remarkable considering the basic similarity of their cellular processes to those of higher plants and animals. The bacterial cell is smaller than the usual plant or animal cell, and, while it shows internal structural detail, certain features of higher cells are absent.

4

Microscopy and Staining

Although much of a microbiologist's work is performed without a microscope, the growth of microbiology depended upon the development of effective undistorted magnification of very small objects. Mastery of the use of the microscope is basic to thorough understanding of this science.

Fundamentals of Optics. When slanting rays of light pass from a material through which they travel easily into a material through which they travel with greater difficulty, the light rays are bent or refracted toward the perpendicular. This principle, the **Law of Refraction,** operates when light passes from air into glass. The rays are bent toward a line perpendicular to the surface of the glass. The light traveling easily through air may be compared to an automobile driving freely over the surface of a dry pavement (Fig. 4.1). If the right front wheel suddenly slips into the muddy shoulder of the road, the car will swerve in the direction of the mud, through which it travels with greater difficulty. The more oblique the angle of entrance into the mud, the sharper the angle of the swerve becomes. On the other hand, if the car is driven directly across the road, both front wheels enter the mud at the same time, and the line of travel is not bent at all.

A portion of glass with a curved surface bends most of the rays

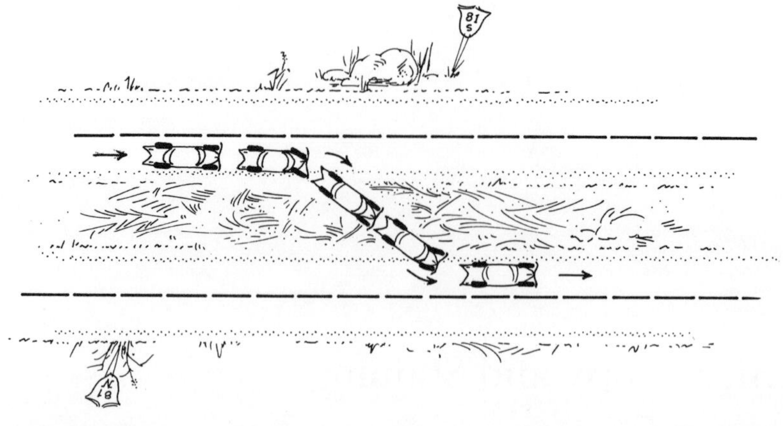

Fig. 4.1. When an unguided automobile enters at an angle on a material which offers greater resistance to its forward progress (such as the unpaved center of this dual highway), it swerves in the direction of the material offering greater resistance. When it leaves the center it swerves again. This is analogous to the bending of light rays encountering an air-glass interface.

which pass through the air-glass boundary. If this lens is properly ground, the rays of light illuminating the specimen and passing through the lens can be focused to form an image. The rays of light reflected from the two ends of a small object will be farther apart when they come into focus as an image than they were as reflected from the object (Fig. 4.2). The point of focus depends on the radius of curvature of the lens. The image of the magnified object appears blurred if it is viewed from any point along the path of reflection other than the focal point. The modern microscope depends on a series of lenses to bring a considerable area into focus at one time without distortions. The lenses of compound microscopes are so arranged that one will further magnify the image formed by another.

The more powerful lenses have the greater curvature, which is obtained by making the lenses progressively smaller. The size is finally limited, as very small lenses do not pass enough light for the human eye to detect the object. However, powerful lights and **condensers** underneath the microscope stage can direct more light up through the lens. The most powerful lens of the light microscope is the oil-immersion lens; a drop of oil placed between the lens and the object eliminates the loss of slanting rays which would otherwise be refracted.

Even if sufficient light were available, the nature of light itself imposes limits to magnification. The wavelengths of light visible to the human eye are between 0.4 and 0.7 micron. Objects smaller than half the wavelength of light do not ordinarily block enough of the light to produce a discernable image. The smallest objects that can be resolved by light microscopes are consequently about 0.2 microns in diameter.

The modern compound microscope usually has an **ocular** or eyepiece lens, which magnifies ten times, and three **objective** lenses attached to a rotary turret at the opposite end of the microscope barrel. The most commonly used objective lenses are: (1) **the low-power objective,** which is 16 millimeters in diameter and magnifies 10 times, (2) the **high-dry objective,** which is 4 millimeters in diameter and magnifies 45 times, and (3) the **oil-immersion objective,** which is 1.8 millimeters in diameter and magnifies 90 times. The total magnification for a given setting is computed by multiplying the magnification of the ocular by that of the type of objective lens being used. Thus the total magnification would be 100× with low power, 450× with high dry, and 900× with oil immersion. Each of these optical systems is composed of several lenses precisely ground to correct distortions and aberrations.

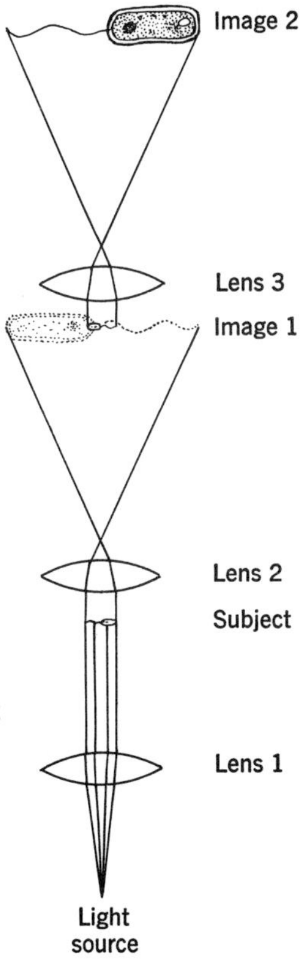

Fig. 4.2. In a complex light microscope the light rays, made parallel by lens 1, pass through the subject, and are magnified by lens 2 to give an image. This image is magnified once more by lens 3.

The other parts of the microscope serve to support the specimen and to allow for adjustment of the optical system. The stage holds the specimen in position relative to the lenses. The **coarse and fine adjustment knobs** regulate the distance between the lens and the stage so that the specimen may be brought into sharp focus. The **condenser** beneath the stage concentrates the light rays on the specimen. The **iris diaphragm** shuts out those light rays which pass through the outer edge of the objective lens and thus limits the view to the center of the lens which gives the truest image.

Other Microscope Methods. The smallest objects detected under the light microscope are observed under **dark-field illumination.** Small objects such as particles of dust, which are completely invisible to the

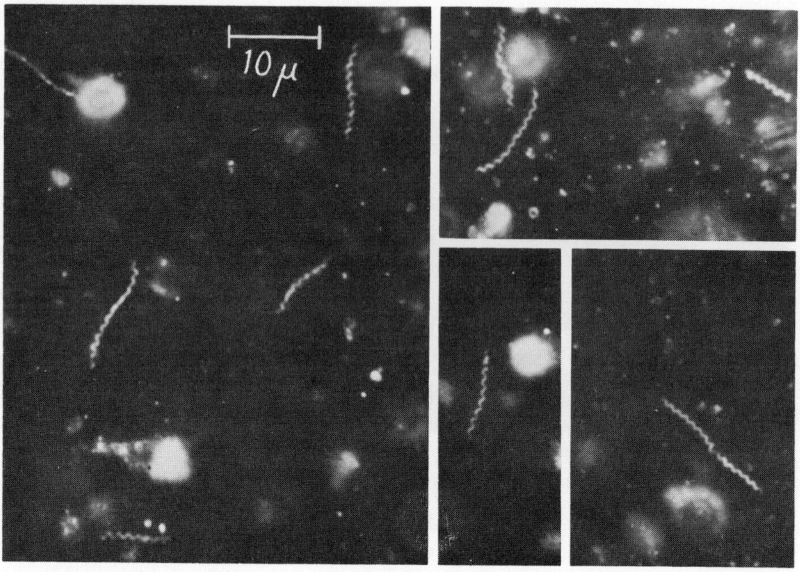

Fig. 4.3. Four photomicrographs of dark-field preparations of *Treponema pallidum*, the causative organism of syphilis. *Photo by Theodor Rosebury, courtesy S.A.B. LS-327.*

naked eye, become visible in a beam of light in a dark room. The small object is not seen but rather the flash of light reflected from it. Dark-field illumination requires a special condenser with a black spot in the center to block out all the rays of light which would pass directly into the objective lens. The resulting dark field allows observation of the flashes of light reflected from small objects on the stage as they are hit by slanting rays of light (Fig. 4.3). Although the resolution is optically no greater than that of the light field microscope, the dark-field technique makes it possible to observe and photograph objects as small as bacterial flagella. Such pictures are, of course, not of the flagella themselves but rather of the flashes of light reflected from them. Dark-field techniques permit general observation of the number, size, shape, and action of the objects so illuminated.

Special lenses and a condenser added to the ordinary light microscope convert it to a **phase-contrast** microscope. The specialized condenser contains concentric rings which illuminate the specimen by cylinders of light not vibrating in the same phase. The objective lenses also contain concentric rings in exact alignment with those in the condenser. Minor differences in the density of parts of the bacterial cell, insufficient to render them visible under the ordinary light microscope, show up as distinct structures under the phase-contrast microscope. The internal structure of bacterial cells can be studied in stained, killed preparations examined under the light microscope; however, observation of similar structures in living cells with the phase-contrast instrument enables differentiation of the parts of the living cell from the **artifacts,** which are apparent yet nonexistent structures produced by staining procedures.

Ultraviolet light, which has a shorter wavelength than ordinary white light, increases the resolution of the microscope and hence makes smaller objects visible. Since ultraviolet rays do not pass through glass, quartz lenses are used in the **ultraviolet microscope.** The magnified object must be photographed since the human eye cannot register ultraviolet impressions. This method resolves objects which are one-half to one-third the size of the smallest, which can be seen with the ordinary light microscope.

The method of magnification of the **electron microscope** does not differ fundamentally from that of a light microscope (Fig. 4.4). A beam of electrons rather than a beam of light is passed through the ob-

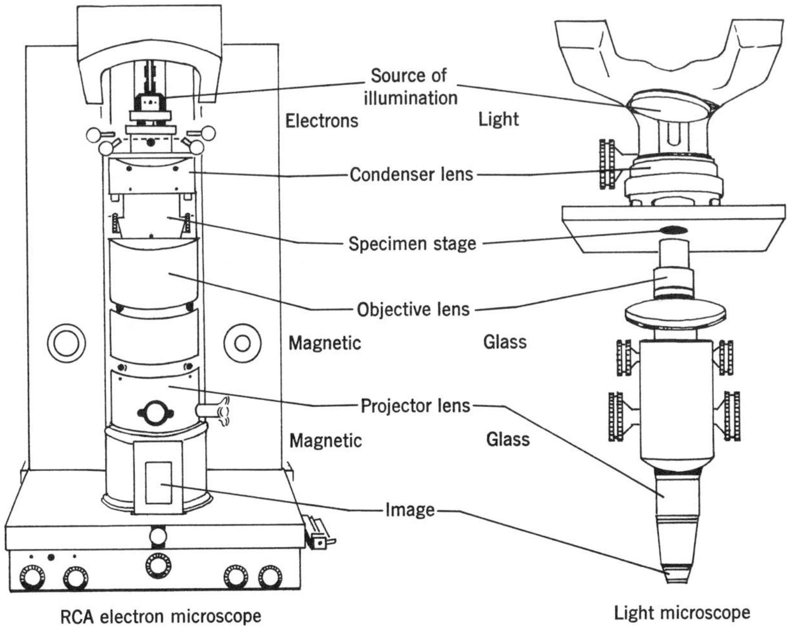

Fig. 4.4. The analogous parts of the electron microscope and the inverted light microscope used in the author's laboratory. *Redrawn from diagram, courtesy RCA.*

ject to be viewed. Three or more ring-shaped electronmagnets serve as lenses to bend the electron beams. Like light rays, the electrons are absorbed or refracted to varying degrees by areas of different "electron density" in the specimen. The emergent electrons can be focused on a photographic plate or upon a fluorescent screen, thus producing a visible image. Since electrons are readily stopped by all forms of matter, studies are carried out in a vacuum. Living materials cannot be used since the specimens must be dried before they are placed in the vacuum. Microbial materials are often mounted on thin films of cellophane or collodion. **Microtomes** are instruments which cut ultrathin slices of bacterial cells for electron microscope studies of the nature of intracellular bodies (Fig. 4.5). Magnifications of 10,000 to 80,000 are possible, and photomicrographs obtained at lower magnifications can be enlarged up to 10 times. The electron microscope, in making possible the first observations of the smaller microorganisms, contributed greatly to the understanding of the basic anatomy of the external as well as internal structures of the microbes.

Preparation of Living Cells. In light-microscope examination bacteria are positioned on a glass slide which is placed on the stage within the light beam that enters the objective lens of the instrument. Living organisms may be suspended in a drop of liquid on a cover slip; the slip is inverted and placed on a **hanging drop slide** which is hollowed to accommodate the drop. The preparation is then sealed with petrolatum and observed with the high-dry objective. Useful for detecting bacterial motility, study of live specimens indicates the presence of flagella on those organisms which are actively motile.

Liquid preparations of living fungi are of little value since identification of such microorganisms depends on the specific characteristics of intact cultures. The **Henrici-slide** permits microscopic observation of growing fungi. Paraffin is applied to a slide to form three sides of a square just smaller than the cover slip. A warm cover slip is then pressed over the paraffin. A suitable melted and cooled agar medium containing fungal spores is poured into the open side of the culture slide chamber. After incubation in the slide, the undisturbed fungal culture can be observed with the high-power objective of the light microscope.

Preparation of Stained Materials. The microbiologist studying bacterial cells under the light microscope generally employs stained preparations. Though staining procedure usually kills the bacteria, it permits better viewing of the organisms and often reveals more than the mere structural arrangement of the cells or their parts.

In the preparation of bacterial smears a thin **film** or **smear** of the organisms is placed on a glass slide. The film is dried in the air and

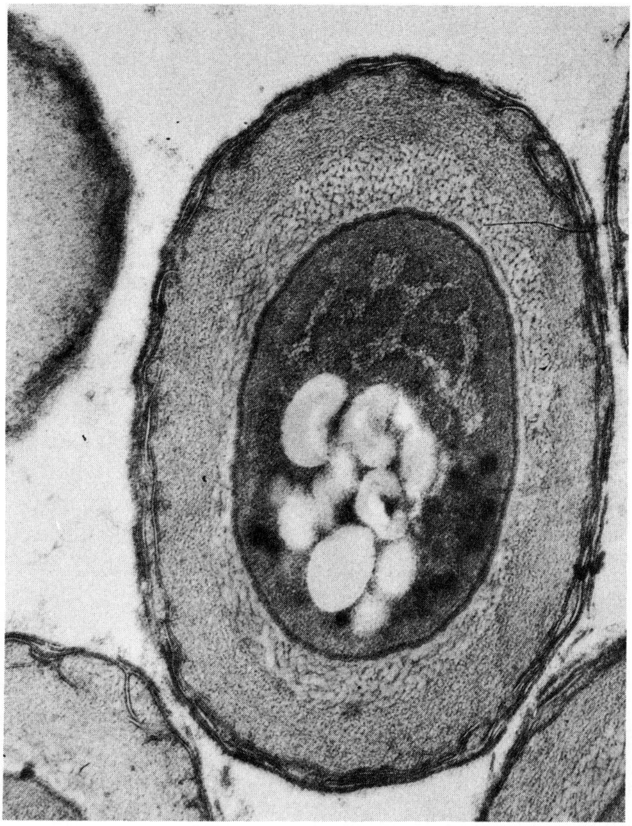

Fig. 4.5. The internal details of this resting cell of the bacterium *Azotobacter* are demonstrable under the electron microscope only after the cells are imbedded in plastic and ultrathin slices (0.05 micron thick) are cut. Compare with unsliced cells in Figs. 5.5 and 17.6.

then subjected to gentle heat or to alcohol which coagulates the proteinaceous material of the bacterial cells. The killed organisms are thus **fixed** or fastened firmly to the glass slide and cannot be washed off during subsequent staining procedures. The film is then covered with a dilute solution of any of a number of colored chemicals which have affinity for the protein substances in the cytoplasmic and nuclear materials of bacterial cells.

The chemicals that are usually employed to stain bacterial cells are termed basic dyes. These include methylene-blue chloride, crystal violet, safranin, and basic fuchsin. Acid dyes, such as acid fuchsin, are rarely used in microbiology.

In preparation of a **simple stain,** an alcohol or water solution of a single dye is flooded over the fixed film on the slide and permitted to remain there for 30 seconds to 5 minutes. The slide is then rinsed in water, blotted dry, and observed under the microscope. The bacterial cells usually stain much more deeply than does any extraneous proteinaceous material. Since bacteria contain a higher proportion of the RNA and DNA types of protein than do the cells of higher plants and animals, the entire bacterial cell takes up the dye and is more evenly stained than are the cells of the higher forms. Simple stains indicate the general shape, arrangement, and size of bacteria but reveal few internal structural details.

Ordinary simple staining procedures do not usually stain such structures as the cell wall, fat globules, capsules, or spores. Though the nuclear matter may take up stain, it cannot be differentiated from the deeply stained cytoplasm. Flagella are probably stained but are too small to be resolved with the light microscope. Chemicals called **mordants** are frequently used to stain specific structures since they cause the dyes to become fixed to them. For example, tannic acid used as a mordant reveals the bacterial cell wall with a simple stain. Bacterial flagella can be demonstrated by adding a mordant which precipitates around each flagellum. This procedure, in reality, manufactures an **artifact** sufficiently thick which, when stained, is visible under the light microscope.

Fat globules may be stained with certain fat-soluble dyes such as Sudan Black. Highly resistant endospores require drastic treatment for staining (Fig. 4.6). They must be heated during the staining process or soaked in the stain for extended periods. Once the endospores have taken up the stain they are equally difficult to destain, as they are unaffected by the gentle washing with acid or alcohol which removes stain from vegetative cells.

Colloidal materials such as India ink, Nigrosin, or Congo red do not penetrate bacterial cells. Called negative stains, they dye the background on the slide leaving the cells colorless in the midst of a dense precipitate. The subsequent secondary staining of such preparations with an ordinary dye of a different color may leave a clear halo around the cells indicating the size and location of the capsule if the cell possesses one. Some cytologists believe that negative stains give a more accurate picture of the size of bacterial cells since the method does not require a fixing procedure which could distort the cells, nor does it involve initial penetration of the cell by the dye.

Some staining procedures distinguish between different types of bacteria. These **diagnostic stains** are specialized to demonstrate certain structural features which have differential significance. For

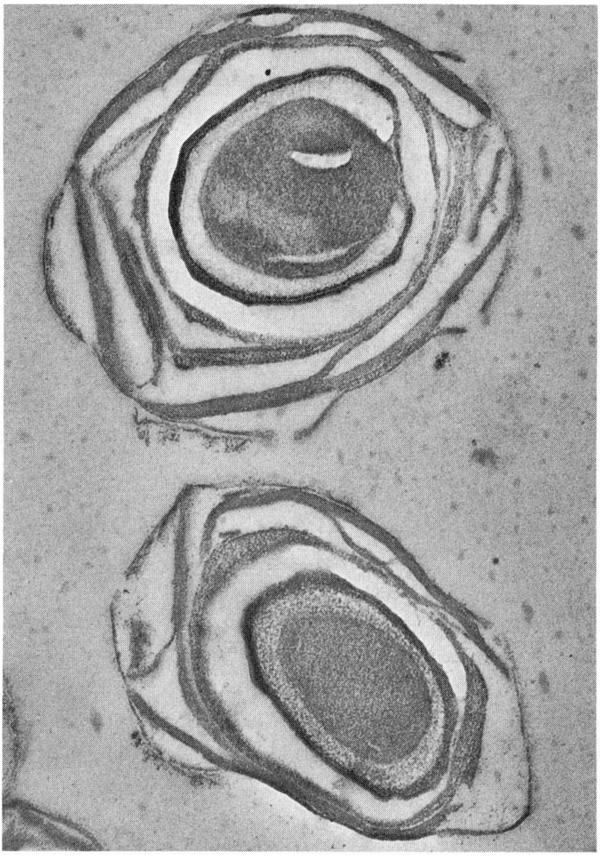

Fig. 4.6. The heavy coats protecting the spore from penetration by chemicals (such as dyes or disinfectants) are shown in this electron micrograph of an ultrathin section of a bacterial endospore.

example, the presence of fat globules, spores, capsules, or flagella may distinguish one bacterium from others which are similar in all characteristics except the absence of one or more of these structures. In some microorganisms, differential staining with solutions of methylene blue reveals **metachromatic granules,** which identify a number of bacteria including those which cause diphtheria.

The tubercle bacilli differ from most other pathogenic microorganisms in that they contain large amounts of fat and wax and are almost as difficult to stain as the endospores. They require long soaking or heating in the dye solution. Once the stain has been driven into the cell, however, even washing with dilute mineral acid will not remove it. Since most other cells are destained by this procedure, the tubercle bacilli can be distinguished from the multitude of other rod-shaped cells found in the sputum, in the throat, or in the tissues. This **acid-fast** stain is routinely used in the medical bacteriology laboratory in diagnosing tuberculosis and in following the progress of the patient during treatment.

The most widely used staining procedure in bacteriology, the **gram stain,** is employed to divide the bacteria into two major groups—gram-positive and gram-negative. The gram reaction has been so extensively studied that it has been correlated with many other properties of the bacteria.

Careful technique is required for the successful use of this staining method since minor variations from the standard procedure give uninterpretable results. Four steps involved in the basic method are demonstrated in Table 4.1.

The gram-positive organisms have certain chemical and physical characteristics which bind crystal violet tightly to the cell when it is mordanted with iodine. Of the many theories advanced to explain these characteristics, one suggests the electrical charges on the surface of the bacterial cell are responsible for the affinity for crystal violet. The gram-positive forms are more negatively charged and hence not as readily decolorized by alcohol. According to another theory, the gram-positive characteristic is directly related to the permeability of the cell membrane or more likely the cell wall. Certainly, the cell walls of

Table 4.1. The Gram Stain

Steps	*Gram-positive Bacteria*	*Gram-negative Bacteria*
1. Crystal violet	Cells stain violet.	Cells stain violet.
2. Iodine solution	Iodine reacts with the crystal violet and "fixes" the dye in the cell.	The crystal-violet dye is not "fixed" in the cell.
3. Alcohol	The alcohol does not remove the crystal violet.	The crystal violet is dissolved in the alcohol, thus removing the dye color.
4. Safranin	The cells are already stained violet by the crystal violet; hence the red safranin is not apparent.	The decolorized cells are stained red by the safranin.

gram-negative bacteria are thinner and they have a unique chemical composition. These cell walls contain about 20% fat, almost ten times that found in the cell walls of gram-positive bacteria. This fatty layer resists penetration by water solutions of certain inhibitory chemicals such as soaps and dyes; on the other hand, alcohol can penetrate it readily and remove the crystal violet-iodine complex.

SUMMARY. The microbiologist is usually a microscopist. The effectiveness of the light microscope can be extended by the use of stains and by the use of dark-field or phase techniques. Differential stains can be used to distinguish different kinds of bacteria and different kinds of cell inclusions. The electron microscope has extended the range of observation of small objects at least one hundredfold. The internal details of the cell are revealed by examining thin sections of bacteria with the electron microscope.

5

The Anatomy and Division of Bacterial Cells

Although in comparison to other cells the bacterial body is small, its structure is well organized, consisting of a protoplast encased in a cell wall (Fig. 5.1). The cytoplasmic membrane on the surface of the protoplast encloses the cytoplasm with its vacuoles, granules, and nuclear material. Outside the cell wall is the capsule and, in the case of motile organisms, the flagella, which originate in the cytoplasm and extend through the cell wall.

The Capsule. The slime layer outside the bacterial cell may vary in thickness from a thin undetectable layer to a mass many times the volume of the bacterial cell itself. When the slime layer is thick enough to be detected, it is called a capsule. The largest capsules are developed by encapsulated bacteria with an abundance of food material; in most organisms the capsule is made of a gummy carbohydrate material. In gram-positive bacilli the capsule material is a proteinaceous substance, and in some organisms it is lipid (fatty) material. The capsule protects certain disease-producing organisms from destruction by the white-blood cells and other defense mechanisms of the animal body. In soil organisms the capsule seems to protect the organism against drying.

The capsular material in the soil is of considerable importance in

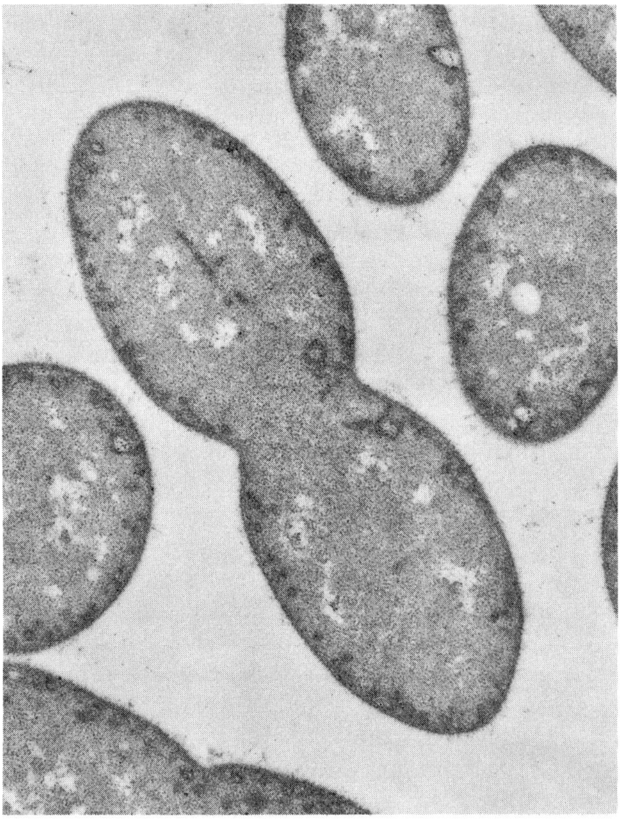

Fig. 5.1. An electron micrograph of the bacterium *Azotobacter*. Careful observation of the edge of the cell shows the cell wall and the cell membrane. The irregular light patches are nuclear material, and the white spherical body is a fat globule. The darkly outlined bodies near the edge of the cell are invaginations or inpouchings of the cell membrane. No other membrane structures can be observed inside the cell.

breaking up the soil into small aggregates and thus contributes to what is called the tilth of the soil.

From capsules of certain organisms, a blood thickener or a blood substitute has been prepared to be administered to shock victims who are losing their blood liquids into the tissue. If whole blood or blood plasma is not available, solutions of these bacterial capsules (**dextrans**) are more useful than plain saline or glucose transfusions since they, like natural blood, are more easily retained by the capillaries. If the capsular material is very water soluble and diffuses away from the microorganism, it is referred to as a slime. In certain industries the development of large numbers of encapsulated organisms is a nuisance; in the paper mills bacteria may stick to the rollers and cause uneven deposition of the pulp, and in the sugar industry they may multiply rapidly and clog the syrup pipes.

The Cell Wall. The bacterial cell wall, though only about 0.01 micron thick, is extremely strong in proportion to its size (Fig. 5.2). This rigid wall, which gives the cell its shape, can be observed in the sectioned cell but does not show up well under the light microscope unless given special chemical treatment. When dried or placed in strong salt solution, the internal contents of the cell may collapse away from the cell wall, but the bacterium will retain its original appearance because the cell wall is not readily distorted. The wall enables the bacterium to retain its shape and integrity even when exposed to great variations in the liquid in which it lives. When the cell walls of any bacteria are removed, the **protoplast** assumes a spherical shape; the cell membrane will burst unless held in a salt or sugar solution with osmotic properties equal to that of the cytoplasm (7% sucrose for *Bacillus anthracis*). Since protoplasts can carry on most of the functions of the intact cell, the cell wall clearly performs a limited function.

In order to observe the fragments of the empty cell walls and to collect them for chemical analyses, bacterial cells are ground with finely powdered glass. Cell walls are composed of proteins, fats, and carbohydrates, the proportions being different in different organisms; but apparently the three substances are arranged in each species in definite, reproducible mosaics. An enzyme called lysozyme, found in tears, egg

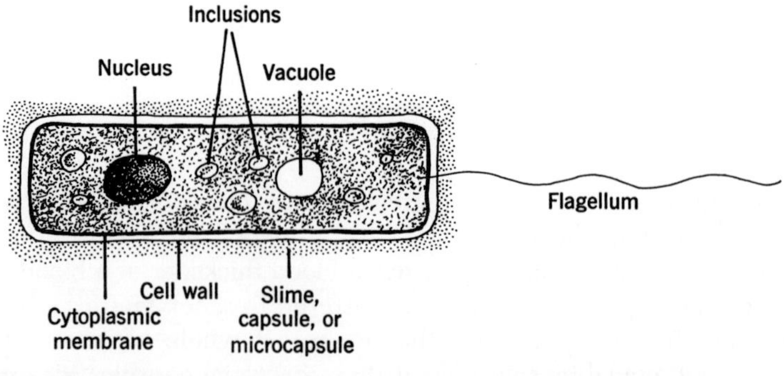

Fig. 5.2. This artist's concept of the bacterial cell reveals the parts to be observed but shows the nucleus as a well-circumscribed body, rather than as diffuse lobes shown by the electron microscope (Fig. 5.1). Those supporting this picture of a bacterial cell argue that the vigorous treatment applied in electron microscopy or by staining disrupts the fragile internal cellular boundaries.

white, and other natural sources, will digest the carbohydrate bonds in the cell wall and cause a general breaking of the structure, usually with subsequent osmotic lysis and dissolution of the protoplast. Lysozyme produces an effect similar to penicillin, and it may have been Fleming's prior discovery of lysozyme that conditioned him intellectually for the more important discovery of penicillin.

Gram-positive bacteria have thicker cell walls than gram-negative organisms, but the latter have a much higher concentration of fat. In addition, gram-negative bacteria contain typical proteins with the entire array of amino acids; gram-positive bacteria contain abnormal proteins devoid of certain amino acids. All bacterial cell walls contain diaminopimelic acid, an amino acid occurring only in blue-green algae and bacteria.

The Cell Membrane. Underneath the cell wall is the cytoplasmic membrane, which is about 0.005 micron thick and stains very easily with dyes. The cell membrane was once thought to consist largely of fat-like materials, but recent studies indicate the presence of high concentrations of nucleic acids, especially on the ends where rapid growth takes place. This concentration of nucleic acids in the growth areas supports the hypothesis that they serve as templates (forms or molds) for building proteins. The cell membrane is very flexible and is equivalent to the outer wall of animal cells. As a living membrane it is differentially permeable, letting some things pass through but not others. Microbes must, by their very nature, live while soaking in their nutrient material; the cell must have the ability to control the concentration of substances which enter the cell, whether these be toxic substances or those needed for structural materials or energy production.

When protoplasts are broken up by diluting the suspending medium, the broken and empty cell membranes appear as cell ghosts in the resulting cell debris. They can be collected by centrifuging, and their chemical and biological characteristics can be studied. They contain specific proteins called **permeases**, which unite with substances on the outside of the cell, carry these substances through the membrane, and discharge them into the cytoplasm. Such permeases require energy for their action, and a number of enzyme systems associated with energy production in bacteria are located in the membrane.

The Cytoplasm and Inclusion Granules. Inside the cytoplasmic membrane is the cytoplasm, a protoplasmic material quite similar to that found in animal and plant cells. It consists largely of a water suspension of enzyme proteins and ribonucleic acid; these are not dissolved evenly throughout the cytoplasm but often occur in particles or granules.

Certain particles called **ribosomes** contain the enzymes involved in protein synthesis. Although early studies of cells treated them as sacks of enzymes, we now realize that the living cell has a geography which holds the secret of many cell processes. Dispersion of granules and vacuoles throughout the cytoplasm suggests considerable localization of materials performing specific cellular activities.

Some of the granules help us identify the bacterium under observation. For example, certain species store granules of the carbohydrate, **glycogen,** which stains red with iodine, while others store starch, which stains blue with iodine. Some organisms store a considerable amount of fat as globules, and other cells may contain granules of sulfur. The diphtheria organism is usually identified by the granules which stain an off-color red when these cells are treated with old solutions of the dye, methylene blue. These metachromatic structures have been called **volutin granules** and appear to be made of ribonucleic acid and polyphosphates.

The Nucleus. Embedded in the cytoplasm is the nucleus (Fig. 5.3), which is difficult to see in the bacterial cell because of (1) the small size of the cell and (2) the high content of ribonucleic acid in the cytoplasm which masks the usual nuclear stains. Although some questions have not been settled to the satisfaction of all cytologists, modern cytological procedures can demonstrate nuclear material in all bacterial cells, and genetic studies with one species suggest its arrangement into a single chromosome. Consequently, complex procedures are not needed in bacterial nuclear division, such as the mitosis, encountered in dividing nuclei of higher animals and plants. The bacterial chromosomes are composed of the same important type of chemical substance, deoxyribonucleic acid (DNA), that makes up the heredity-governing units (the genes) in the cells of higher animals and plants and which direct the activity of the cell. Nuclear membranes and centrioles appear absent from bacterial nuclei, but the chromosome replicates and undergoes division in such a manner that the decendants inherit equal shares of the material controlling the heritable characteristics of the parent cell.

Endospores. Some of the rod-shaped organisms form spherical or oval bodies called spores; since these are formed within the bacterial cell, they are called **endospores.** The ordinary bacterium is called a vegetative cell in order to distinguish it from the spore. Spores are observed in older cultures when readily available food is no longer present. Spore production is indicated by condensation of the protoplasm of the organism and formation of a specialized body within the organism. Although alive, spores appear inert, exhibiting practically no metabolism and a

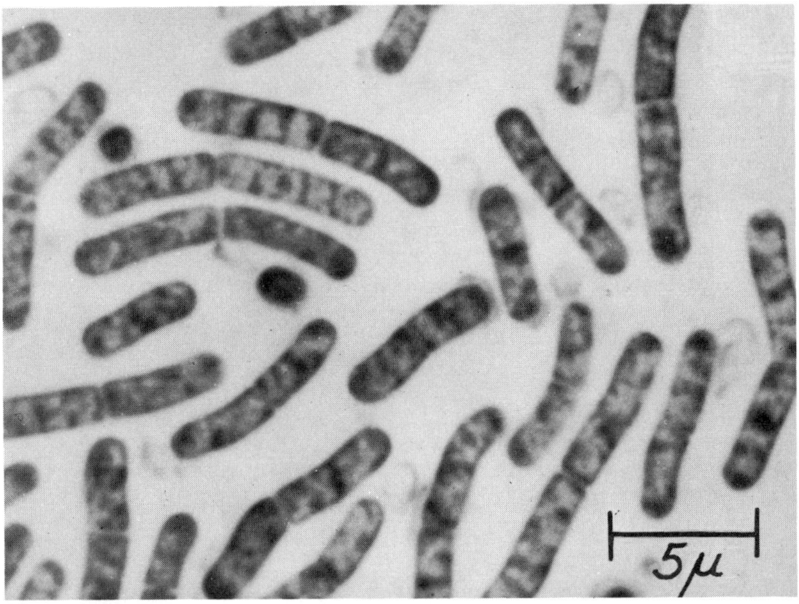

Fig. 5.3. *Bacillus megatherium* fixed and stained with 0.01% aqueous basic fuchsin for 20 seconds. The uneven staining of the cell contents is due to the greater affinity of the basic fuchsin for the cytoplasm than for nuclear material. Empty spore cases are visible. In some cases a clear band is seen in the bacteria which represents the unstained transverse cell wall. *Photo by C. F. Robinow, courtesy S.A.B. LS-237.*

high resistance to the killing action of heat or chemicals. The spore may remain dormant for long periods of time, but, when placed in food material proper for growth, it germinates to form a rod, which will produce a new cell like that from which the spore was formed. The spore permits the organism to live through periods and in places where the conditions for growth are temporarily undesirable. As a spore, the organism may be spread throughout the world, since spores are readily carried by air currents and are not killed by the drying process.

Spores are found in the center of some cells, while in others they may be near the ends of the rods. Most spores are no larger than the diameter of the cell, but in some species they may be large enough to cause a bulge in the cell wall (Fig. 5.4); thus the cell may be spindle-shaped if the spores are in the center, or club-shaped if the spores occur near one end. Since a single endospore is formed from a single rod, sporulation is a survival mechanism rather than a method of multiplication.

The resistance of spores has been attributed to the tough, imperme-

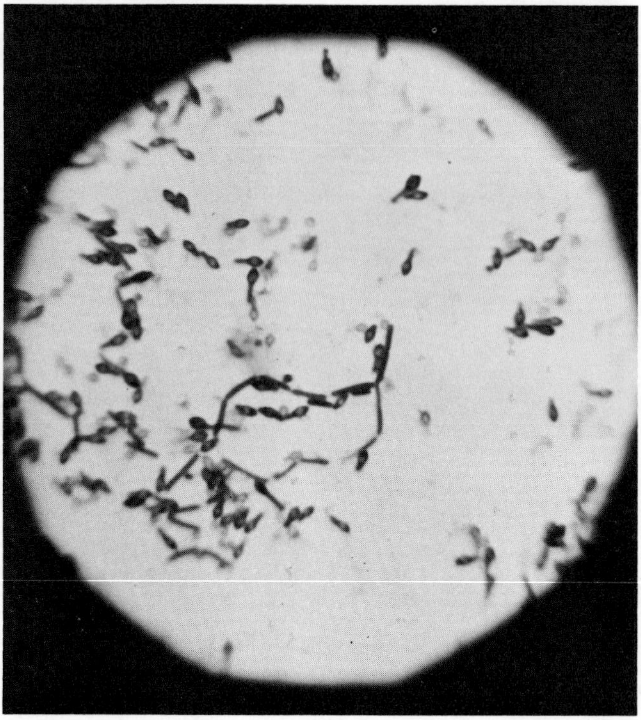

Fig. 5.4. A light microscope picture of spores forming in rod-shaped bacteria. In this species the spores cause a bulge in the rod; such a structure is called a clostridium.

able spore coat which is called the **exine.** When the exine is mechanically broken the spore loses much of its resistance. The interior of the spore contains nuclear and cytoplasmic material but differs from vegetative cells in having a very low moisture content. In the absence of moisture the spore proteins are resistant to the denaturing effects of heat. Spore formation, therefore, may be regarded as a procedure by which protoplasm is condensed, partially dehydrated, and surrounded by an impermeable wall to resist re-entrance of water and dissolved materials. Germination occurs when the exine is rendered less impermeable by spore enzymes activated by a germination medium.

The extreme resistance of spores presents some serious problems. The heat treatment used in canning foods is aimed at destroying spores since the sensitive vegetative cells are easily killed. In any situation where elimination of all microbes is sought, the treatment employed must be sufficiently drastic to destroy the most resistant microbial form, that is, the bacterial spore.

Flagella. Essentially all of the spiral shaped bacteria and about half of the bacilli are capable of independent motion. Any particle may be carried by water currents or be imparted vibratory motion as a result of being bombarded by molecules of the suspending fluid. But these bacteria are able to move independently in a moist environment. True motility can be observed in the organisms in a drop of water; whereas nonmotile forms vibrate back and forth in almost the same area or move about in currents of water, the motile forms have definite motion in relation to each other and can be observed moving about as if proceeding to some destination. The motile bacteria swim actively by means of a flagellum or several flagella (Fig. 5.5).

Many bacteriologists believe that the most primitive bacteria were probably the spiral water bacteria, which swim by means of a single

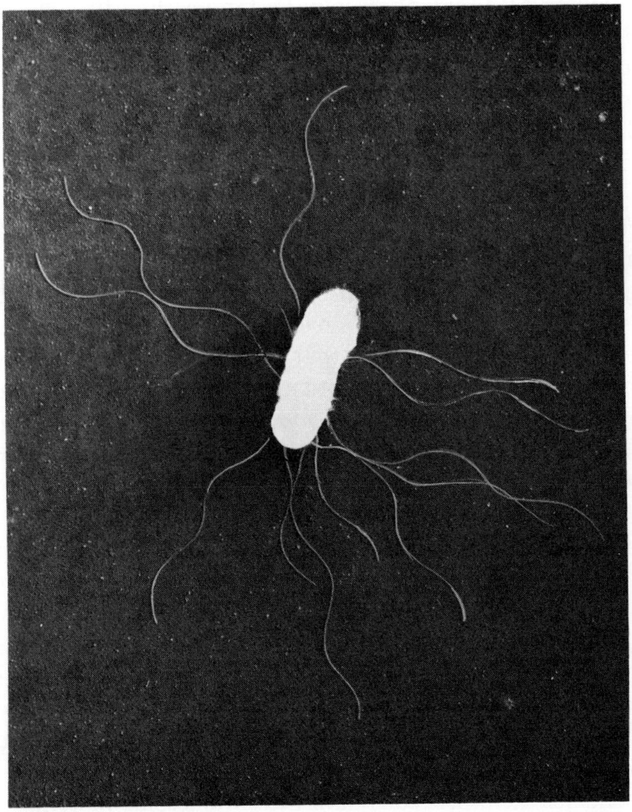

Fig. 5.5. An electron microscope picture of a bacterial cell showing peritrichous flagella. Since this cell has not been cut into ultrathin sections, no internal detail is evident.

flagellum located at one end of the cell. Evolving from these were rod-shaped organisms with single flagella, followed by spiral and rod-shaped bacteria with tufts of flagella. These organelles permitted swimming even as the organisms moved to less watery environments. The motile bacteria found in such places as the intestinal tract of man usually have numerous flagella extending from all sides of the cell. Such an adaptation permits them to move around in the films of water found on dryer particles. Other bacteria which have moved out of the water to a terrestrial existence, such as the organisms found on the surface of the skin, in the dryer parts of the soil, or on the surface of plants, have abandoned motility entirely and exhibit no flagella.

The flagella are long, threadlike structures, often several times the length of the cell to which they are attached. From their attachment to a basal granule in the cytoplasm, the flagella pass through the cell membrane and cell wall and capsule and project into the surrounding environment. Although they may be longer than the cell, they are ordinarily less than one twentieth the diameter of the cell (less than 0.05 micron) and, therefore, are quite invisible under the light microscope unless they are stained by a special procedure which precipitates material around each flagellum. The resulting structure is much bigger than the flagellum itself and can be seen by the better light microscopes. The true size and shape of the flagellum is demonstrated by the electron microscope. The flagella seem to act by contraction and rotation, moving about in the rear of the bacterium like a propeller. Not only do they drive the bacterium forward, but they also act as rudders, governing the direction of movement. The flagella are composed of protein somewhat similar to that found in muscle. An organism with a single flagellum is referred to as **monotrichous**, while one with a tuft of flagella on the end is called **lophotrichous**. If the flagella are scattered over the entire surface of the cell, it is referred to as **peritrichous**.

Reproduction of Bacteria. Bacteria would be of little consequence if it were not for their prodigious rate of reproduction when placed in a suitable environment. Bacteria reproduce by transverse binary fission, splitting crossways, never longitudinally, and dividing into two approximately equal parts. This process of splitting is preceded by delicate movements in the nuclear material: The nucleus contains those substances which govern the inheritance phenomena in the cell, and these must be reproduced before the cell divides. An increase in the deoxyribonucleic acid proceeds until the chromosome material has been replicated. The chromosome then splits longitudinally, each half having a full complement of the genes. An elaborate mechanism for moving the two sets of chromosomes to opposite sides of the cell is implemented in higher cells by formation of spindle fibers attached to opposite poles of the cell. Each set undergoes reorganization into a new nuclear body, after which the cell splits in half; each daughter cell then contains a nucleus with a complement of heredity-controlling components identical to that of the mother cell. While such a process is unnecessary in bacterial cells with a single chromosome, pictures have been presented which imply that in certain bacteria these events may take place.

At some stages during bacterial growth the nuclear division may proceed more rapidly than cell division; each bacterial cell may then contain two or even four nuclear bodies. But generally, after the nuclei divide, a cell plate grows between them, starting from the cell wall and growing toward the center. This cell plate splits to form the end walls of two new cells, though the cells may be connected by a thread of cytoplasm through the center of the walls after the other processes of division are complete. This thread, called the **plasmodesm**, has been observed in bacteria such as streptococci and chain-forming bacilli.

After the cell has divided, each daughter cell grows until it, in turn, is able to divide its nuclear material and undergo a cell division. Under ideal conditions bacteria have been known to divide once every nine minutes, but the species of organisms commonly dealt with in the laboratory usually have a generation time of 20 to 30 minutes. The generation time is the minimum time it takes for the organism to undergo separation from a sister cell and fission into two daughter cells. Certain slow-growing bacteria, even under the optimum conditions for growth, divide no more often than once every 3 to 4 hours.

If a single bacterium in a test tube containing one milliliter of broth began to grow at its optimum rate, it would make about 30 divisions to produce a population of a billion cells; if it were undergoing fission every 30 minutes, this population would be achieved in 15 hours. After that time the organism would stop growing because of the exhaustion of food material or because of the toxic nature of the waste materials produced. If we consider binary fission as a division of one organism into two and the two into four, the four into eight, and so forth, we observe that there is an infinite series of 1, 2, 4, 8, 16, etc., produced within succeeding generations. A little arithmetic will show us that in 10 generations one cell will become 1024 cells. Therefore, if instead of one cell 1000 are placed in the test tube, the process will take 10 generations less (or 5 hours less) to achieve the maximum population of one billion per tube. If 500 million organisms are placed in the tube, the population will arrive at the figure of one billion in the next cell division, 30 minutes later. This type of reproduction is called asexual because it does not involve the combination of hereditary materials from two individuals.

In certain strains of some species of bacteria, a mating of organisms has been demonstrated resulting in inheritance of some of the characteristics of each of the parents. This sexual process is probably not very widespread in nature, but it demonstrates the rather interesting thesis that a fundamental process in higher animals and plants has its counterpart among the bacteria.

SUMMARY. Bacterial cells, though of microscopic size, are extremely highly organized entities. They possess most of the characteristics of the cells in higher plants and animals and are adapted so they may function as individuals. Bacteria undergo division at rates which guarantee their survival in all but the most perverse environments.

6

Growth of Bacteria

Only a relatively small part of the everyday activity of the modern microbiologist involves examining organisms under the microscope. Most laboratory effort involves the growing or culturing of microorganisms in tubes or flasks containing food materials called **culture media.** A culture medium is any substance which provides food for microbial growth. It must contain a utilizable source of the elements of which the bacterial cell is made. For example, some bacteria can build their nitrogenous cell substance from gaseous nitrogen (N_2); others can use ammonia (NH_3); and still others require amino acids (RNH_2COOH).

A few bacteria are **autotrophic** and can use carbon dioxide (CO_2) as their sole source of carbon; the majority are **heterotrophic** and require organic carbon, that is, that incorporated in carbohydrates, fats, proteins, and organic acids. All bacteria can obtain hydrogen and oxygen from water. Most can obtain mineral elements from simple salts of sulfur, phosphorus, calcium, potassium, iron, magnesium, sodium, zinc, copper, molydenum, cobalt, and so forth; a few types need sulfur already built into amino acids, or cobalt already built into vitamin B_{12}.

A nutrient medium must not contain toxic concentrations of salts or other growth inhibitors, and it must not be excessively acid or alkaline. The pH scale measures the acidity or alkalinity of a medium by checking on a logarithmic scale the concentration of hydrogen ions

($H_2O \rightleftarrows H^+ + OH^-$). This scale ranges from 0 to 14; most microbes grow best at pH 7, which is neutral. Values below 7 indicate acidity and those above 7 indicate alkalinity. Electrometric instruments or dyes that change color at different pH values may be used to measure pH. If a medium is too acid or alkaline, adjustments can be made by appropriate addition of alkali or acid.

Broth. The simplest culture medium is meat broth, which was used by the earliest bacteriologists. Although many diverse extracts of animal and plant origin as well as mixtures made from synthetic chemicals are now used, all such liquid culture media are termed **broths**. Since microbial cells are composed largely of protein, additional proteinaceous substances are often added to broths by adding peptones (products of protein digestion), which dissolve in water to give clear solutions; thus an excess of the necessary nutrients is supplied. A liter of water in which is dissolved 5 to 10 grams of peptone (made from partially hydrolyzed meat, milk, or soy bean protein) makes an excellent broth for many bacteria.

When bacteria grow in a broth, the medium becomes cloudy or **turbid**. The degree of turbidity is a measure of the number of organisms present (Fig. 6.1). Some microbes form thin films called **pellicles** on the surface of broth; some form sediment at the bottom of the tube. To stimulate growth, peptone broths are supplemented with sugar, starch, or vitamins, or, if the culture contains fastidious organisms which ordinarily grow in the animal body, blood may be added.

Solid Media. For some purposes a solid medium is superior to a liquid medium. To solidify a broth we can add gelatin, but by far the most commonly used solid media are made by adding about ½ to 1½% agar to a nutrient broth. Agar, a carbohydrate obtained from seaweed, will melt at 98°C and will remain liquid until it cools to about 40°C. Once it has solidified it will not melt again until heated to almost the boiling point. Unlike gelatin, agar itself can be used as food by very few microbes, and so it is not liquefied by microbial growth.

Sterilization. Since bacteria and other microorganisms are found everywhere in nature, the bacteriologist who prepares a culture medium will find that immediately hundreds of microorganisms from the air, glassware, and chemicals will begin to grow in this material. Any bacteriological experiment which he might attempt would be hopelessly confused by this mixture of unwanted organisms called **contaminants**. The battle against contamination constitutes much of the effort in the microbiology laboratory. After a culture medium is made, it is placed in containers that will prevent the further entrance of any other micro-

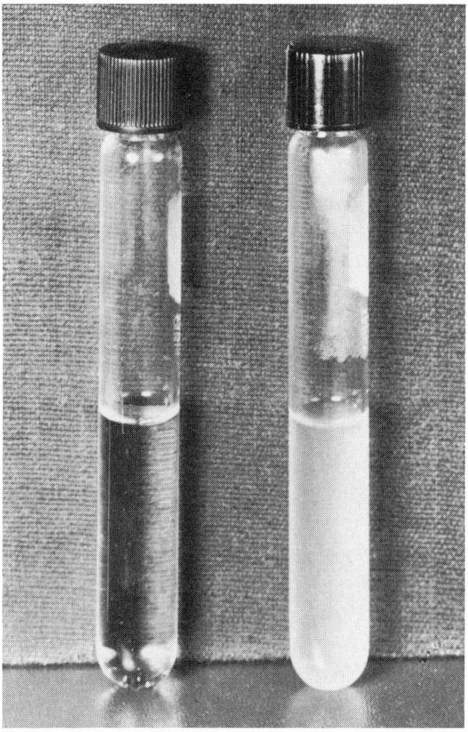

Fig. 6.1. Left, a control tube of sterile broth; right, a turbid bacterial culture.

organisms from the air and dust. The classic method of keeping contaminants out of flasks and tubes is by plugging them with cotton. With moderately compressed cotton plugs the passage of air and other gases in and out of the container is not impeded, but microbes are effectively prevented from either entering or leaving.

Next the contaminants already present in the medium must be destroyed. The procedure used to free the culture medium and equipment from all living forms is referred to as **sterilization**. A number of different methods are routinely employed in the bacteriological laboratory. For glassware, such as test tubes and flasks, **dry heat**, such as that produced by an oven, is ordinarily applied. When 170°C heat is applied for 2 hours the organisms found in culture equipment are completely destroyed: The material is sterile. Cotton-stoppered tubes and flasks and petri dishes and pipettes that are wrapped in paper may be oven-sterilized since this heating will not cause charring of the paper or the cotton.

Broths and agar cannot be placed in the oven at 170°C because they will evaporate; such materials are sterilized in **moist heat.** By placing them for 20 minutes in a large pressure cooker, called an **autoclave** (Fig. 6.2), where they are subjected to live steam at 15 pounds of pressure, contaminants are destroyed. The pressure has no direct effect on the sterilizing process, but at 15 pounds of pressure the temperature of the steam reaches 121°C. Since this produces sterility quite as effectively as the dry-heat oven treatment, it is evident that moist heat is more efficient for destroying microorganisms: Not only does a lower temperature suffice, but also a much shorter time is required. When steam contacts cool objects it liberates large amounts of latent heat, which promptly raises the temperature of the articles to that of the steam. Therefore, moisture, together with the rapidly elevated temperature, results in effective sterilization in the autoclave.

Equipment that is not damaged by heat may be sterilized by a direct flame, which destroys microorganisms by incineration. This procedure is used to sterilize the inoculating needle, a piece of platinum or nichrome wire attached to a handle with which microorganisms are transferred from one test tube to another. Some materials are sterilized with chemicals. The desk tops on which microbiologists work are ordinarily washed down with a germ-killing chemical, such as phenol or cresol. Glass rods that are used to spread microorganisms over solid medium surfaces are dipped in alcohol, which is burned off before use. Ethylene oxide gas is an efficient cold sterilizing agent for materials held in it in a closed container for several hours.

Solutions of chemicals that are heat sensitive can be sterilized by filtration. A culture medium containing heat labile substances may be sterilized by passing it through a bacterial filter with such fine pores that all bacteria are filtered out. Heat-sensitive liquids such as blood serum may be sterilized in this manner.

Special Media. While standard bacteriological culture media are supplemented agars or broths, certain organisms and special experiments demand the use of other culture media. For many organisms sterile milk is an excellent culture medium. An indicator dye, such as litmus, may be added, which will change in color when acid is produced by fermentation of the milk sugars. Since milk is too cloudy to permit observation of turbidity, the dye is used to indicate the changes produced during the growth of organisms. Tomato juice and other vegetable juices provide an excellent liquid medium for the cultivation of organisms characteristically found in plants. **Differential media** are employed to differentiate between types of bacteria. For example, on an agar medium containing the chemical, bismuth sulfite, the typhoid organism

Fig. 6.2. The autoclave is used for routine sterilization in the microbiology laboratory. *Photo courtesy American Sterilizer Co.*

will grow as a black colony and can be distinguished from a mixture of other organisms (Fig. 6.3). **Selective media** may contain substances which stimulate the growth of the type of organism that is desired or which inhibit unwanted types. The selective device may involve the addition of a dye that inhibits gram-positive bacteria but permits growth of gram-negative bacteria; it may involve the addition of acid to lower the pH to a value unfavorable for skin bacteria but not for the ringworm fungus; it may involve the incorporation of a special food, such as cellulose, if we desire to isolate cellulose-decomposing microorganisms.

In order to study the complex nutrition of bacteria, a chemically de-

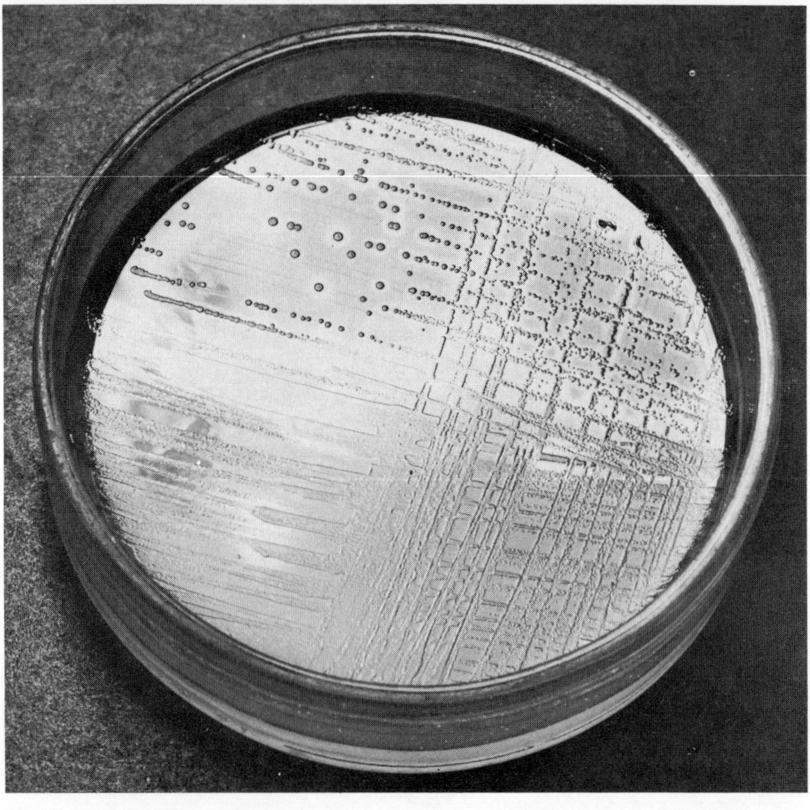

Fig. 6.3. A streaked plate of *Salmonella typhosa* on bismuth sulfite agar. The isolated colonies in the upper left can be picked as pure cultures. This is a differential medium because the typhoid bacterium grows better on it than many bacteria usually found with it; it is also a diagnostic medium since the typhoid colonies on it show a distinctive shiny surface and a halo.

fined medium is often required. Instead of using extracts of natural materials, mixtures of pure chemicals are made which contain utilizable forms of the necessary elements. Such media are called **synthetic media** or **chemically defined** media, since they are compounded from known chemical substances.

Growth on Living Systems. Some organisms will not grow on nonliving material. The viruses that cause diseases in plants are cultured in the greenhouse on growing plants protected from contamination by plastic or glass hoods. As the host plants age and die, the greenhouse cultures of viruses are transferred to young healthy plants, and the stock culture is maintained. Similarly, microorganisms are grown in laboratory animals such as monkeys, guinea pigs, rabbits, rats, and mice.

The most convenient laboratory animal is the developing chick embryo, since it is enclosed in its own covering, the eggshell, which keeps out contaminating organisms. When a fertile egg has been incubated for a few days, we can observe the development of the baby chick. This embryo serves admirably for the growth of many microorganisms that are not easily grown in any other type of laboratory medium.

Animal cells are grown in test tubes and flasks by application of the procedures worked out earlier for bacteria (Fig. 6.4). Although very complex media are required, it is now no great problem to grow skin tissue, tissues from certain types of cancers, and kidney or heart tissue in sterilized flasks containing the proper nutrient formula. Microorganisms requiring living cells for growth can be grown and studied in these test-tube conditions without the complication of using a whole living animal.

Many kinds of culture media are required, although microorganisms, in their ability to thrive under diverse conditions, are the most flexible of all the living forms. Man and other higher animals live under moderate temperatures and pressures, in contact with relatively inert gases and chemicals; microbes are not so restricted. Many species, it is true, favor the conditions under which higher animals and plants thrive. Other species may prefer temperatures much higher or lower than those which we regard as compatible with life: Some will thrive in strong acid or under high pressure. The microbiologist utilizes knowledge of these factors in preparing culture media and in regulating the growth and death of microorganisms.

When microbes are inoculated into a sterile medium and placed in an incubator at a suitable temperature, growth occurs. The term growth as applied to bacteria almost always connotes increase in numbers, that is, multiplication. The individual organism grows both be-

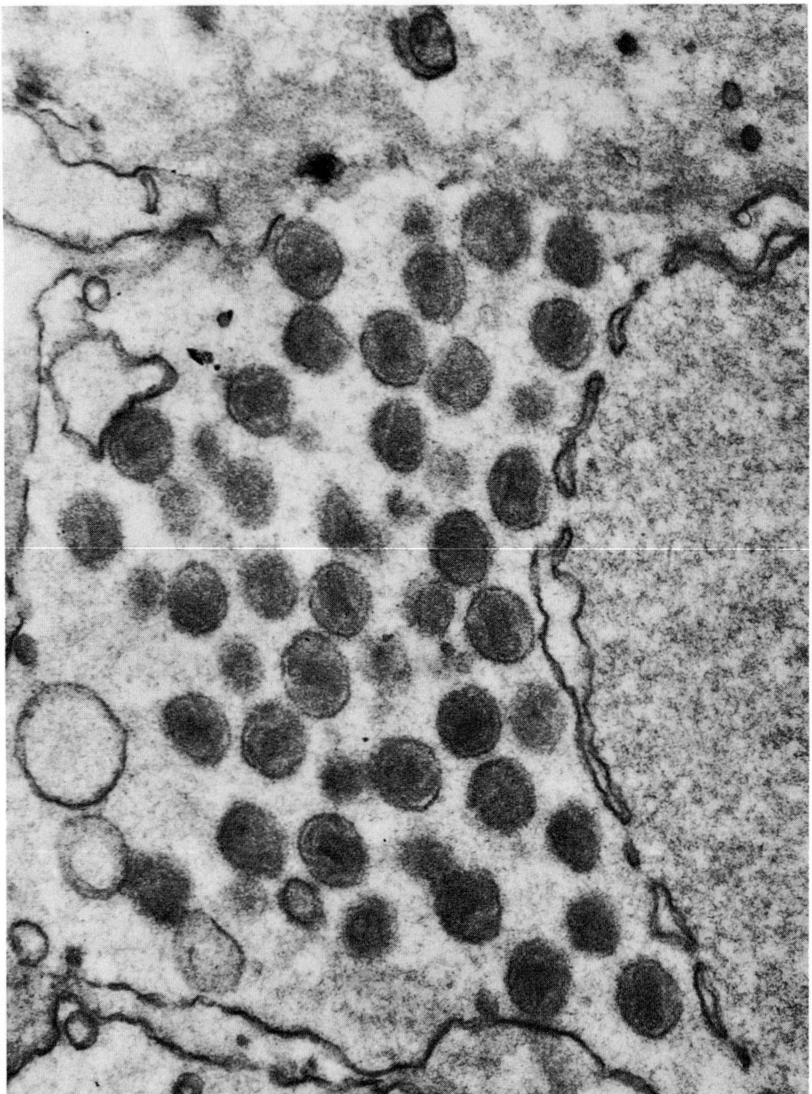

Fig. 6.4. The dark spots in this electron micrograph of a part of a cell from an infected chick embryo are vaccinia virus particles. Around each appears to be a membrane and, inside of some, a dumbbell shaped nucleus-like area is visible. The nucleus of the chick cell on the right is separated by a nuclear membrane from the cytoplasm in which the viruses multiply. *Photo by Norton McDuffie, Univ. of Texas.*

Table 6.1. Summary of Methods for Determining Bacterial Growth

Total Numbers (Multiplication)	*Total Mass (Growth)*
Total Quantity of Growth	
1. Counting chamber	1. Turbidity
2. Stained slides	2. Total cell volume
3. Proportional count	3. Weight
4. Electronic particle counter	4. Colony diameter
Viable Quantity of Growth	
1. Plate count	1. Oxygen uptake
2. Dilution count	2. Nutrients (sugars) consumed
3. Membrane filters	3. Metabolic products (acid, CO_2, or NH_3)

fore and after cell division occurs, but the growth of the culture involves the production of more cells and is most often measured by determining the number of cells produced. However, techniques are available for measuring cell mass, and the growth of multicellular microorganisms, such as molds, is often followed in that manner. By measuring the inoculum and then by determining the amount or number of microbes some hours later, the growth rate may be estimated. Procedures are available for measuring either the total amount of protoplasm produced or for measuring the amount of viable (i.e., living) protoplasm. The methods are summarized in Table 6.1.

Bacterial cells may be counted directly under the microscope in much the same manner as blood cells are counted in the hospital laboratory. **The Counting Chamber** (also called the Petroff-Hauser bacteria counter) is a thick glass slide with a small depression carefully machined to 0.02 mm deep (Fig. 6.5). On the bottom of the chamber are etched lines which divide it into squares. When the liquid containing the bacteria is placed in the depression and covered with glass, the slide may be examined under the microscope, and the bacteria in each of a number of the squares may be counted. Since there is a definite volume of liquid above each square, the number of bacteria per milliliter can be computed from the average count per square. The direct microscope count cannot be used with turbid materials, as particles of solids, such as soil, make counting impossible. Thus this technique is restricted to determining the number of organisms in broth or clear liquids; however, because living and dead cells look alike, it does not distinguish them. Stains applied to a culture may indicate whether cells are living or dead. For example, dead yeast cells stain deeply when suspended in a dilute solution of methylene blue, while living cells are colorless. By such staining the quality of a yeast preparation is determined.

Sometimes a rough estimate of the total number of bacteria is all that is required. By mixing a drop of the bacterial suspension with an equal volume of human blood, smearing it on a glass slide, and staining, a proportional count can be made. A comparison of the number of bacteria and the number of red-blood cells is made under the microscope. If bacteria and cells are present in equal numbers, the original material contains about 5 billion bacteria per milliliter, since that is approximately the number of red cells in normal human blood. Similarly, a proportional count of viruses can be made by taking electron microscope pictures of a mixture of the virus with a finely divided colloid in which the number of particles is known.

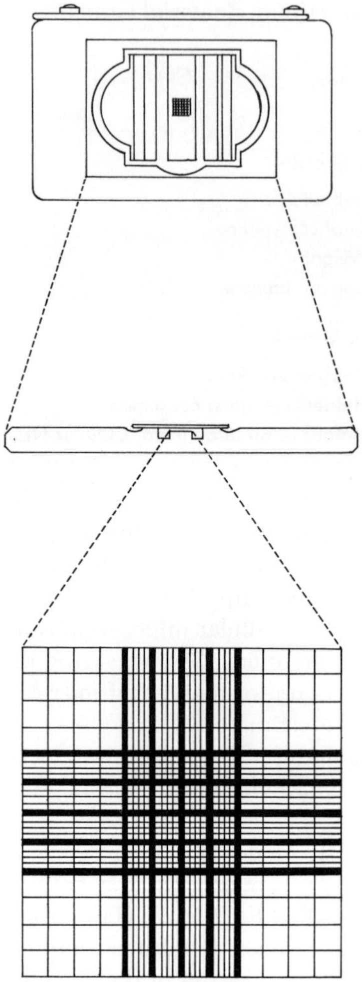

Fig. 6.5. A Petroff-Hauser counting chamber for making direct microscopic counts. The top representation is the front view, showing area which has etched rulings; in the center is a side view, and at the bottom is a diagram of the ruled area.

Bacteria are regarded as alive only if they can multiply; that is, (1) produce an infection in an animal, a plant, or a tissue culture, (2) make a tube of broth turbid, or (3) produce a colony on a solid medium.

The number of living cells is most often determined by a cultural method such as the **plate count**, which is also called the **colony count**. A measured amount of the material containing the microorganisms to be counted is mixed with melted nutrient agar, which has been cooled to about 45°C. After the microbes are thoroughly mixed with the nutrient agar, the mixture is poured into a culture dish called a petri plate. Upon solidification each cell or clump of cells is trapped in a definite place in the gel. Since nutrient agar contains all the material necessary for microbial growth, the organisms will begin to multiply when the plate is incubated at the proper temperature. After 24 to 48 hours, wherever an organism had been trapped in the gel there will be a pile of organisms or **colony**, which can be readily seen with the naked eye. A count of the number of colonies reveals how many organisms there were in the original material. If too many organisms are planted on a plate, there will be neither space nor food material enough for each to form a visible colony. In that case the whole plate is covered with tiny microcolonies, which may run together in a solid mass. For good plate counts it is desirable to have less than 300 colonies per plate. Materials containing more than 300 organisms per milliliter must be diluted in sterile water so that a countable number can be planted. This procedure is called a **dilution plate count** and is used to determine the number of viable cells in a culture or in other bacteria-containing materials. Less than 30 colonies per plate is undesirable since with such small numbers the chance variations become large.

While each colony is often regarded as the progeny of a single cell, actually, organisms stuck together in a clump will give rise to only one colony. Plate counts on milk usually show about one-fourth as many organisms as are counted by the direct microscopic method, due to clumps and dead organisms. Only a relatively small fraction of the bacteria of soil may appear on the plate count, since it is impossible to have the medium and the conditions of cultivation favorable to all organisms.

When culturing bacteria from air or from fairly pure water, **membrane filters** can be used to concentrate them before making a plate count. These membranes have uniform pores with diameters sufficiently small to seive bacteria from air or water. Measured quantities of gas or liquid are drawn by suction through the filters. The membranes, which are thin sheets made of cellulose acetate or similar materials, are then placed on the surface of a nutrient medium. The nutrients soak through the filter, and the microorganisms trapped on the filter grow to form colonies that can be counted.

Plate counts of viruses can be made by spreading properly diluted preparations over a layer of growing susceptible animal, plant, or bacterial cells; during incubation, each virus particle gives rise to a visible plaque which may be counted. A plaque is a circular area of infected

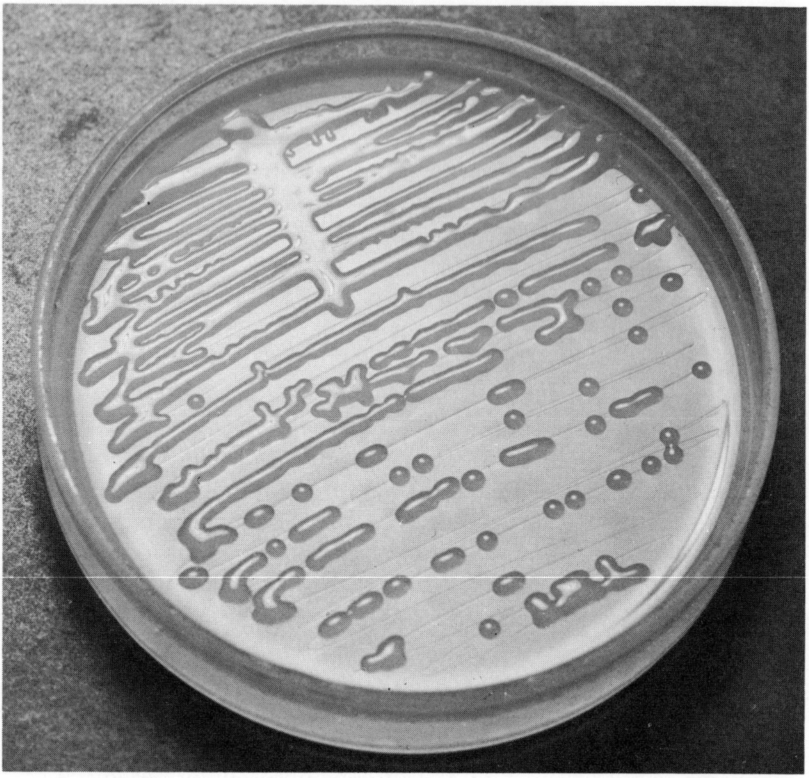

Fig. 6.6. A streak plate showing isolated colonies of *Azotobacter vinelandii.*

or dead host cells caused by the multiplication and radial spread of the virus. Estimates of the numbers of virus particles in the original preparations are thus made in a manner similar to colony counts of bacteria.

Well-separated bacterial colonies on an agar plate serve as a starting point for the isolation of a pure culture. The entire population in the colony is presumed to have descended from a single individual. A small amount of the cell mass from such colonies is transferred aseptically to a sterile tube of nutrient medium as the inoculum for the new culture. Since it is easier to pick surface colonies, plates for the isolation of pure cultures are usually prepared by streaking the organisms on the surface of an agar plate by means of a cotton swab, a glass rod, or an inoculating needle (Fig. 6.6). To insure the absence of latent contaminants, colonies are usually restreaked on sterile media at least one additional time before picking for the isolation of a pure culture.

Counts of living bacterial cells can be obtained by the **dilution method**

(Fig. 6.7). Tubes of nutrient broth are planted with a series of dilutions of the material containing the bacteria. After incubation the highest dilution showing growth gives a basis for estimating the number of organisms originally present. For example, if growth occurs in a tube inoculated with a milliliter of sewage that was diluted 1:1000, but not in a tube inoculated with the dilution 1:10,000, it is evident that at

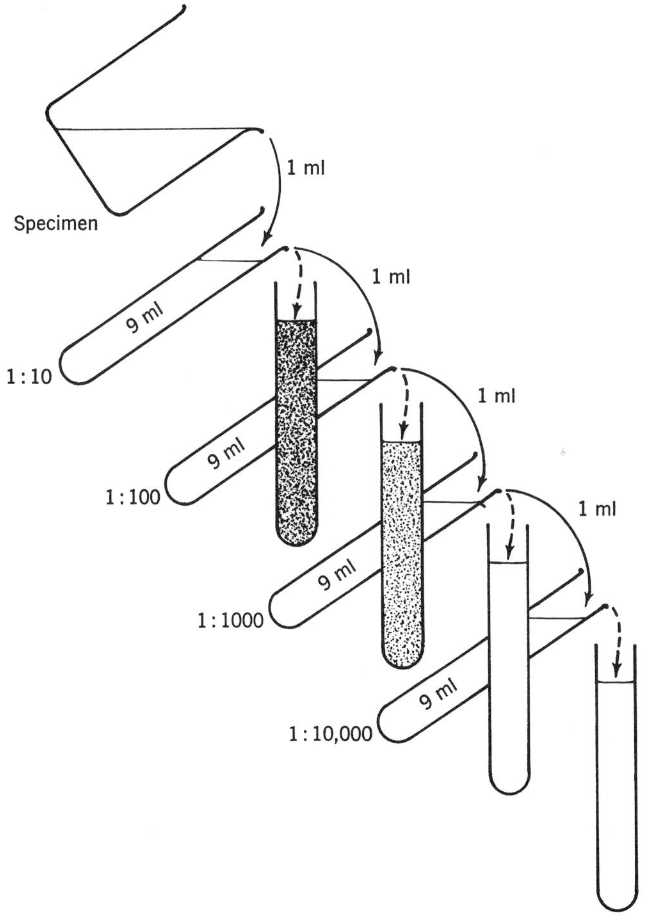

Fig. 6.7. Estimation of bacterial population by serial dilutions. A one ml portion is transferred to the succeeding dilution tubes and another one ml portion is seeded into a tube of broth. In this example the broth tubes seeded with the 1:10 and the 1:100 dilutions became turbid while those seeded with the 1:1000 and the 1:10,000 dilutions remained sterile. Therefore, the specimen has more than 100 bacteria per ml but less than 1000. Greater precision can be obtained by using multiple tubes.

least 1000 organisms but not as many as 10,000 were present per milliliter of the original sewage. By using several tubes at each dilution, it is possible to obtain a reasonably accurate estimate of the microbial population. This method can sometimes be used for determining the numbers of a particular kind of organism when it occurs together with a larger number of other bacteria. In water bacteriology a count of organisms capable of producing gas from lactose sugar can be made in a sample containing many other bacteria. A number of dilutions of water are inoculated into broth containing lactose sugar; after incubation only those tubes producing gas are recorded. For example, growth may occur in the 1:1,000,000 dilution, but if only the 1:10 dilutions show gas, the conclusion is that although there are many organisms present, only about 10 organisms per milliliter of the gas producers are to be found in this sample.

The total cell mass can be measured in the following ways.

1. ***Turbidity.*** Growth in broth cultures is determined by the turbidity resulting from the presence of bacterial cell bodies. With most bacterial cells the broth becomes slightly clouded when it contains about 10 million cells per milliliter. In a good broth an average bacterial culture attains a maximum population of the order of several hundred million to one billion cells per milliliter. When a single cell grows into a fully developed culture, more than 20 cell divisions occur before visible turbidity results. Turbidity is a useful measure of the suitability of a culture medium. For accurate measurements photoelectric devices are used to determine the extent of the turbidity by measuring the interference offered to the passage of a beam of light.

2. ***Volume.*** Centrifuge tubes are made with a graduated capillary in the bottom so that when 10 ml of the microbial culture fluid is sedimented by centrifuging, the volume of the cell mass is evident. This test is valuable in the yeast industry where interest centers on the amount of marketable cell material.

3. ***Weight.*** Centrifuged cells can be dried and weighed. Weight is used as a measure of mold growth, for most molds grow as a pellicle on the surface of a liquid medium, and the pellicle can be fished out, rolled into a ball, dried, and weighed.

4. ***Colony diameter.*** When a microorganism is inoculated on an agar plate, its rate of growth can be followed by the increase in colony size or by the rate of progression of the edge of the colony across the agar. This procedure is especially useful in measuring mold growth. Depending on the mold and cultural conditions, the growth may vary from several millimeters per hour to barely measurable progress per day.

The activity of the protoplasm does not always parallel its mass.

With older cultures much dead or relatively nonreactive material may be present. Molds generally contain more supportive and structural tissue and less metabolically active tissue than bacteria. The most common measurements involve (1) the uptake of oxygen, (2) the utilization of food, and (3) the accumulation of metabolic products.

Oxygen Uptake. Special instruments employing flasks attached to manometers are used extensively for determining oxygen uptake by microorganisms. The Warburg respirometer is an example. The growth of the organisms (i.e., the increase in metabolically active tissue) can be followed by measuring the rate of increase of oxygen utilization.

Disappearance of Food. In fermentation industries the microbiologist is often concerned with the conversion of sugar into some useful product. Under such circumstances the disappearance of the sugar measures the progress of the microbial development; when the sugar is all gone, the fermentation is complete.

Accumulation of Metabolic Products. Measurement of the metabolic products of bacteria is often simpler and of more immediate interest than numbers or amount of the microbes. For assaying vitamins the amount of acid produced in a given time is a measure of the amount of active organisms, and this in turn is directly proportional to the amount of an essential vitamin originally present in the culture medium. Acid is easy to measure by titration with alkali, using an indicator dye to determine the end point. The gas, CO_2, is produced by many organisms, and since the amount produced is dependent on the amount of active cell material, measurement of CO_2 serves as a convenient count of active cell numbers or active cell mass. Under special conditions other metabolic products may be measured to determine the rate of development of a microbial population.

When growth starts from a single cell and the number of cells doubles regularly, the increase in viable count occurs in steps. Such cell divisions are said to be synchronized. Soon, however, the cells get out of step, and a graph, made of the number of living cells plotted against time, proceeds upward in a reasonably smooth curve. Certain chemical studies on bacteria cannot be accomplished on one or even a few cells, but require a large population growing synchronously. By holding the cells at a temperature slightly below that required for cell division, the individual cells continue to grow slowly, but each stops at some point prior to division. When such cells are placed at a more desirable temperature, a sudden doubling of the population results as all the cells divide at about the same time. After a period equal to the generation time, a second doubling of the population occurs. Synchronous growth will occur for several such doubling steps, but the population of bacteria exhibits slight generation-time variation with individual cells and soon gets out of phase. Another method of obtaining a temporary synchrony of some bacteria is to filter out and discard the larger cells; the smaller cells have just divided and will on further incubation show a stepwise growth.

Under normal conditions when microbes are inoculated into a new environment, the developing bacterial culture follows a typical growth pattern. The cultural history is represented by a graph, which shows the logarithms of the cell numbers on the vertical axis and the time on the horizontal axis (Fig. 6.8). The typical growth curve shows first a period of delayed reproduction, which is called the **lag** phase.

The lag phase may be very short if a large number of actively growing bacteria are inoculated into a medium that is ideal for their growth. In the cultivation of microbes in industry every effort is made to create conditions which shorten the time of the unproductive lag phase. When only a few cells or cells that are old or injured are inoculated, the lag phase is longer and may be prolonged still more if the growth conditions are unfavorable.

In the dairy and food industry, quality control depends on limiting the initial count of microbes and holding the products at low temperatures to prolong the lag phase of those organisms that cannot be excluded. Transfer to a different type of medium lengthens the lag phase because adjustments must be made within the organisms, and

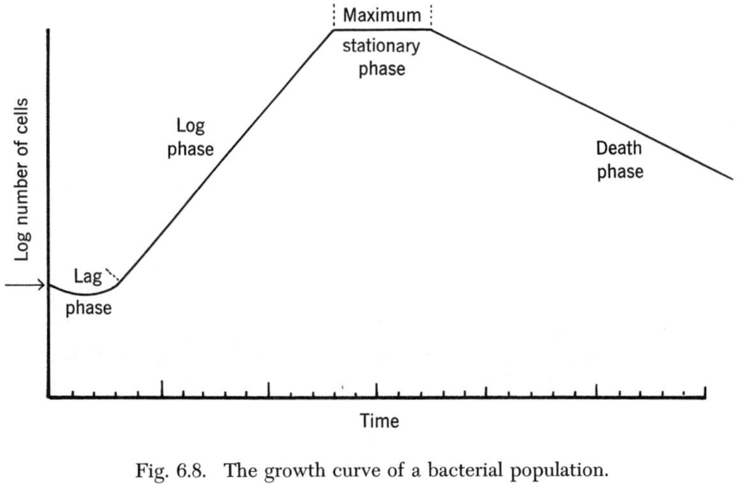

Fig. 6.8. The growth curve of a bacterial population.

often only a few individuals in the inoculum can grow well in the new environment. When an unwashed milk container is again filled with milk, the lag phase may be very short, not only because of the large inoculum, but also because the population is being introduced into an environment with which it has had previous experience.

The **log** phase is that part of the culture history represented as a straight line slanting upward, indicating the numbers of organisms plotted against the time; during this time the organisms are increasing in number exponentially. The rate of growth during this time is represented by the steepness of the slope; a steep slope indicates a short generation time determined by the suitability of the medium, the conditions for growth, and the type of organism. The explosive nature of exponential growth yields hundreds of millions of new organisms within a few hours when proper conditions are available.

When the organisms become numerous their growth is limited by the exhaustion of food, by their toxic excretion products, and, in natural situations, by the presence of their living enemies—protozoa that eat the bacteria and viruses that infect them. When the multiplications and the deaths exactly balance, the culture enters the **maximum-stationary phase.** The height of the maximum stationary phase is a measure of the total crop of cells. This number can be increased to some extent by supplying additional food material or neutralizing toxic excretions. but eventually the culture must arrive at this resting state after which is the death and dissolution phase. The maximum stationary phase is so short in some species that transfers to new cultures must be carried out daily if the stock is to be maintained. With other cultures this stationary phase may persist for weeks or months. It can be lengthened by placing the cultures in a refrigerator.

The last phase, the **death phase,** often follows an exponential course, and the graph shows a straight line sloping downward. In some dying cultures abnormal, distorted cells appear, which are called **involution forms;** in others, the cells digest themselves by a process called **autolysis.** In nature they rarely die off to the last cell before a change in the environment permits a new surge of growth. To the microbes every crumb of soil, every hair follicle on the skin, or every particle of waste in the intestine may represent a microenvironment for such cycles of growth and death.

SUMMARY. The classical growth curve is not restricted to laboratory cultures, but is a significant factor governing microbial populations in nature. Interest usually centers on (1) the length of the lag phase, (2) the steepness of the log phase, (3) the height and length of the maximum stationary phase, and (4) the slope of the death phase.

Two factors explain the survival of the numerous microbial species in nature: (1) Logarithmic growth with the short generation time exhibited by bacteria is an explosive type of growth which insures maximal occupancy of any available environment; (2) A few of these millions of organisms will survive and wait for the next suitable environment to become available.

7

Classification of Bacteria

Scholars characteristically arrange the objects of their study in an orderly fashion, grouping related forms and assigning descriptive names. In the case of a plant or an animal, the anatomy, or morphology, indicates relationships to other plants or animals. Therefore, an understanding of similarities between individual organisms allows the scientist to form groups, to write descriptions, and to assign names on the basis of evolutionary relationships. However, morphology is not sufficiently varied among bacteria to afford very extensive groupings. Furthermore, in bacteria, similarities in form do not necessarily indicate natural relationships. In classifying these simple, unicellular organisms, such nonmorphological characteristics as physiological, biochemical, and, in some instances, serological differences must be considered. Consequently, the schemes of classification suggested for bacteria are not based on evolutionary criteria, are subject to frequent revision, and probably can never be fully satisfactory.

Bacteria were first considered animals. Leeuwenhoek spoke of them as "little beasties." To some workers they constituted a third kingdom of living things—the *Protista.* It was early recognized that they had characteristics which made them more plant-like than animal-like, so they were placed in the plant kingdom. Most microbiologists are in accord with this idea.

Even though bacteria cannot be classified satisfactorily on the basis of their natural relationships, the same general principles laid down for the classification and naming of plants and animals are followed. That branch of biological science which deals with classification is termed taxonomy; the system of names is called **nomenclature.**

Descriptions and names of various plants, animals, and microorganisms have been assembled over the years into a volume on taxonomy with a key which permits tracing an unknown to its proper place in the scheme. There is no official system of taxonomy for bacteria, but a semi-official system, presented in Bergey's *Manual of Determinative Bacteriology* is very widely accepted (Table 7.1). Descriptions of almost 2000 organisms are included in this publication. It should be noted that some bacteriologists do not accept the Bergey system in all its details.

Table 7.1. Classification of Bacteria according to Bergey's Manual, Seventh Edition

Division I. **Protophyta**—primitive plants.
  Class I. **Schizophyceae**—blue-green algae.
  Class II. **Schizomycetes**—bacteria.

Gram-negative rods and curved forms with polar flagella (or nonmotile related forms) (orders I to III).

Order I. **Pseudomonadales**—polar flagella, true bacteria.
  Suborder I. **Rhodobacteriineae**—pigmented, photosynthetic bacteria.
    Family I. **Thiorhodaceae**—purple sulfur bacteria.
    Family II. **Athiorhodaceae**—purple and brown nonsulfur bacteria.
    Family III. **Chlorobacteriaceae**—green sulfur bacteria.
  Suborder II. **Pseudomonadineae**—nonphotosynthetic bacteria.
    Family I. **Nitrobacteraceae**—nitrifying bacteria.
    Family II. **Methanomonadaceae**—methane, carbon monoxide, or hydrogen oxidizers.
    Family III. **Thiobacteriaceae**—sulfur oxidizers.
    Family IV. **Pseudomonadaceae**—ordinary heterotrophic bacteria.
    Family V. **Caulobacteraceae**—stalked bacteria.
    Family VI. **Siderocapsaceae**—capsules encrusted with iron.
    Family VII. **Spirillaceae**—comma-shaped and spiral forms.
Order II. **Chlamydobacteriales**—filamentous, colorless alga-like species.
    Family I. **Chlamydobacteriaceae**—free filaments, motile swarm cells.
    Family II. **Peloplocaceae**—folded filaments.
    Family III. **Crenotrichaceae**—attached, differentiated filaments, with conidia.
Order III. **Hyphomicrobiales**—spherical to pear-shaped cells, often reproducing by budding on stalks.

Table 7.1. (Continued)

Family I. **Hyphomicrobiaceae**—buds formed on fine stalks.
Family II. **Pasteuriaceae**—multiply by budding or by longitudinal fission.

Peritrichous bacteria (or nonmotile related forms) (Order IV).
Order IV. **Eubacteriales**—true bacteria.
Family I. **Azotobacteraceae**—gram-negative, nitrogen-fixing bacteria.
Family II. **Rhizobiaceae**—gram-negative, symbiotic nitrogen-fixing or violet-pigmented bacteria.
Family III. **Achromobacteraceae**—gram-negative cells with little fermentative ability.
Family IV. **Enterobacteriaceae**—gram-negative, active fermenters, often found in enteric tract.
Tribe I. **Escherichieae**—generally nonpathogenic.
Tribe II. **Erwinieae**—plant pathogens.
Tribe III. **Serratieae**—red pigmented.
Tribe IV. **Proteeae**—lactose not fermented, urea hydrolized.
Tribe V. **Salmonelleae**—generally pathogenic.
Family V. **Brucellaceae**—small, gram-negative, obligate parasites.
Family VI. **Bacteroidaceae**—gram-negative anaerobic rods.
Family VII. **Micrococcaceae**—gram-positive, non-chain-forming cocci.
Family VIII. **Neisseriaceae**—gram-negative cocci.
Family IX. **Brevibacteriaceae**—gram-positive, asporogenous rods, form little acid from sugars.
Family X. **Lactobacillaceae**—gram-positive cells, generally form lactic acid.
Tribe I. **Streptococceae**—cocci (chain forming).
Tribe II. **Lactobacilleae**—rods.
Family XI. **Propionibacteriaceae**—gram-positive, propionic or butyric acid-forming rods.
Family XII. **Corynebacteriaceae**—gram-positive, pleomorphic rods, weak fermenters.
Family XIII. **Bacillaceae**—gram-positive, aerobic or anaerobic, sporeforming rods.

Generally nonmotile, filamentous, mold- or alga-like bacteria (Orders V-VIII).
Order V. **Actinomycetales**—slender, often branching, mold-like cells which may form spores.
Family I. **Mycobacteriaceae**—acid-fast, asporogenous rods.
Family II. **Actinomycetaceae**—mycelial growth, divide by segmentation.
Family III. **Streptomycetaceae**—conidia formed on sporophores.
Family IV. **Actinoplanaceae**—sporangiospores, some flagellated.
Order VI. **Caryophanales**—large, filamentous, segmented cells.
Family I. **Caryophanaceae**—coenocytic, tubular cells, no spores.
Family II. **Oscillospiraceae**—large, partitioned, motile, sporogenous parasites.

Table 7.1. (Continued)

Family III. **Arthromitaceae**—large, apparently septate, nonmotile, sporogenous parasites.

Groups of cells which often creep or glide over moist surfaces (Orders VII-VIII).

Order VII. **Beggiatoales**—filamentous, alga-like cells; some filaments may be motile.

Family I. **Beggiatoaceae**—oxidize sulfide, deposit S granules.

Family II. **Vitreoscillaceae**—organotrophic rather than S oxidizers.

Family III. **Leucotrichaceae**—organotrophic, tapering threads from hold-fasts, only gonidia motile; gonidia form rosettes.

Family IV. **Achromotiaceae**—spherical to ovoid cells, may deposit S and/or $CaCO_3$ granules.

Order VIII. **Myxobacterales**—slime-forming, slender, flexible rods, creeping motility.

Family I. **Cytophagaceae**—no fruiting bodies or spores.

Family II. **Archangiaceae**—fruiting bodies of no definite shape, elongate spores (microcysts).

Family III. **Sorangiaceae**—cysts usually angular, cells usually thick and short with blunt, rounded ends.

Family IV. **Polyangiaceae**—cysts usually rounded, cells with pointed ends.

Family V. **Myxococcaceae**—microcysts spherical to ellipsodial, fruiting bodies formed except in genus **Sporocytophaga.**

Slender, flexuous cells, motility serpentine or by spinning (Order IX).

Order IX. **Spirochaetales**—spiral cells, some resemblance to protozoa.

Family I. **Spirochaetaceae**—large, mostly free-living forms.

Family II. **Treponemataceae**—small, generally parasitic cells.

Small, fragile, pleomorphic, nonmotile, often filtrable cells (Order X).

Order X. **Mycoplasmatales**—the pleuropneumonia group.

Family I. **Mycoplasmataceae**

Obligate parasites, microscopic to ultramicroscopic in size (Class III).

Class III. **Microtatobiotes**—smallest life.

Order I. **Rickettsiales**—small, intracellular parasites often associated with insects.

Family I. **Rickettsiaceae**—do not occur in erythrocytes.

Tribe I. **Rickettsieae**—cause human rickettsioses.

Tribe II. **Ehrlichieae**—cause animal rickettsioses.

Tribe III. **Wolbachieae**—arthropod, not vertebrate, hosts.

Family II. **Chlamydiaceae**—found in tissues, not transmitted by insects.

Family III. **Bartonellaceae**—occur in or on erythrocytes.

Family IV. **Anaplasmataceae**—parasites in erythrocytes of lower animals.

Order II. **Virales**—the filtrable viruses.

1. Bacteriophages—bacterial hosts.
2. Plant viruses.
3. Animal viruses.

The Bergey *Manual* suggests that the blue-green algae, the bacteria, the viruses, and rickettsiae be placed in a division known as Protophyta, or primitive plants. The blue-green algae, placed in a class known as the Schizophyceae, are studied along with the other types of algae and the higher fungi in cryptogamic botany. Those organisms which are normally regarded as bacteria, the so-called higher bacteria, and a number of less familiar types have been placed in the class Schizomycetes. Organisms, so small that they will pass through filters which retain the more familiar bacterial types, have been allocated to a class designated Microtatobiotes.

Bacteria occur in nature in mixed cultures; pure cultures are uncommon. In order to establish the characteristics of an unknown organism and assign it a name, a study of a pure culture is necessary. Pure cultures may be obtained by standard procedures, and the culture so obtained, prior to identification, is referred to as an **isolate.** If there is some reason why a particular isolate should be differentiated from other isolates, it may be designated as a **strain.** This designation may be a number, as putrefactive anaerobe No. 3679; it may be a letter, or letters, or the name of a place or person, as *Staphylococcus aureus,* H, or *Bacillus subtilis,* Marburg.

Often the isolate is identified in taxonomic study by determining its characteristics, organizing the data obtained, and comparing the data with that given in the taxonomic key. The bacterial characteristics commonly studied include some or all of the following:

1. **Cell morphology,** including, in addition to cell shape: staining reaction, size, flagella (if present, the mode of arrangement), the presence or absence of a capsule, spore formation, and cell inclusions.
2. **Culture morphology,** including the size and shape of colonies, the appearance of the growth in liquid, solid, and special media.
3. **Physiological and biochemical reactions,** including the temperature range of growth, growth in the presence or absence of oxygen (aerobic or anaerobic), utilization of various carbon and nitrogen compounds incorporated into the medium, and formation of end products of metabolism, such as acids, gases, sulfide, ammonia, and so forth.
4. **Pathogenicity,** either for animals or for plants in those cases where there is some indication that the organism under study is pathogenic.
5. **Serological reactions** (serology: the study of the properties and reactions of blood serum), both of nonpathogenic and pathogenic organisms, sometimes may be a determining factor in identification of an unknown. The organism is injected into an animal, in which it stimulates the formation of specific chemical antibodies. These antibodies, which are contained in the fluid serum portion of the blood, will react specifically in laboratory test systems with all cultures of this

species or variety (**serotype**), but not with unrelated species and serotypes.

Since sexual reproduction is not common in bacteria, a species cannot be defined in the terms used for plants and animals. Modern microbiological research indicates that the results of genetic recombination usually confirm the relationships defined by other taxonomic criteria. Nevertheless, some adjustments are necessary. Recent experiments reveal that when organisms are closely related, the melting points as well as the chemical composition of their DNA are similar. Furthermore, their DNA, isolated from closely related organisms, will intertwine when a mixed aqueous solution containing these chemicals is heated and cooled. However, until such research progresses much further, bacterial species must be regarded as a group of isolates more like each other than like any other group. In some instances individuals within a species may differ but not sufficiently to justify creation of another species designation. For these minor variations designations of **subspecies, serotype,** or **variety** may be added as a part of the species name.

The isolate is the smallest unit of bacterial taxonomy. The possible number of isolates is infinite, since it is limited only by the amount of work done in securing additional pure cultures. To prepare a classification scheme identical or nearly identical, isolates are grouped into species. More commonly the problem confronting the microbiologist is that of classifying a newly isolated organism.

Once the characteristics of an isolate have been determined and organized, the organism is traced to its proper place in a descriptive key such as Bergey's *Manual.* Bacteria are representatives of the **plant kingdom** and members of the phylum *Protophyta* and the class *Schizomycetes.* The sequence of divisions, or categories, remaining which must be followed in tracing through the key are:

Order. The Schizomycetes are divided into ten orders, designated by the suffix *-ales.* The largest order is Eubacteriales, with 607 named organisms and about 350 serotypes. The smallest order is Hyphomicrobiales, with only four organisms included.

Suborder. Some of the orders are divided into suborders, representing a slight narrowing of the characteristics of a broadly related group of organisms. The suborder consists of organisms which share certain significant characters not shown by other suborders of the parent order. The suffix which designates a suborder is *-ineae*, as in Pseudomonadineae.

Family. Further narrowing of shared characteristics results in the grouping known as the family. The suffix which designates the family is *-aceae*, as in Enterobacteriaceae.

Tribe. Sometimes the family constitutes such a broad group that it must be subdivided into tribes in order to make the descriptive key readily usable. The ending which denotes a tribe is *-eae*, as in Salmonelleae.

Genus. The tribe (or family, if there is no division into tribes) is subdivided still further to give the genus for which there is no special ending.

Species. The final narrowing of characters gives the **species**, which like the genus has no characteristic ending.

The first described member of a species is the **type species**. The type species should be thoroughly characterized, in order that comparisons will readily identify later isolations.

If a previously undescribed organism is isolated, certain principles of nomenclature must be followed in assigning a name. The name should be a binomial, the first word designating the genus; the second, the species. These names are Latin, and though they may be derived from some other language, they must be Latinized. The generic name is a noun in the singular and is written with a capital letter. It may be masculine, feminine, or neuter. It may be descriptive of some characteristic of the organism, such as *Aerobacter*, a gas-producing bacetrium, or it may be given in honor of an individual, usually a scientist who has studied the organism; *Escherichia* is named for Escherich, who first described the organism. The generic name should always represent some important feature of the organism.

The second word of the binomial is the specific epithet, which is not capitalized. It may be an adjective, in which case it must agree in gender with the noun it modifies, as *Bacillus albus*, the white bacillus, and *Sarcina alba*, the white sarcina. It may be an adjective in the form of a present participle, in which event the ending will be the same for all genders, as *Clostridium putrefaciens* or *Bacillus putrefaciens*. It may be a noun in the genitive case modifying the generic name, as *Clostridium belfantii*, the clostridium of Belfant, who was an Italian bacteriologist (Table 7.2).

Taxonomic studies of a number of strains of a species may establish more precisely the characteristics significant for classification. Variability is characteristic of all living matter, hence comparative studies often reveal variations in characteristics. Theoretically, each test applied to the group permits division into two groups, those which react positively and those which react negatively. Some judgment is, therefore, essential in choosing which characteristics have taxonomic significance. The number of types possible increases at the rate of two raised to the power indicating the number of tests. This is the 2^n principle in taxonomy. If a

Table 7.2 Genus and Species Names

Name	*Meaning*
Bacillus (generic name)	Rod-shaped
subtilis (species name)*	Slender
mycoides (species name)	Fungus-like
cereus (species name)	Wax-colored or waxen
Serratia (generic name)	Honoring the Italian scientist Serrati
marcescens (species name)	Decaying
Escherichia (generic name)	Named for the bacteriologist, Escherich
coli (species name)	Living in the colon
Streptococcus (generic name)	Flexible chain of cocci
pyogenes (species name)	Pus-producing
equi (species name)	Causing a disease of horses
agalactiae (species name)	Causing a disease which stops milk production
Staphylococcus (generic name)	Irregularly clustered cocci
aureus (species name)	Golden pigment
Proteus (generic name)	Referring to marine god who could assume any shape
vulgaris (species name)	Common
Clostridum (generic name)	Spindle-shaped (as a common name with a small c)
botulinum (species name)	Sausage-shaped
perfringens (species name)	Breaking through
Pseudomonas (generic name)	False (pseudo) and a unit (monad)
fluorescens (species name)	Producing a fluorescing pigment
synxantha (species name)	Producing a yellow pigment
syncyanea (species name)	Producing a blue pigment
mephitica (species name)	Producing a skunk-like odor

*Used alone this is the specific epithet; the species name results when used in combination with the generic name, as **Bacillus subtilis.**

single test is applied only two groups are possible—one positive and one negative. If a second test is applied, a positive and a negative group is possible for each of the original two groups. For three tests the number of groups becomes 2^3 or 8 and for n tests it is 2^n. Reasonable and workable limits demand that only tests which yield significant data should be considered.

SUMMARY. Taxonomy, or descriptive bacteriology, is not a glamorous or exciting subject. However, it is of great importance in every aspect of the science, and students should become familiar with it early in their study of bacteria. A presentation of the classification of bacteria, actinomycetes, rickettsia, and viruses is given in Table 7.1.

The algae, fungi, and protozoa show greater complexity, and their taxonomic position follows precisely that used for higher plants and animals.

8

Molds, Yeasts, and Actinomycetes

Molds and yeasts are closely linked to bacteria but somewhat more complex in structure and higher in evolutionary development. Diverse forms and transitional stages occur between the groups of molds and yeasts, making group boundaries difficult to draw. For example, some of the water molds are very similar to some protozoa. Transitional forms also occur between all of the groups and some bacterial forms. In spite of the complexity of classification, a study of the classical and typical forms offers a good beginning to the understanding of the molds and yeasts.

THE MOLDS

Occurrence. The molds are nonphotosynthetic microorganisms grouped with the yeasts and mushrooms under the term fungi (Fig. 8.1). The molds demand the attention of the bacteriologist because they are the weeds of the laboratory, appearing with aggravating frequency in other cultures. Molds frequently contaminate other organic substances because their environmental demands are less particular than those of other plant forms. (1) Molds are widely distributed, as they produce tremendous numbers of spores that are readily spread through the air. (2) No

Fig. 8.1. *Pleurotus ulmarius.* The fruiting bodies of a *Basidiomycete* growing from a tree trunk. The mushrooms are supported by a vast network of mycelium submerged in the substrate of wood or soil. These aerial structures bear the fungus spores which are disseminated after the mushrooms dry. *Photo courtesy C. M. Christensen.*

organic substance is free from mold destruction, as the mold can consume a wide variety of foods. (3) Molds require some moisture but can absorb water from moist air in regions of high humidity. While substances can be dried sufficiently to prevent mold growth, slight moisture will cause molding of grain, clothing, etc. (4) Molds thrive in fruit and vegetable tissues which are too acid for bacterial growth. In the isolation of molds the pH can be adjusted to 5.0, which will be inhibitory to most bacteria but permit vigorous mold growth. (5) Mold spores can survive many years in the dry state. (6) The resistance of molds to chemicals permits their growth in a chemical solution such as photographic developer.

Mold growth is limited by its aerobic nature. Molds will not grow in the absence of oxygen and are therefore limited to surface growth. In liquids they grow as a floating mat or pellicle; in solids they penetrate only as far as oxygen can diffuse. Molds grow more slowly than bacteria and consequently do not participate in the early stages of organic decomposition. When a plant residue decomposes in the soil, the sugars and proteins are consumed rapidly by bacteria. The rapid growth of aerobic bacteria removes oxygen and delays mold development. Only when these readily available food materials are gone does the bacterial respiration slow down sufficiently to allow oxygen to diffuse into the material at a rate sufficient to support mold growth on the more resistant portions of the plant material. Of course, if the material is too dry or too acid for bacterial growth, molds will participate in the earlier stages of decomposition.

Structure. Typical molds are composed of branching thread-like filaments called mycelium, which are about 5 to 10 microns in diameter. A single branch of a mycelium is called a hypha (pl. hyphae). Some of the hyphae are embedded in the food material or medium on which the mold grows; these anchor the mycelium and absorb nutrients (Fig. 8.2). Those that are not submerged are aerial hyphae, which function by absorbing oxygen. Water from the air may condense on aerial hyphae and support mold growth on a fairly dry medium. Aerial hyphae also bear the fruiting bodies or asexual spores. In some molds the mycelial threads have crosswalls dividing the hyphae into cells. A pore or hole in the crosswalls permits the cytoplasm to pass from one cell into another. If a bit of a hypha consisting of at least one intact cell from any part of the mycelium is torn off and replanted, it will grow into a new mycelium. Some molds have no crosswalls but are made of long mycelial tubes containing cytoplasm and nuclei. A bit of a hypha containing at least one nucleus and enough cytoplasm to support it can be torn from the mycelium and successfully start a new culture. Since molds produce tremendous numbers of asexual spores, the new culture usually arises from a germinating spore.

Sexuality. When mold colonies of two different strains of the same species are grown close to each other, the hyphae may fuse, and nuclei from one mycelium may pass into the other. The resulting mold with

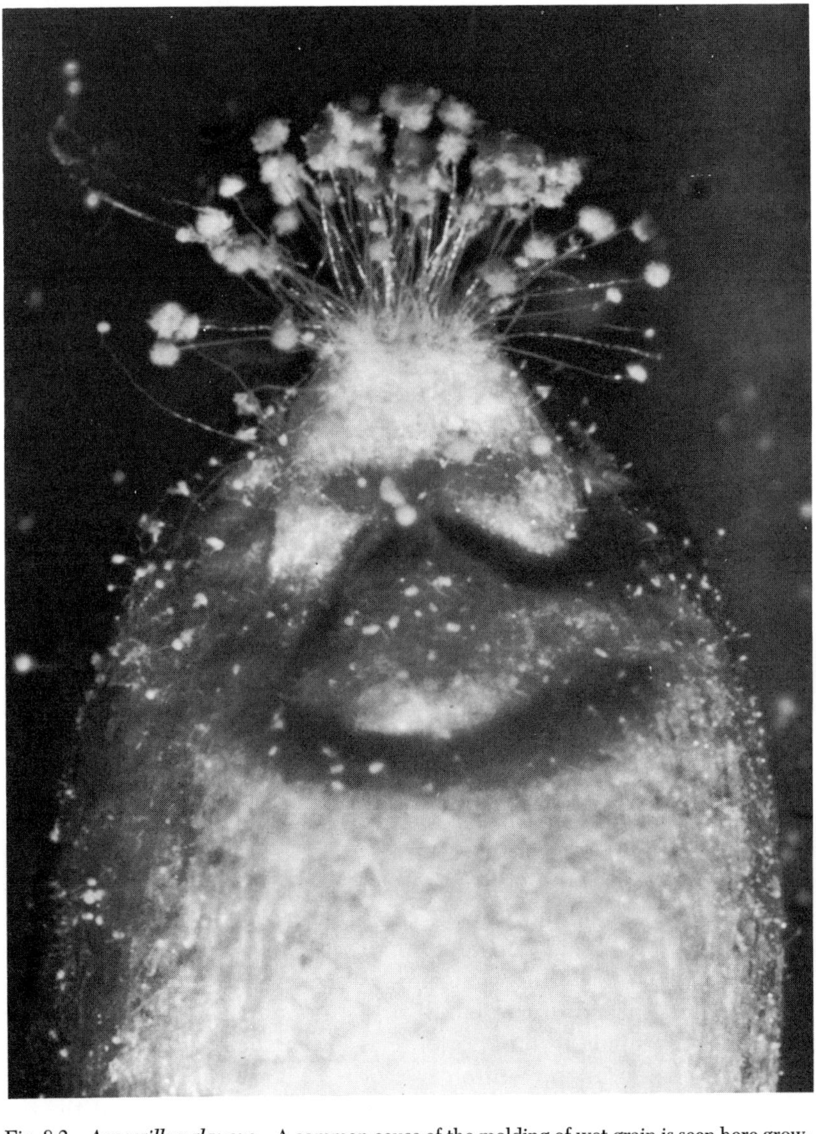

Fig. 8.2. *Aspergillus glaucus.* A common cause of the molding of wet grain is seen here growing from the tip of a kernel of wheat. The fruiting bodies bearing the conidia grow out of the mycelium anchored to the grain. *Photo courtesy C. M. Christensen.*

two different nuclei in the same cytoplasm is known as a **heterokaryon.** The nuclei will divide independently as the mycelium grows so that the heterokaryon will exhibit the hereditary characteristics of both nuclei, being thus a sort of hybrid. This heterokaryotic condition, which is widespread in nature, may be maintained indefinitely and permits the development of a mold possessing desirable properties from *both* of the parent strains even though actual sexual union does not take place.

Sexual reproduction occurs when the nuclei fuse after union. In those molds in which sexual union occurs only a strain designated as + exchanges nuclei with a strain designated as −; two + strains or two − strains never recombine. Since both partners in the recombination are morphologically indistinguishable and behave in an identical fashion, they cannot be designated as male or female. Where + and − strains are required for sexual union, the mold is said to be **heterothallic.** When fusion occurs between all strains, the mold is said to be **homothallic.** Following fusion of the nuclei, the resulting cell called a **zygote** undergoes further division to produce the sexual spores. These will have *some of the characteristics* of each of the parents as a result of the reassortment of the genetic material from the two nuclei that fused before division into the sexual spores. The mycelium that arises from the germination of sexual spores is not to be confused with the heterokaryon, which contains nuclei from both parents and therefore *all the characteristics* of both parents.

REPRESENTATIVE MOLDS

The Ascomycetes. A large group of molds of the class Ascomycetes reveal the formation of sexual spores in a sac called an *ascus.* Well-known representatives of this class are the green and gray molds of the genus *Penicillium* and the black and brown molds of the genus *Aspergillus.* All of the Ascomycetes have septate mycelium (with crosswalls) and special fertile hyphae which bear the asexual spores called **conidia.** These asexual spores are the major method of reproduction and spread of the molds. In the penicillia, the conidia are green or gray spheres (about 5 microns in diameter) growing in brush-like tufts on top of the white or colorless mycelium. The brown or black spores of the aspergilli grow on a club-like structure at the top of aerial hyphae (Fig. 8.3). Some ascomycetes are simple and some more complex; for example, the common bread yeast is a simple ascomycete.

The Basidiomycetes. The best known basidiomycetes are the mushrooms, which produce a vast mycelial network and, under favorable

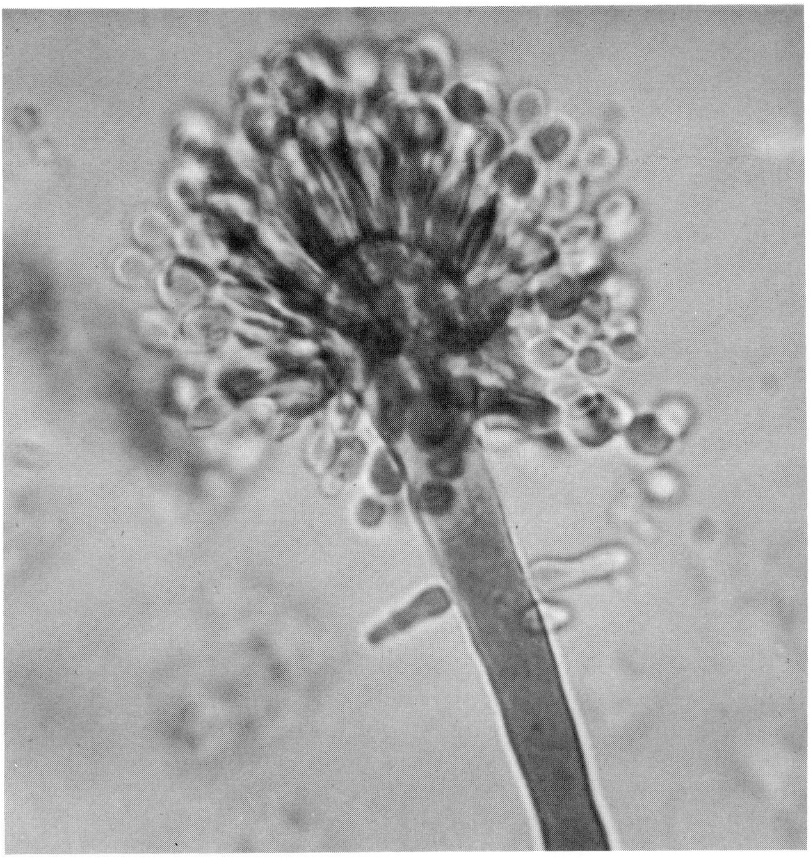

Fig. 8.3. Detail of a more highly magnified fruiting body of *Aspergillus* showing the conidia and the club shaped cell to which they are attached. *Photo courtesy C. M. Christensen.*

conditions of moisture and temperature, send up the fruiting body. The visible cap of the mushroom is made of densely packed hyphae. The spores are borne on club-shaped cells, that result from the fusion of two nuclei, on the gills on the underside of the cap. Like other molds, the mushrooms produce tremendous numbers of spores and thrive on decomposing organic matter. The basidiomycetes also include important plant pathogens, the rusts and smuts.

The Phycomycetes. This class includes the water molds, which grow on decaying plant material floating in water, and some closely related soil molds. All phycomycetes have nonseptate mycelium (no cross-walls) and all bear their asexual spores inside a sack called a **sporangium.**

Most of them are anchored to their substrate by root-like mycelial structures called **rhizoids**. The sexual stage involves the fusion of hyphae from two different mycelia. In some forms the two hyphae that fuse are morphologically distinct. One passes its nuclei into the other; hence the former can be designated as male, and the latter, female. In other phycomycetes the fusing hyphae are indistinguishable, and the strains must be designated as + and −. The water phycomycetes produce motile spores, but all spores of the soil or terrestrial phycomycetes are nonmotile. A typical example of the latter is the black bread mold, *Rhizopus nigricans.*

The Fungi Imperfecti. Another class of fungi includes a diverse group in which no sexual spores have as yet been found. Consequently, they are termed **imperfect fungi** (Fig. 8.4). When and if sexual spores are discovered in any members of this class, they will be classified in one of the other three groups.

IMPORTANCE OF MOLDS

Molds are used in the production of penicillin (Fig. 8.5) and gluconic and citric acid. Soya sauce is produced by the decomposition of soy beans by a selected strain of *Aspergillus*. Roquefort and Camembert cheese are ripened and flavored by mold action. In aerobic soils the molds participate in the decomposition of organic matter. The destructive action of molds is observed on posts, railroad ties, and piling as well as in tent fabrics, ropes, paints, papers, and leather. Mold spoilage of foods and feeds constitutes a major part of the economic loss in the food industry. Molds are the most important causative agents of plant diseases; in addition to the rusts and smuts, the mildews, rootrots, and many of the blights are caused by molds.

Very few molds produce disease in animals and man. Because of their aerobic nature, molds attack surface tissues. Those infecting the skin are called **dermatophytes**. Dermatophytes of the genus *Microsporum* invade the hair and skin to produce ringworm. Scrapings from infected areas when properly stained and examined microscopically show the mycelium of the filamentous fungus. Typical mold colonies are produced when infected material is planted on acid agar. Other dermatophytes invade the nails and the skin producing athlete's foot. These diseases are spread by contact and occasionally the parasitic dermatophytes are harbored by cats and dogs.

Aspergillosis is a fairly common mold infection of the lungs of birds, which on rare occasions may be spread to man. Most infections by aspergilli in man involve the ear canal, but lung infections occasionally occur, especially among persons working with infected birds. A few other infections in man, such as **sporotrichosis,** are produced by molds, but fungus infections of the deeper tissues usually involve yeast-like

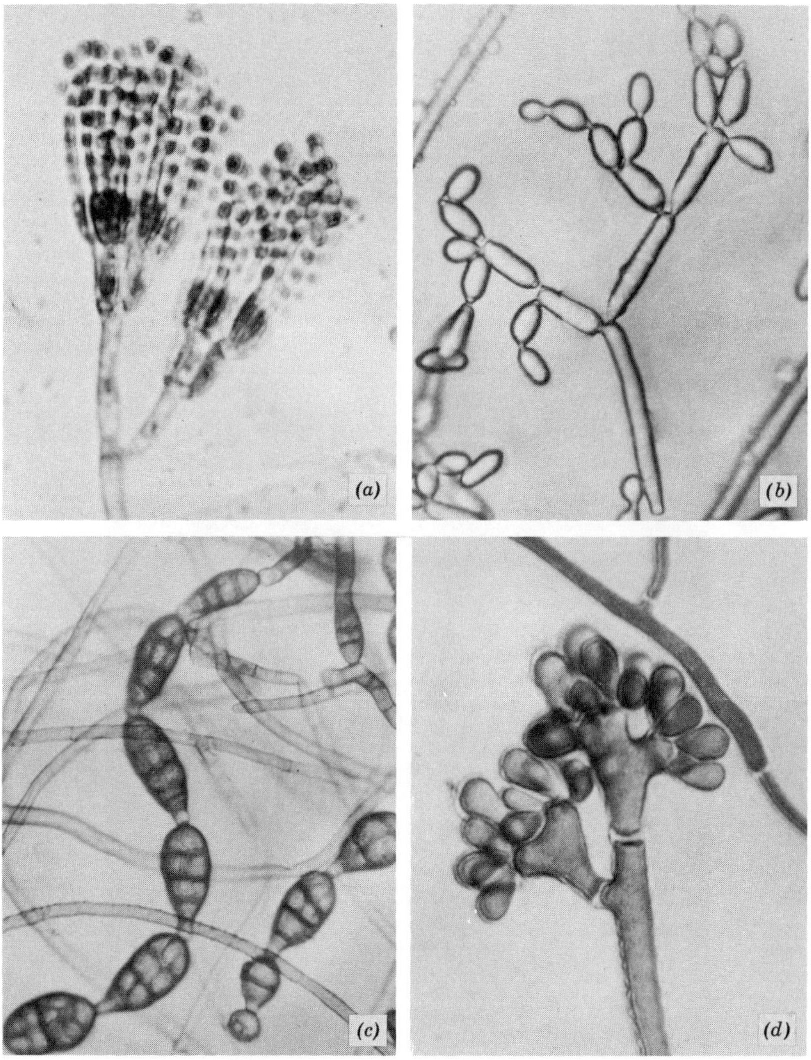

Fig. 8.4. The fruiting bodies and some mycelium of four frequently encountered genera of the *Fungi imperfecti.* (*a*) *Penicillium,* (*b*) *Cladosporium,* (*c*) *Alternaria,* (*d*) *Botrytis.* *Photos courtesy C. M. Christensen.*

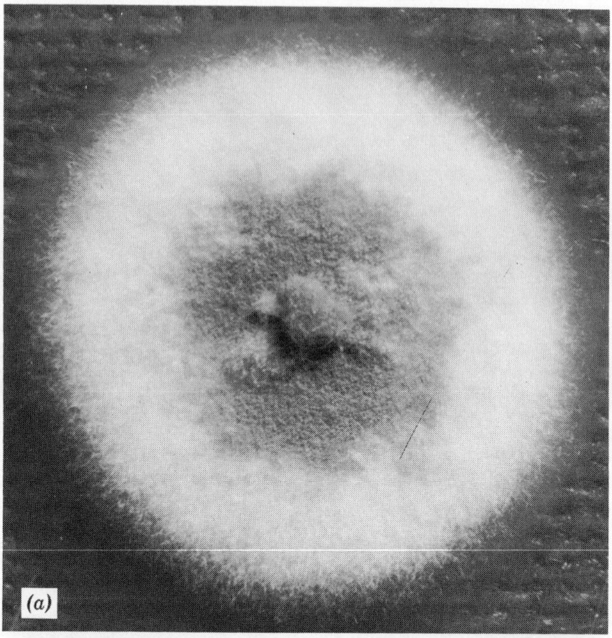
(a)

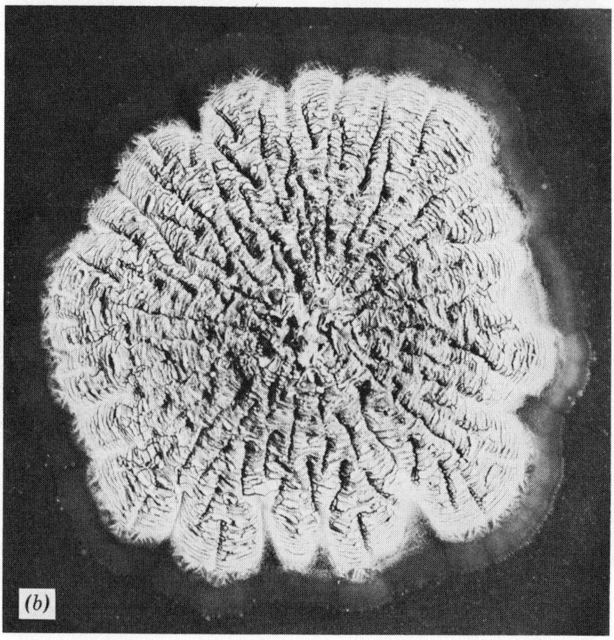
(b)

Fig. 8.5. Colonies of molds showing distinctive details; (*a*) *Penicillium chrosogenum*, which produces almost all of the commercial penicillin; (*b*) *Streptomyces rimosus*, which produces the tetracycline antibiotic, terramycin; (*c*) *Penicillium herquei*, which has no commercial use. *Photos courtesy Chas. Pfizer & Co.*

forms. Some pathogens are **dimorphic**, that is, they produce filamentous mold-like growth on culture media but show only unicellular yeast-like growth in tissues.

YEASTS

Fungi that have lost their mycelial nature and live as unicellular organisms are called yeasts. These organisms, less widespread than molds or bacteria, are found primarily on the surface of plants in the soils of orchards and in the digestive tracts of insects. Most yeasts range from 4 to 6 microns in diameter, which is sufficiently large to allow observation of internal structures such as the nucleus and vacuoles under the light microscope, especially after staining (Fig. 8.6). The typical asexual reproduction of yeast occurs by budding. Some of the protoplasm produces a bulge in the cell wall; the bud separates when it approaches the size of the mother cell. A few yeasts reproduce by

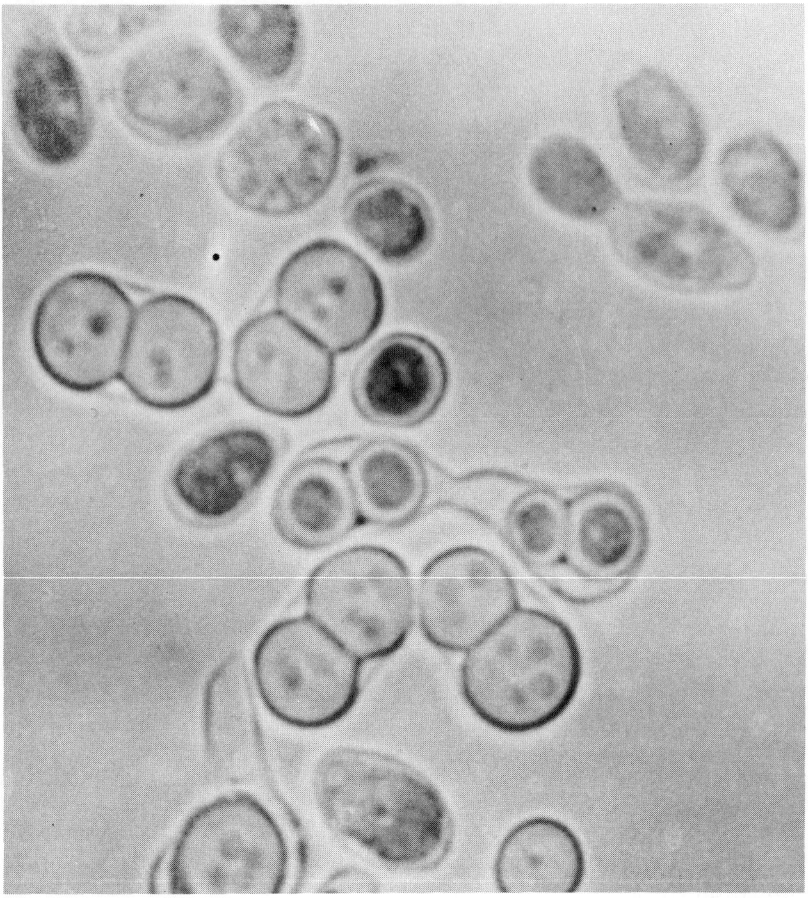

Fig. 8.6. Yeast cells showing the budding method of cell reproduction. Yeasts are much larger than bacteria and show definite compartments within the cell. Note the budding cell in the upper right hand corner and the four ascospores in the center.

fission, like bacteria. All yeasts are nonmotile. Some reproduce sexually by forming ascospores; other form basidiospores, and in still others sexual spores do not occur.

The baker's, brewer's, and distiller's yeast is an ascomycete named *Saccharomyces cerevisiae*. Anaerobically these organisms convert sugar almost quantitatively to ethyl alcohol and carbon dioxide. The budding vegetative cells contain the diploid number of chromosomes. When the cell stops budding and ascospores are formed, a division takes place that reduces the chromosomes to the haploid number in the newly formed ascospore. In the rather unusual life cycle of the yeast, the ascospores fuse before germinating to yield diploid vegetative cells. In most other biological forms, fusion takes place prior to the formation of the sexual spore. Certain wild yeasts called film-forming yeast or **torula** grow on the surface of organic solutions. They oxide the solutions of sugar, alcohol, or organic acid to form carbon dioxide. Yeast spoilage may occur in those foods which contain sugar but are too acid for bacterial growth and too anaerobic for mold growth.

A number of yeasts produce plant diseases and a few cause animal diseases. The most common pathogenic yeasts and yeast-like fungi are: (1) *Cryptococcus neoformans,* which forms deep-seated cutaneous ulcers, may spread to other organs including the viscera, lungs, and central nervous system; (2) *Candida albicans,* which invades mucous membranes, the skin, and the lungs; an older name for this organism is **Monilia;** and the disease it causes is called **moniliasis;** (3) *Coccidiodes immitis,* which causes lung infections especially in the San Joaquin Valley in California; (4) *Histoplasma capsulatum,* which causes nodular infections in the spleen, lungs, skin, or intestine.

THE ACTINOMYCETES

The mold-like bacteria of the order Actinomycetales, commonly called actinomycetes, are filamentous forms but differ from the true molds because the mycelium is of bacterial dimensions (about 1 micron in diameter). The typical actinomycete has a branched mycelium and produces such compact colonies that removal of a portion with an inoculating needle is extremely difficult. Unlike yeasts and molds, the actinomycetes do not grow on acid medium. While they are often studied with the molds, evolutionary hypotheses on their origin tie them closely to the bacteria.

The genus *Streptomyces* comprises the most mold-like of the actinomycetes; it produces conidia on aerial hyphae. The surface of the colony has a powdery appearance like some mold colonies. The branched cells are aerobic gram-positive filaments and some species are thermophilic. They carry out a significant part of the decomposition of organic matter in the soil; the characteristic odor of *Streptomyces* is evident in freshly turned soil. The plant disease, potato scab, is caused by a *Streptomyces scabies.* Many actinomycetes produce antibiotic substances; the useful antibiotics, streptomycin, the tetracyclines, chloramphenicol, and neomycin are produced by species of the *Streptomyces* genus.

The anaerobic actinomycetes of the genus *Actinomyces* and the aerobic members of the genus *Nocardia* are less complex in structure. These produce no conidia, but young cultures form a mycelium which later breaks up into short rods or cocci. The disease "lumpy jaw" in cattle as well as lesions in other animals and man are caused by actinomycetes of the genus *Actinomyces*.

The genus *Mycobacterium*, which includes the tubercle bacillus, is classified with the actinomycetes; it produces no mycelium and is a transitional form between the mold-like organisms and the true bacteria. The actinomycetes are classified with the bacteria in the Schizophyta. The molds and yeasts are classified in the Thallophyta.

SUMMARY. The actinomycetes are filamentous schizomycetes and occupy an important position in modern microbiology. They produce many of the useful antibiotic substances and are the transitional forms between the bacteria and the molds. Because of the larger dimensions of the mold mycelium, molds were studied by biologists before the advent of bacteriology. Though tremendously diverse in their structure and in their sexual cycles, the molds are classified in four large groups. Dimorphic forms are the transitional groups between the multicellular molds and the unicellular yeasts. On media equally favorable for all three types of organisms, yeasts and molds generally grow more slowly than the bacteria.

9

The Algae, Protozoa, and the Complex Schizomycetes

These extremely diverse groups of microorganisms have distinctive types as well as members that appear to be transitional forms between the various groups of microorganisms.

THE ALGAE

Algae such as the seaweeds, pond scums, and water blooms are chlorophyll-containing plants without differentiated roots, stems, and leaves. Over 15,000 species have been described ranging from the tiny primitive blue-green algae, closely allied with the bacteria, to the masses of brown algae which make up the giant kelps (Table 9.1). Algae are found in greatest abundance in the upper layers of water bodies; few thrive at depths greater than 25 feet because of the lack of light. They also appear on the surface of the soil, on rocks, and on the bark of trees. In the water they may be free-floating or attached to rocks or bottom sediments in the shallow or shore line areas.

Chlorophyll in the algae is usually associated with accessory pigments. Often its green color is masked by the reds, browns, yellows, or blues of other pigments which assist in the photosynthetic process. The pigment is usually contained in distinct cellular bodies called

Table 9.1. Classification of Algae

Phylum **Thallophyta**
Subphylum **Alga**
Class I **Chrysophyceae**—diatoms
Class II **Cyanophyceae**—blue-green algae*
Class III **Chlorophyceae**—green algae
Class IV **Phaeophyceae**—brown algae
Class V **Rhodophyceae**—red algae

*Microbiologists usually classify the cyanophyceae in the phylum Schizophyta, and the class, Schizophyceae.

chloroplasts. All algae absorb water, carbon dioxide, and minerals from the medium and use light for energy. Algae are cultivated in a mineral salts solution placed in the light. Some of the blue-green algae can fix atmospheric nitrogen, but other algae use ammonia or nitrates for their nitrogen nutrition. Some algae require vitamins and other growth factors in the medium.

CLASSIFICATION OF ALGAE

The red algae are large marine plants usually found in the subtropical and tropical seas. The cell walls of some species contain a gelatinous carbohydrate called agar. The agar is extracted with hot water for use in bacteriologists' culture media. Brown algae also exist primarily in large multicellular forms. The pillbox-shaped **diatoms** are algae with cell walls impregnated and hardened with silica (Fig. 9.1). On division each daughter cell retains either the cover half or the bottom half of the pillbox and grows a new matching member. Some diatoms are motile and others are not. Most diatoms are unicellular forms but a few species are filamentous or colonial types. The remains of the silica walls of the diatoms accumulate on the ocean floor, and deposits of fossil diatoms over 3000 feet thick have been discovered in oil-well drilling.

The green algae are similar to higher plants in that all have cellulose in the cell walls, starch as the storage product, and the same four pigments in the chloroplasts (Fig. 9.2). Yet, morphologically they are a very diverse group ranging from flagellated forms, indistinguishable except for the chloroplasts from certain protozoa, to multicellular filamentous forms that are obviously closely related to the higher plants.

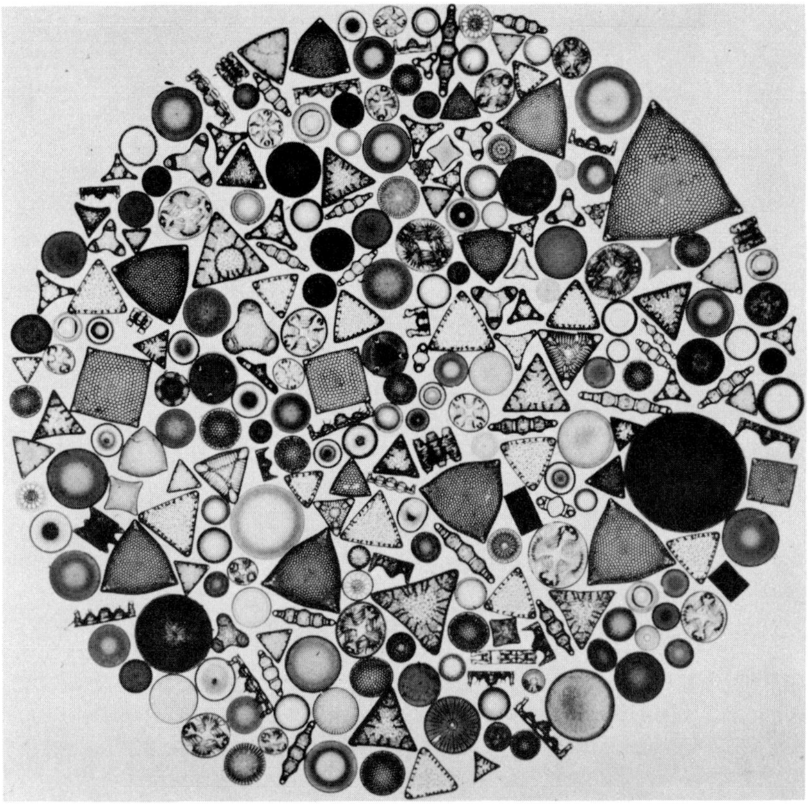

Fig. 9.1. The silica shells of diatoms are pillbox-like structures of diverse shapes. An old favorite method for determining the quality of a microscope is to see how well it resolves the lines and other markings on diatom shells. *Photo courtesy Smithsonian Institution.*

These complex green algae reproduce by means of motile spores, which are similar in structure to the unicellular green algae.

The blue-green algae are more similar in chemistry and structure to the bacteria. Classified with the Schizophyceae, they are unlike the other algae; chloroplasts are absent, and the pigments are distributed throughout the cytoplasm. Reproduction occurs by cell division and by spores. Sexual stages have not been observed. In some species the cells separate on division and are free living. In others, the cells are held together by gelatinous sheaths in colonies or in filaments. The blue-green algae will grow in a medium composed of mineral salts and water. Their ability to utilize gaseous nitrogen obtained from the air permits their growth in areas where nitrogen compounds are absent

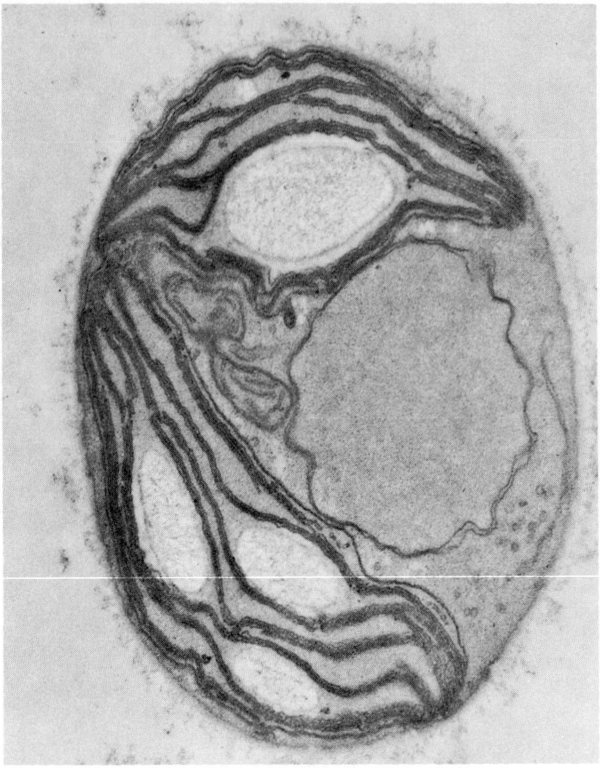

Fig. 9.2. An ultrathin section of the green alga *Chlorella pyrenoidosa* as shown by electron microscopy. Note the internal membranes, which are not demonstrated in similar sections of the bacteria or blue-green algae.

from the medium, and it accounts for their growth on volcanic rock and in similar areas where other plant life fails to develop.

Importance of Algae. The algae are an important link in the biological nutrition chain in the sea. They are the builders of organic material used by the small sea animals, which in turn serve as food for the larger animals. They have been termed the "grass of the sea." Scientists anticipate that, with the development of proper methods of collection and culture, algae may some day be a direct source of human and animal food. Diatomaceaous earth (fossils of diatoms) is used as an abrasive; it can be manufactured into an insulating material and is used as a filter aid in chemistry. Vitamins A and D, originally synthesized by algae, are concentrated in the livers of certain fishes from which they are processed for medical use.

Photosynthesis by algae promotes fish life by releasing oxygen into the water. In areas of intense sunlight, sewage purification procedures have been developed which involve the oxygenation of the effluent by algal photosynthesis.

The tremendous growth of algae in lakes may ruin the lake for recreational purposes during the height of the water bloom. Even worse is the following period when the decomposition and putrefaction of algal cell bodies releases decomposition products, that are extremely unpleasant in odor and taste.

Algae are the only major group of microorganisms with no pathogenic species, but the decomposition products produce illness and even death in animals drinking the water during the period of greatest algal decay. Even relatively minor growth of certain species of algae in drinking water may be responsible for obnoxious odors and tastes.

PROTOZOA

Although these single-celled organisms are classified as animals, the protozoa include forms so closely related to the algae that some botanists include them in the plant kingdom as chlorophyll-less variants of the algae. On the other hand, other protozoa are very similar to the water molds, and still others are clearly similar to the bacterial spirochaetes (Fig. 9.3). As might be expected of such a diverse group, they are widely distributed in nature. In surface waters and in the upper six inches of soil, they live on the small algae and bacteria. In the gut of the termite and in the rumen of cud-chewing animals they feed on the cellulose-digesting bacteria, thus performing an indispensable function in the conversion of cellulose into absorbable nutrients. The intestines of animals and insects contain protozoa; a few species are parasitic.

Protozoa are divided into four groups, the rhizopods, the sporozoans, the flagellates, and the ciliates. The rhizopods move by means of **pseudopodia** (false feet). These organisms have no fixed shape but constantly change in form and size as the cell membrane is stretched into temporary projections by the flowing of the protoplasm. Since the genus *Amoeba* is one of the best known rhizopods, this flowing type of movement is called ameboid movement. The cells engulf food particles such as bacteria and algae by flowing around them, thereby enclosing the food in a vacuole where it is digested. Other vacuoles collect excess water and waste material inside the cell and move to the cell boundary where it is discharged.

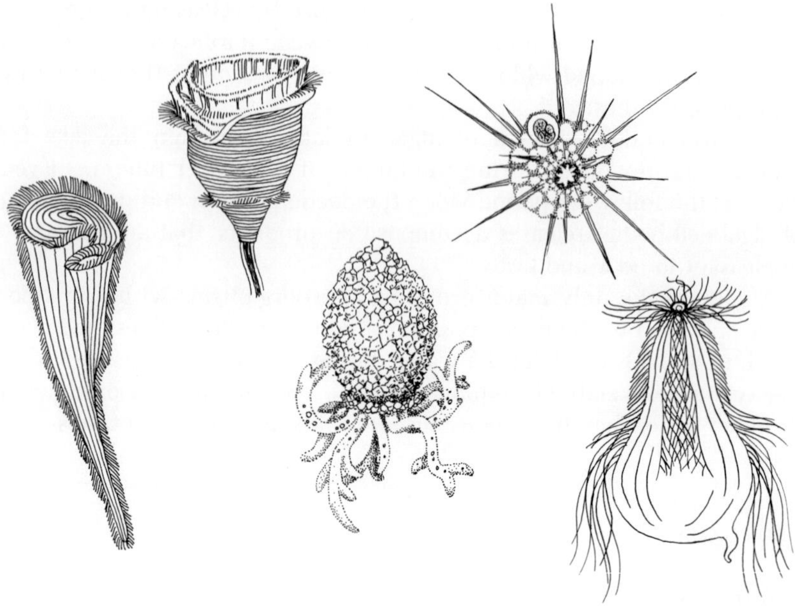

Fig. 9.3. Protozoa exist in a tremendous variety of shapes and cell arrangements. Some representatives are shown in this figure.

Asexual reproduction involves simple division of the nucleus, followed by cell division. When sexual reproduction occurs the cells may fuse (or in some cases flagellated gametes produced by the cells conjugate) to form a zygote which, in turn, develops to produce daughter ameboid cells.

One group of marine species develops as flexible amebae but secrete silica as they grow, forming either an external shell or an internal skeleton. During the millions of years that these forms have been living and dying and leaving skeletons and shells on the earth, they have been changing in structure. Experts in microscopic examination of geological deposits can determine the age of layers of sedimentary rock by the appearance of these fossil protozoa. This information is especially useful in the identification of the geological formation in which the drill is operating during oil-well explorations.

Endamoeba histolytica is prevalent in the tropical and subtropical areas where, as the causative agent of amebic dysentery, it produces an occasionally fatal, but more often chronic, debilitating disease. Many healthy carriers are involved in its spread. Diagnosis is made upon finding the organism by microscopic examination of the stool.

The **sporozoans** are parasitic protozoa with complex life cycles. Malarial parasitism involves both an animal (man or monkey) and an insect (the *Anopheles* mosquito). The mosquito injects motile spores into the blood stream of the animal; these attack and destroy red blood cells. The development of the organism is synchronized so that emergence of each new generation from the red blood cells causes the recurring and periodic chills and fever. A few of the parasites mature into sexual forms, which do not develop further in the human body. A feeding mosquito, however, will pick up the zygotes that result from sexual combination, and the protozoa complete their life cycle in the body of the insect; there, the sporozoites eventually form and invade the salivary glands of the mosquito. When the mosquito feeds, the sporozoites may enter the new victim.

The flagellate protozoa move by long whip-like flagella which push or pull the flexible cells through their liquid environment. Flagellates generally have a leaf-shaped structure often elongated like a spirochaete. Reproduction is almost always asexual; these cells split longitudinally unlike the transverse fission of bacteria. Cysts are formed by enclosure of the cytoplasm in a thick cell wall which protects the organisms during long periods of drying. A group of parasitic flagellates are called **trypanosomes**; most trypanosome diseases involve an insect vector. *Trypanosoma gambiense* causes African sleeping sickness and is transmitted to man by the tsetse fly.

The ciliate protozoa are exceedingly highly developed. The movement of these single-celled animals is controlled by short hair-like projections, the cilia, which move as if coordinated by a nervous system. In the best known ciliate, the *Paramecium* (Fig. 9.4), food enters the

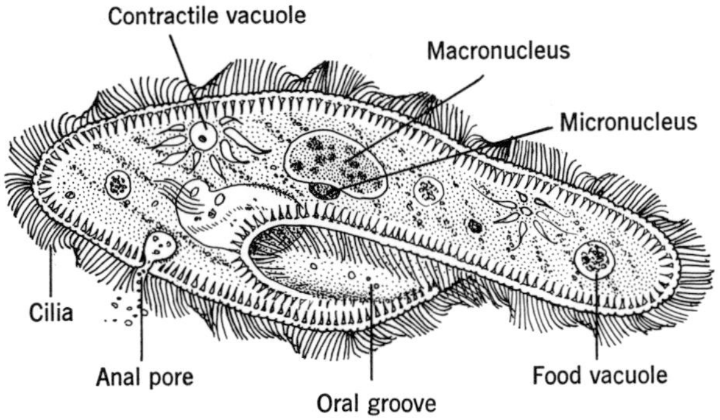

Fig. 9.4. The protozoa, *Paramecium,* is frequently encountered in pond water where it feeds on bacteria and small algae. Although a single cell, it shows structural detail far more complex than that observed in bacteria.

body through an oral groove and, moving in a food vacuole, passes lengthwise through the cell. The vacuole finally empties the undigested food into the medium through an anal pore. Other vacuoles carry water and dissolved substances through the cytoplasm.

These organisms usually contain two nuclei: a **macronucleus**, which controls the ordinary activities of the cell, and a **micronucleus**, which is involved only in sexual reproduction. In asexual reproduction both nuclei divide prior to longitudinal fission. In sexual reproduction, however, the macronuclei disappear following conjugation of two cells; division of the micronucleus in each cell is followed by reciprocal nuclear exchange between the conjugating partners—thus each fertilizes the other. In each species of *Paramecium* there may be from two to six mating types; conjugation does not take place between members of the same mating type.

Only one species of the ciliates is known to be parasitic for man—*Balantidium coli*, an intestinal parasite which causes a type of dysentery.

Protozoa are of importance to microbiologists for many reasons, among them are:

1. They cause a few diseases of man such as dysentery, malaria, and sleeping sickness.
2. They aid in the control of the bacterial populations in soil and water.
3. They are a link in the food cycle in the sea; they consume the smaller algae and bacteria and are themselves consumed by larger animals.
4. Fossil protozoa reveal the age of sedimentary rock.

COMPLEX SCHIZOMYCETES

In the classification of the Schizomycetes (see Chapter 7, Table 1), Orders I and IV constitute the true bacteria; the other eight orders contain more complex forms, the "higher" bacteria. Some are transitional forms between the true bacteria and the algae, protozoa, yeasts, and molds. Others represent evolutionary deviations from the bacteria which have not led to currently existing higher forms of life. Except for the order Actinomycetales (see Chapter 8), study of these extremely interesting biological entities has been neglected.

The order Spirochaetales includes the single-celled spiral bacteria (commonly called spirochetes), which are flexible, not possessing a rigid cell wall. In their flexibility these motile bacteria resemble animal cells and are often considered transitional forms between the bacteria and some of the protozoa. The Spirochaetales are divided into two families; the large water forms, the Spirochaetaceae, and the smaller parasitic forms, the Treponemataceae. Many spirochetes stain poorly with ordinary stains and are best observed either in a living preparation under the dark-field microscope or in negatively stained preparations.

Of the parasitic group, the best known is *Treponema pallidium* (Fig. 9.5), the causative organism of syphilis and the tropical disease, yaws. Organisms of the genus *Leptospira* are found in scrapings taken from the base of the teeth and gums of most individuals—even those with seemingly healthy mouths. Infectious jaundice and relapsing fever are other diseases caused by spirochetes.

Some of the larger spirochetes, such as the genera *Cristaspira* and *Spirochaeta*, exhibit long cells, some ranging up to 500 microns in length.

The slime bacteria of the order, Myxobacteriales move by a creeping or gliding motion, and appear to be nonphotosynthetic relatives of the free-living (nonfilamentous) blue-green algae. In this respect they are alga-like bacteria. The actively growing vegetative cells are flexible, thin, nonflagellated rods multiplying in a slimy matrix. It has been suggested that the gliding movement results from secretion of the slime. In some species, as the spreading colonies of myxobacteria age, the cells round up and mass into distinctive fruiting bodies. Some of these have complex-branched stalks, and others exhibit spherical masses similar to the asexual spores of molds. Yet in the slime bacteria these structures are masses of undifferentiated cells; the mechanisms leading to the piling of these cells into shapes resembling more complex organic forms are unknown. Slime bacteria can be readily isolated by inocu-

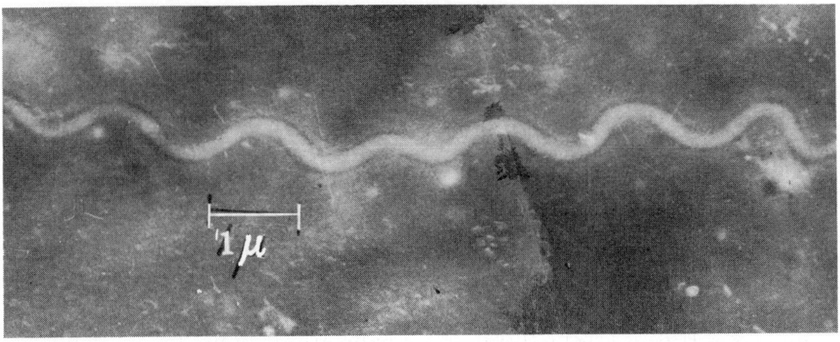

Fig. 9.5. This spirochete, *Treponema pallidum*, was observed in an electron micrograph made from exudate of a lesion of a syphilis patient. *Photo by Oskay, courtesy H. E. Morton, W. F. Ford, and S.A.B. LS-254.*

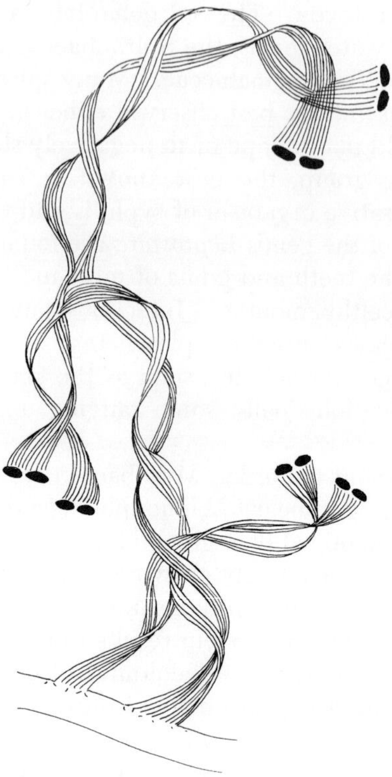

Fig. 9.6. The small rod-shaped *Gallionella* secrete iron hydroxide from one side of the cell to produce the complex twisted ribbons which anchor the cells to a surface.

lating manure on an agar plate which contains only the cells of true bacteria or fungi. The slime bacteria kill and digest these cells utilizing them as food. Such experiments infer that the slime bacteria play a role in the control of microbial populations. Some species of slime bacteria grow well on cellulose: These may be isolated on a piece of filter paper soaked in a mineral salts medium.

The order Beggiatoales includes other filamentous bacteria which move by gliding or waving filaments; morphological evidence suggests that these are nonphotosynthetic relatives of the filamentous blue-green algae. These organisms live in sulfide springs and other places where hydrogen sulfide is available. The hydrogen sulfide, oxidized to sulfur, is deposited in granules within the cells. In the absence of sulfide, the sulfur can be oxidized further to sulfuric acid. A widely occurring species in this order is *Beggiatoa albus,* which multiplies by fragmentation of short pieces from the ends of the filaments.

The sheathed bacteria of the order Chlamydobacteriales produce colorless filaments surrounded by a gelatinous sheath. The sheath appears as a tube of cells and in some genera, such as *Leptothrix* and *Crenothrix*, the sheath is encrusted with iron hydroxide. These are water-dwelling species, and the filaments are either free-floating or attached to the bottom or sides of the water body in which they live. The end cells in the sheath may slip out and form new filaments, or conidia may be produced in the sheath. Some of the sheathed bacteria produce motile conidia. At intervals these can be observed swarming away from the parent filament.

The stalked bacteria, the Hyphomicrobiales, reproduce by buds which form on the ends of stalks. Cell division may also occur by longitudinal fission. The Gallionellae were once thought to be complex Schizomycetes because of the interesting stalk associated with the cell (Fig. 9.6). However, it is now known that the stalk is an excretion product of iron hydroxide appearing as a twisted ribbon which anchors the cell to a solid surface, and that the organisms are small, gram-negative, kidney-shaped rods. When the gallionella cell divides, either the ribbon branches or one of the daughter cells breaks free to start a new colony. As with the sheathed iron bacteria, these organisms can create rusty water problems in city-water systems.

SUMMARY. Algae are the grass of the sea and the producers of organic matter in water. Microbiologists are concerned with them because of the nuisances they create in recreation areas, their role in the food cycle of the sea, and the special products obtained from them. The one-celled animals, the protozoa, are scavengers of bacteria and of the smaller algae. While there are no pathogenic algae, the protozoa are involved in a number of human diseases. The spirochaetes occupy a position between the protozoa and the true bacteria, and because of their somewhat greater complexity, they, together with the slime bacteria, the stalked bacteria, and the sheathed forms, are referred to as "higher" bacteria.

10

Viruses, Rickettsiae, and Pleuropneumonia-like Organisms

The microbiologist encounters organisms that are smaller and in some respects less complex than the bacteria. As science has become aware of the role of viruses in human disease, the techniques of bacteriology have been modified to deal effectively with the special problems of viral culture and study. These modified techniques have been useful in studying rickettsiae and pleuropneumonia-like organisms.

VIRUSES

A number of transmissible diseases are caused by agents so small that they can pass through the pores of filters which will retain bacteria. These agents, too small to be viewed with the light microscope, are called viruses, or filtrable viruses. Variation among members of the group is so wide that no simple definition can describe all viruses, but they can be characterized by a number of common features.

The most striking properties of viruses are their size, their obligate intracellular parasitism, and their general resistance to currently available chemotherapeutic agents. The unit of measure for viral particles is the millimicron (mμ), which is 0.001 micron (Fig. 10.1). The smallest bacteria are of the order of 300 mμ. Since viruses were first detected

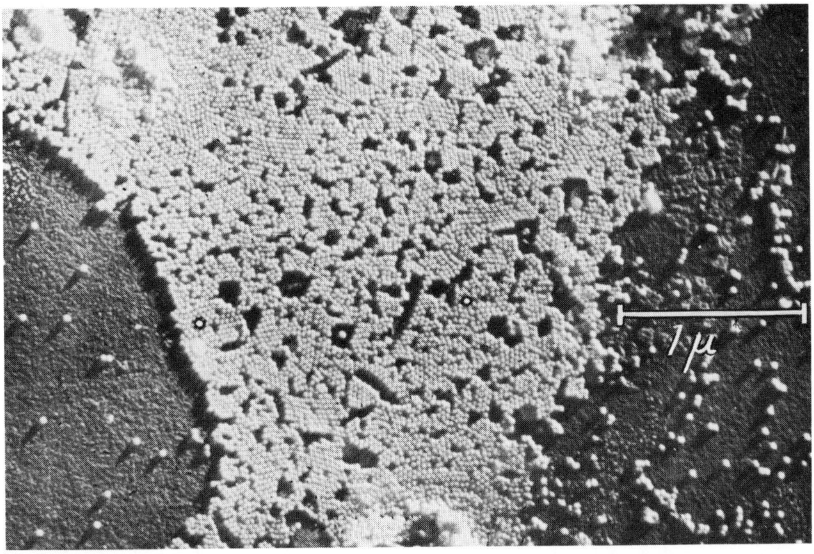

Fig. 10.1. Electron micrograph of bushy stunt virus particles. The three-dimensional effect results from shadowing the preparation with gold metal before the picture is taken. This is done by blowing the vaporized metal over the preparation from one side so that the metal accumulates on the leeward side of the particles to give the shadowed appearance. Each particle is .03 μ (30 mμ in diameter). *Photo by R. C. Williams, courtesy S.A.B. LS-169.*

as those organisms which passed through a bacterial filter, filtrability was the early criterion of a virus. More meaningful determinations of size have been made chiefly by three independent methods.

Ultrafiltration. Membranes of graded pore size can be prepared by drying solutions of varying concentrations of collodion. Pore size is measured by determining which molecules of known size will pass the filter. The approximate size of the infective unit of a virus then can be measured by finding the smallest pore size which will permit passage.

Ultracentrifugation. The rate at which particles can be thrown out of suspension by a high-speed centrifuge operating at a known speed of rotation is a function of size and density. Measurements of size which have been made by this method may not be fully accurate since variations in virus density influence the results.

Electron Microscopy. The electron microscope utilizes the short-wave length of a beam of electrons in place of light waves, and focuses with magnets instead of glass lenses. Estimates of the size of viral particles made from such micrographs may not be fully accurate because of distortions caused by the procedures of preparation for examination, but this measuring device is currently the most widely used. Measurements by the other methods are in fair agreement.

Viruses range in particle size from about 10 to 300 mμ. Electron micrographs demonstrate no uniformity in shape. Particles may be spherical, ovoid, rod shaped, cubical, or tadpole shaped (Fig. 10.2).

The obligate intracellular parasitism of the viruses is a reflection of nutritional requirements such that multiplication can take place only in susceptible host cells. Taken by themselves viruses do not respire, nor do they show any of the enzymatic activity characteristic of metabolism. The virus itself is little more than a piece of genetic material with the ability to penetrate a susceptible cell. Once inside the cell, the virus provides a code which directs the enzymatic apparatus of the host cell to produce more viruses. When this process causes no observable damage to the host, the virus infection is termed **latent**. When much of the host-cell activity is diverted from its own necessary activities, observable cell damage or destruction results, and a diseased condition is recognizable.

Because the reproduction of a virus is accomplished through the

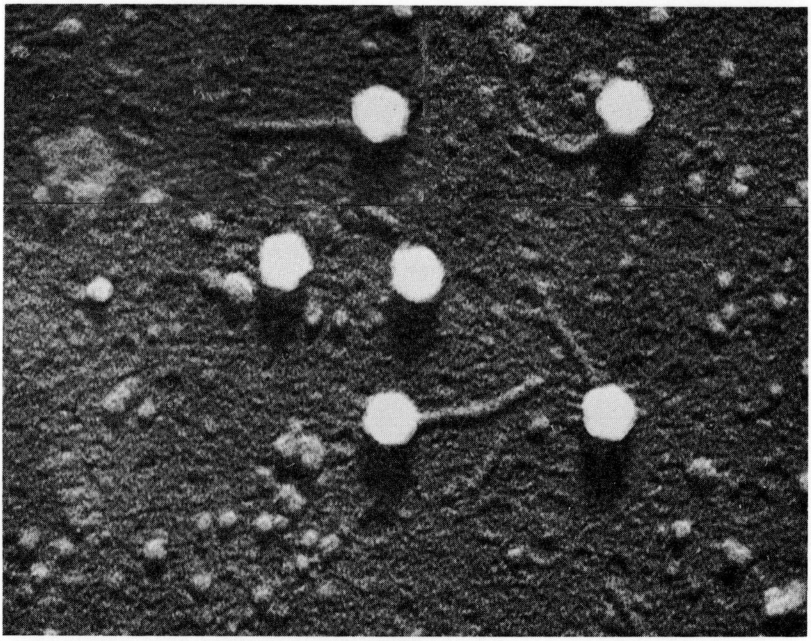

Fig. 10.2. Most bacterial viruses (bacteriophages) are tadpole-shaped. This phage for *Azotobacter* has a head almost 100 mμ in diameter and a tail 30 × 200 mμ.

reactions of the host cell, scientists have had difficulty in finding chemical substances that will selectively check virus growth without poisoning the host. Some antibiotics do work against the very largest viruses, such as those of parrot fever (psittacosis) and related diseases. But, although there are a few exceptions, those diseases that do not respond to the currently available chemotherapeutic agents may be correctly diagnosed as of viral origin.

In comparison with other organisms, viruses have a simple chemical structure. All contain nucleic acid and protein and some contain certain metal ions, vitamins, and enzymes. A few even have lipid material which forms a membrane to protect the genetic material in the free viral stage outside the host cell. The essential part of the virus is the nucleic acid, which may be either DNA (deoxyribonucleic acid) or RNA (ribonucleic acid). When only the nucleic acid of a virus is introduced experimentally into a host cell, complete viruses are produced.

Crystalline preparations of viruses have been obtained which appear to retain their infectious ability indefinitely. This observation suggests that viruses are inanimate and should not be classified as living. Certainly the free virus, as it is observed under the electron microscope and is subjected to chemical analysis, is only the resting stage in the cycle of viral development.

Viruses have two important attributes: the ability of reproduction coupled with the ability of variation. Of the several attributes of "living" things, most biologists regard these two as definitive. Viruses must make use of another living cell for reproduction, but all other forms of life reproduce only in a suitable environment. The suitable environment for a virus exists within a host cell. The property of variation permits living things to survive in a changing environment and to participate in organic evolution. In viruses these changes appear to be analogous to genetic changes, which have been more extensively studied in higher forms, and, like these, have been termed mutations. Recorded viral mutations include alterations in virulence, adaptation to a new host, development of new nutritional requirements, alterations in tissue affinity, and emergence of antigenic variants. Naturally occurring viral mutations are exemplified in the almost unlimited ability of the influenza virus to produce antigenic variants and, possibly, in the evolution of vaccinia virus from variola virus. Viral adaptation to a laboratory host with simultaneous loss of virulence for the natural host has been induced in a number of instances. This tendency toward adaptation has been exploited in immunization against naturally occurring disease, as in rabies and yellow fever.

In some viral diseases the affected cells show inclusion bodies not present in normal cells (Fig. 10.3). These may appear only in the

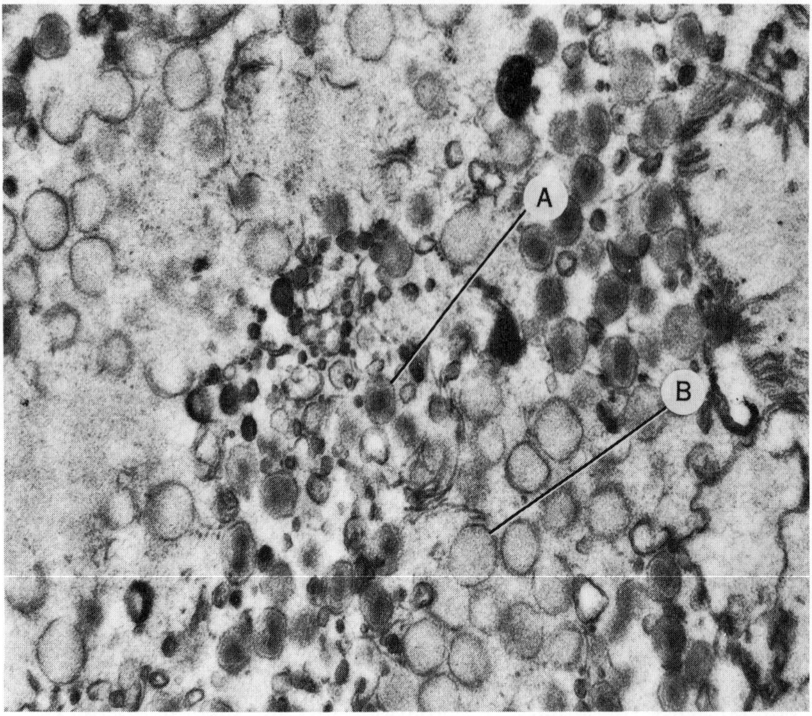

Fig. 10.3. An electron micrograph of a thin section cut through a Guarnieri body reveals the developing vaccinia virus. (A) A mature virus particle showing dark center. (B) An immature virus particle. *Photo by Norton McDuffie, Univ. of Texas.*

cytoplasm, as is the case with the negri bodies in rabies and the Guarnieri bodies in smallpox, or they may be found only in the nucleus, as in warts and in herpes simplex. Many scientists believe that the inclusion bodies consist of aggregations of viruses. Certain types of cancer in animals are definitely known to be of virus origin (Fig. 10.4).

Free viruses and vegetative bacterial cells show about the same susceptibility to heat. Most viruses can be preserved for long periods in a freezer held at the temperature of solid carbon dioxide ($-76°C$). Many survive long periods in the dry state, and a number have been crystallized. Viral strains vary greatly in their resistance to chemical agents; however, any chemical which denatures proteins will destroy viruses.

Animal Viruses. For years animal viruses could be maintained in the laboratory only by culture in susceptible animals. Characteristically, viruses require specific-host species and even certain tissues or cells in the host organism. Fortunately, such specificity applies less to embryonic tissue, and most viruses can now be cultured in embryonated chick eggs (Fig. 10.5) and in test tube cultures of young or cancerous mammalian cells. Consequently, vast research areas on animal viruses are now open.

Animal viruses may be classified very simply according to the nature of the disease which each produces. In **generalized diseases** the virus is spread throughout the body, as in dengue, yellow fever, measles, and smallpox. In the **diseases of specific organs or tissue systems** the viruses are localized. Some of the generalized group may show prominent

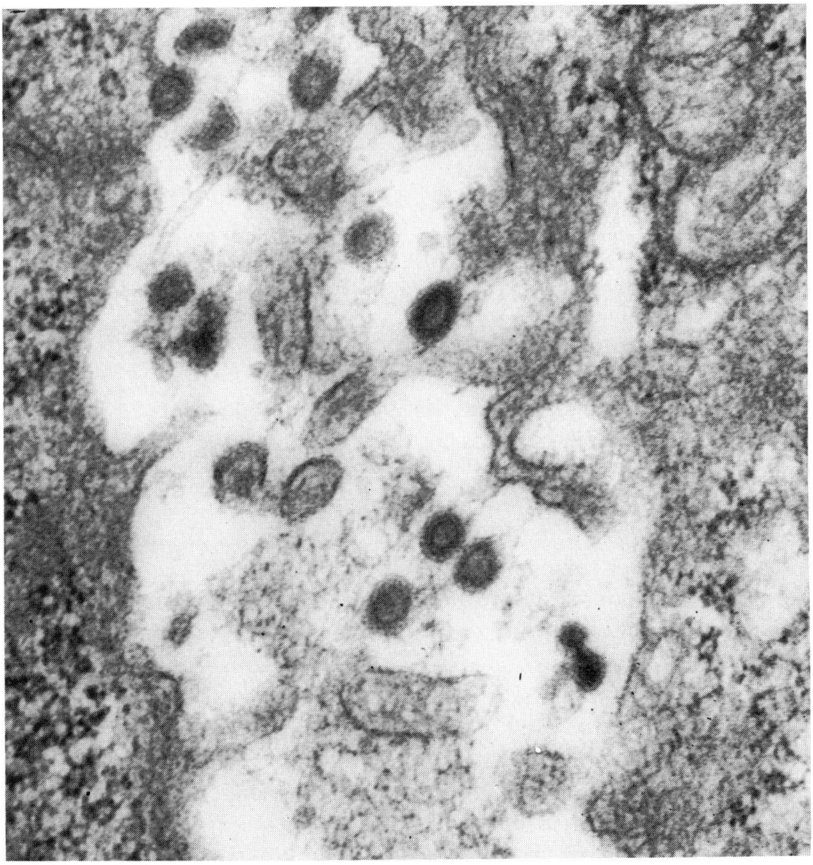

Fig. 10.4. An electron micrograph of material from mouse mammary carcinoma showing viral particles. *Photo by Norton McDuffie, Univ. of Texas.*

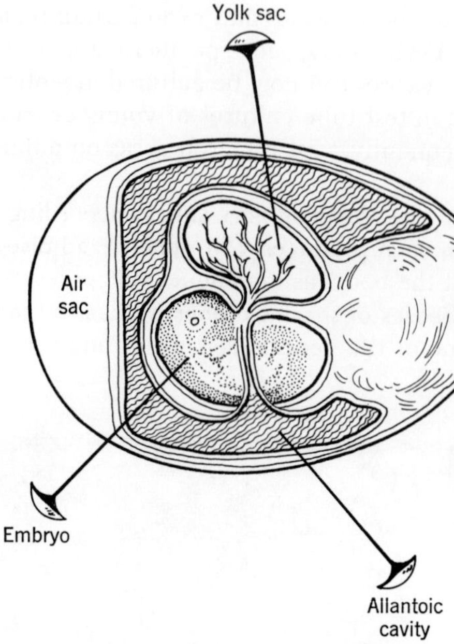

Fig. 10.5. The diagram of a developing chick embryo showing sites of virus inoculation, yolk sac, the allantoic cavity, and the embryo itself. By puncturing the shell over the air sac, the outer membrane of the embryo (chorioallantoic membrane) drops away from the shell and can be inoculated with virus.

changes in a particular tissue system, such as the skin in the pustules of smallpox and the rash of measles. Likewise viruses of the localized group may show generalized symptomatology. Virus diseases which affect primarily a specific organ or tissue include mumps, which affects the salivary glands, trachoma and the several types of viral conjunctivitis, which affect the eye, and hepatitis, which affects the liver. The dermotropic group, such as herpes simplex (fever blisters) and warts, localizes primarily in the skin and mucous membranes; the neurotropic group (such as rabies, poliomyelitis, and the encephalitides) attacks the nervous system, and finally the pneumotropic group, including influenza, the common cold, and the atypical pneumonias, attacks the respiratory system.

Most animal viruses show a high immunizing ability. Second attacks of such viral diseases as measles, smallpox, or mumps are uncommon. The apparent lack of immunity to the common cold results from the dozens of strains of the cold virus. Immunity to one strain gives no protection against the others.

Important viral diseases of animals include:

Primarily Human	*Primarily Animal, but Transmissible to Man*	*Animal, not Transmissible to Man*
Smallpox	Cowpox	Distemper
Chicken pox	Rabies	Hog cholera
Measles	Psittacosis	Fowl pox
Mumps		
Influenza		
Poliomyelitis		
Yellow fever		
Dengue		
Encephalitis lethargica		
Infectious viral hepatitis		

Insect Viruses. Only three orders of insects are known to be susceptible to viral disease: the Lepidoptera (butterflies and moths), the Hymenoptera (ants, bees, and wasps), and the Diptera (true flies). Only larval forms are susceptible to frank viral disease. The most common insect virus causes **polyhedral disease**, in which large polyhedral crystals occur in infected tissue. These protein crystals contain virus particles. The polyhedral bodies may appear in the host-cell nucleus or in the cytoplasm. The nuclear polyhedral viruses cause the body contents to liquefy. The larval skin easily ruptures and liberates the virus-rich fluid contents. In the cytoplasmic polyhedral diseases the caterpillar host tends to dry up rather than liquefy. Thus the cytoplasmic infections spread more slowly than the nuclear polyhedroses.

The second largest group are the **granuloses**, in which virus particles are enclosed in a granule or capsule. Polyhedral bodies are not seen. The granuloses viruses are restricted to caterpillars of the order Lepidoptera. Some of the hosts of this group are insects of great economic significance. A highly infectious suspension of granulosis virus is readily prepared from only a few infected insects. When the suspension is sprayed over caterpillar-infested fields, the ensuing viral infection produces biological pest control.

The third group of insect viruses, the **nonencapsulated**, is similar to the viruses of animals and plants. The virus is disseminated throughout the insect body, producing neither polyhedral bodies nor granules.

The studies of insect viruses have developed in laboratories peripheral to the main stream of microbiology. Control of certain insect pests through induced epidemics of viral disease shows considerable promise. Since only three orders of insects are known to be affected by viral disease, control of insect populations by viral infection is limited in applicability.

Plant Viruses. Viral infections are widespread throughout the plant kingdom. Only the conifers and lower forms such as the ferns are not susceptible to viral disease. Affected plants do not ordinarily die of the infection, but disease may cause considerable reduction in yield from plants of economic significance.

The tobacco-mosaic virus causes the loss of millions of pounds of tobacco annually (Fig. 10.6). The same virus can cause disease in the tomato with a great reduction in yield. The "curly top" disease infecting sugar beets may destroy an entire crop. "Potato blight" and "Peach yellow" are similarly destructive.

The manifestations induced in plants by viruses are varied and may simulate mineral deficiencies, fungal diseases, or even genetic mutations. The symptoms may be classified broadly in three major groups:

Mosaics. One of the most common plant virus diseases is the mosaic. One type of mosaic disease affects the reddish and bluish pigments of flowers, causing a variegated or mottled effect, the so-called flower breaks, which may be quite attractive. Another type of mosaic virus

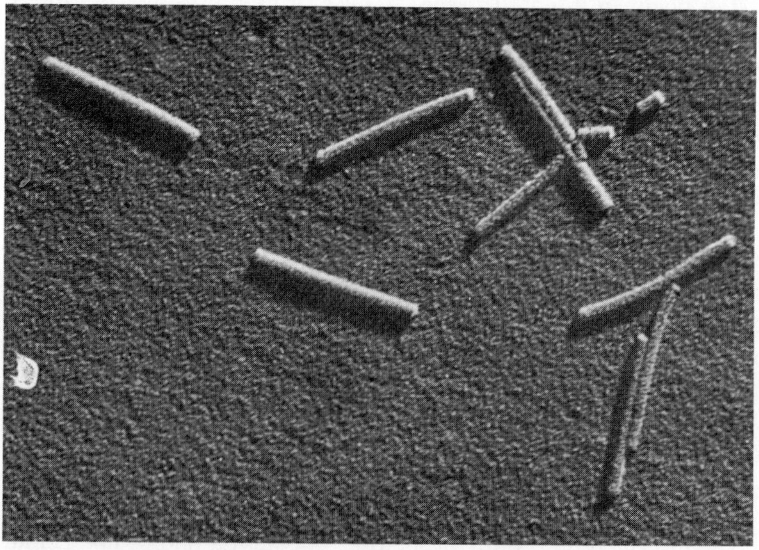

Fig. 10.6. Electron micrograph of shadow-cast tobacco mosaic virus. The particles are about 20 × 300 mμ and consist of 94% protein and 6% RNA. *Photo courtesy Virus Laboratory, University of California, Berkeley.*

seems to inhibit the production of chlorophyll in leaf tissues in an irregular pattern over a range from a scarcely visible mottling of various shades of green to a brilliant variegation of yellow or even white areas.

Malformations. Most mosaics cause some slight leaf distortion; however, in extreme cases, viruses cause deformity and abnormal growth of part or all of an affected plant. The entire plant may be stunted or dwarfed; rosette formations or abnormal growths in the form of tumors and galls may appear.

Ring spots and necrosis. Many viruses cause the formation of rings by altering chlorophyll or by killing the tissue.

Bacterial Viruses. Early microbiologists observed a special sort of degenerative change in laboratory cultures of bacteria. The change could be transmitted by placing a drop of filtrate from an infected culture onto an agar culture of the susceptible bacteria. The filtrable agent was identified as a virus, parasitic upon bacterial cells. Since the agar culture colonies appeared "nibbled," the name **bacteriophage,** commonly abbreviated to **phage** (from the Greek word, *phagein,* meaning to eat), was applied.

While any particular phage is highly host-specific (it will attack only one species and perhaps only a few strains of that species), probably every known type of bacterium is susceptible to one or more phages. Phages against actinomycetes and yeast have also been reported, but none have been found which attack algae, molds or protozoa.

Bacteriophages affect susceptible bacteria by causing **lysis** or dissolution during the stage of active growth. Infection occurs when a few drops of a filtrate containing phage are added to the surface of an agar plate which has been heavily seeded with an organism sensitive to the phage. If the filtrate has not been diluted, no growth, or at most a few colonies of resistant bacteria, will appear. If sufficiently diluted, the filtrate addition produces small clear areas called **plaques** (Fig. 10.7) distributed in the background or lawn of growth of the bacteria. Each plaque corresponds to a phage particle in the inoculum; thus a phage count may be made just as dilution plating is used to count bacteria. Differences among phages can be recognized by differences in size, turbidity, and formation of the plaque edge.

Bacteriophage can be demonstrated also by adding phage-containing filtrate to broth cultures of a susceptible organism. Phage should be introduced when the bacteria are inoculated into the broth or in the early stages of bacterial growth. Clearing of the culture, either partial or complete, will occur as a result of phage action. Prolonged incubation may produce clouding from the growth of mutant cells which are resistant to phage action.

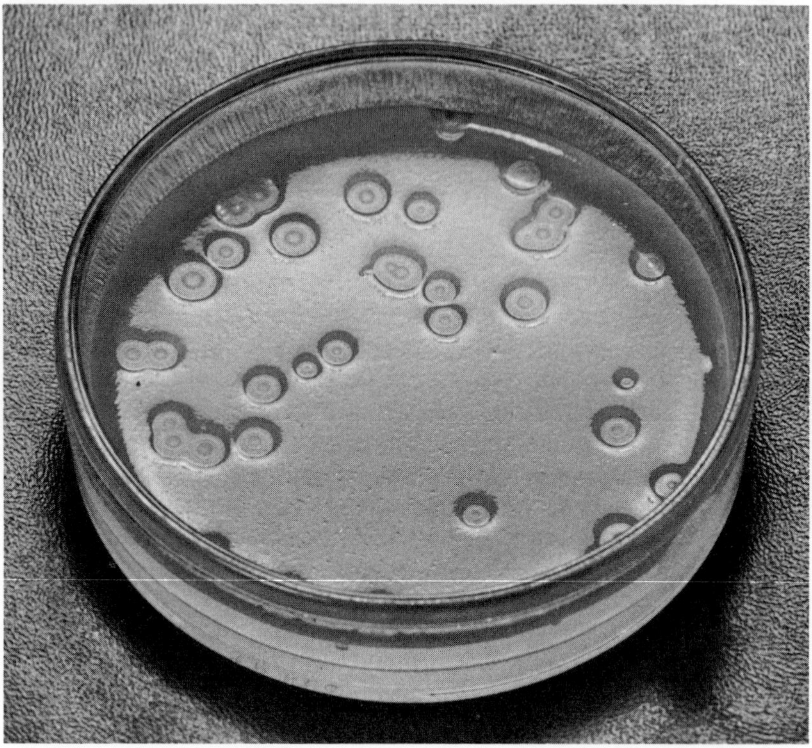

Fig. 10.7. To isolate bacteriophages and to make quantitative studies, plate counts of plaques are made which appear as holes or negative colonies in a lawn of bacteria growing on agar.

The most widely studied phages are tadpole shaped. The tail in some species may be so short as to escape detection, while in others it may exceed 200 mμ in length. The head in various species ranges from a diameter of about 50 mμ to as much as 90 to 100 mμ. The head contains the DNA surrounded by a protein coat.

When virulent phage particles are inoculated into a culture of sensitive bacteria, the course of development involves **adsorption, penetration, multiplication,** and **release.** During the adsorption process the phage particle becomes attached to a receptor site on the bacterial cell wall (Fig. 10.8). Phage-resistant mutants have cell walls so modified that the receptor sites are absent.

Using the tail as an inoculating needle, the phage penetrates the bacteria, and the phage DNA enters the bacterial cytoplasm. The viral-protein coat remains outside the bacterial cell. Adsorption and penetration usually take place in about five minutes. The phage DNA

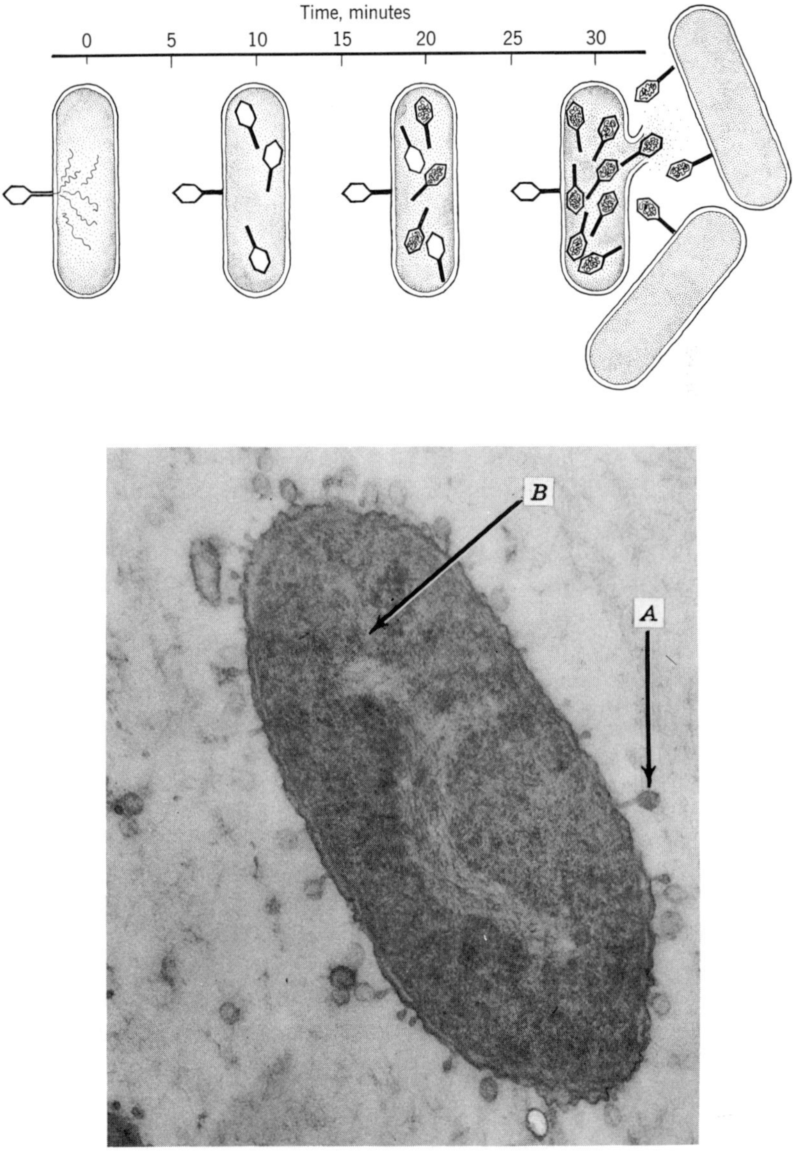

Fig. 10.8. Top: The phage is adsorbed tail first on the bacterial cell wall, and the thread-like DNA from the head penetrates into the bacterium. It serves as the code directing the bacterium to make the parts of a new crop of phages. When these are assembled they burst from the cell and attack other bacteria. Bottom: The phage *A* is shown attached to the bacterium *B* in the electron micrograph. In other attached phages the DNA has already entered the bacteria leaving, outside the phage, "ghosts."

now seizes control of the economy of the cell, and the cell ceases to produce bacterial structural elements. The cell continues its energy-producing activities, but its entire biosynthetic capabilities are directed to the synthesis of phage materials. After about 20 to 60 minutes a crop of new phages is assembled from these newly synthesized phage precursors. The cell bursts releasing the phages and thus completing the cycle. An average burst releases about 200 phage particles; however, the burst size varies with different phages from 20 to over 1000.

In addition to virulent phages there exist temperate phages, which are carried in many bacterial cells only occasionally showing evidence of their existence. When the DNA of a temperate phage penetrates the bacterial cell, it attaches itself to the bacterial chromosome and behaves as if it were part of the heredity apparatus of the bacterium. When the nuclear material of the bacterium is reproduced, the phage DNA, now called **prophage,** is reproduced with it and passed on to the daughter cells. This process may continue for many generations. Bacterial cells containing prophage are immune to attack by related virulent phages. In old cultures or in cultures exposed to radiation, the balance between the prophage and the bacterial DNA is disturbed. The prophage detaches from the chromosome and assumes control of the cell economy as with virulent phages. The cell lyses releasing a burst of free phage particles which will attack sensitive cells. Because of this latent potential for lysis, cultures containing prophage are called **lysogenic,** and the whole phenomenon is called **lysogeny.** Such loss of individual cells in old cultures is more than balanced by the immunity against virulent phages that lysogeny confers.

Bacteriophages have not been effective in the control of disease-producing bacteria. Much of our knowledge of virus multiplication and of host-parasite relationships has been acquired through phage studies. Since phages are principally genetic material, such studies have made major contributions to modern genetic theory. Epidemiology has been advanced through studies of the sensitivity to phages of strains of pathogenic bacteria isolated from different human carriers. Phage typing of such strains often indicates the individual source of an epidemic.

THE RICKETTSIAE

The rickettsiae are microorganisms, intermediate in size between the viruses and bacteria (Fig. 10.9). Morphologically they resemble the bacteria; biologically, because of their obligate parasitism, they are related to the viruses. The generic name *Rickettsia* was given in honor

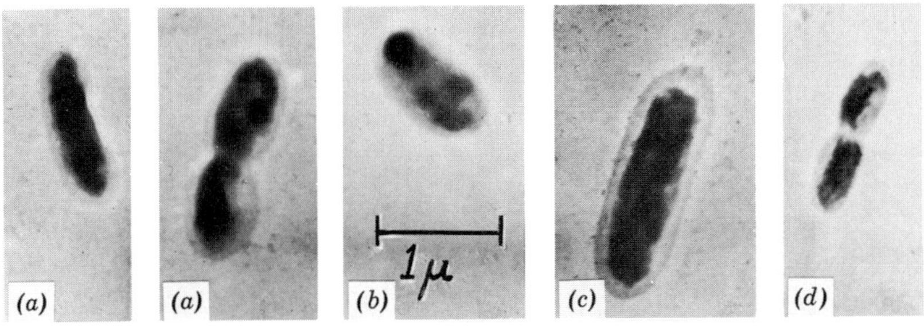

Fig. 10.9. Electron micrographs of the rickettsiae associated with human disease. (*a*) Epidemic typhus, (*b*) Endemic typhus, (*c*) Rocky Mountain spotted fever, and (*d*) American Q fever. *Photos by Plotz, Smadel, Anderson, and Chambers: J. Exp. Med., LXXVII, 355–358, April 1943, courtesy* S.A.B. LS-25.

of Dr. Howard Taylor Ricketts, who in 1909 first described bacillary bodies in the blood of patients suffering from Rocky Mountain spotted fever. In 1910, in the course of studies on typhus fever, which led to his death from the disease, he saw similar organisms in patients and in infected body lice. His observations have been confirmed and extended by many later workers.

Rickettsiae are widespread in nature in arthropods. With the exception of the louse, which is killed by the rickettsiae of typhus fever, they do not harm the natural host. Disease results when rickettsiae infect man or an arthropod species other than the natural host. The diseases they cause in man are characterized by fever and rash. A high fatality rate is reported for untreated cases.

Rickettsiae are coccobacilli which show considerable variation in size, ranging around the limit of visibility with the light microscope(i.e., to about 0.2 μ). Diplococcoid forms are seen frequently. With one exception (the Q fever rickettsiae), they are not filtrable. Since they stain poorly with the ordinary bacterial stains, special stains must be employed (such as Giemsa's stain for blood and protozoa). Like viruses they are obligate intracellular parasites, although they are found at times in body fluids and excretions. Cultivated only in living cells, they seem to grow most luxuriantly in resting or slowly metabolizing cells. In the laboratory they are most conveniently grown in the yolk sac of embryonated eggs, from which they can be recovered and concentrated by centrifugation into pure preparations. As both deoxyribonucleic and ribonucleic acids have been found in pure preparations, rickettsiae probably have a nucleus or nuclear material. Unlike viruses they contain enzymes concerned in metabolism and are sensitive to a number of chemotherapeutic agents.

Table 10.1. Groups of Pathogenic Rickettsiae

Group	Type of Disease	Casual Rickettsia	Natural Hosts Arthropod	Mammal	Mode of Transmission to Man
I Typhus	Epidemic	*R. prowazekii*	Body and head louse	Man	Infected louse feces into broken skin
	Endemic	*R. typhi*	Rat flea	Small rodents	Infected flea feces into broken skin
	Scrub	*R. tsutsuga-muchi*	Mite	Small rodents	Mite bite
II Spotted fevers	Rocky Mountain	*R. rickettsii*	Ticks	Small wild rodents; Dogs	Tick bite
	Mediter-ranean (Boutonneuse fever)	*R. conorii*	Dog tick	None known	Tick bite
	South African Tick bite	*R. conorii var. pijperi*	Ticks	None known	Tick bite
	Rickettsial pox	*R. akari*	Mite	House mice	Mite bite
III Q Fever		*Coxiella burnetii (R. burnetii)*	Ticks	Cattle, sheep, and other animals	Contact, inhalation, tick bite
IV Trench fever		*R. quintana*	Body louse	Man	Louse feces into broken skin

Rickettsiae appear to divide like bacteria, all stages of divisions having been observed in microscopic preparations. In electron micrographs they show a dense inner area surrounded by an envelope or capsule-like structure. Like the vegetative cells of bacteria, the rickettsiae can resist heat and bactericidal chemicals but most exhibit low resistance to drying. Four groups of rickettsia are pathogenic for man (Table 10.1).

THE PLEUROPNEUMONIA-LIKE ORGANISMS

The pleuropneumonia-like organisms (PPLO) have no cell walls and are extremely variable in shape. They appear as large bodies, filaments, ring structures, and filtrable granules (Fig. 10.10). The large bodies may reproduce by fragmentation. No special cell structures such as flagella or spores are seen. They produce tiny colonies on agar; even when the culture medium is enriched with serum, the colonies are seldom large enough to see with the naked eye. In diseased animals and in tissue culture, they grow in the cytoplasm of the infected cell.

The actual pleuropneumonia organism causes a diseased condition of the pleural membranes and lungs of cattle, sheep, and goats. On the other hand, the pleuropneumonia-like organisms grow in sewage and in the mouth and genito-urinary tract of man. Though they are occasionally associated with irritations of the mucous membranes, a causative relationship has not been firmly established.

Certain true rod-shaped bacteria may give rise to soft, protoplasmic forms exhibiting all the variations in size and shape (including the

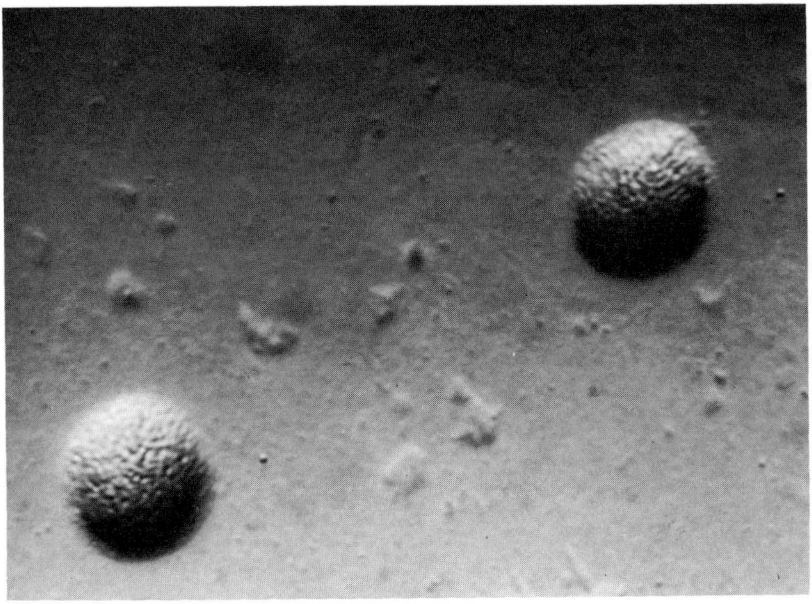

Fig. 10.10. The colonies of PPLO are so tiny that they must be observed under the microscope. The individual cells of the PPLO culture may be smaller than the largest viruses. *Photo by H. J. Morowitz and M. E. Tourtellotte: Scientific American, CCVI, 122, March 1962.*

filtrable particles) observed in the PPLO cultures. Termed **L-forms** (after the Lister Institute where extensive studies on these types were conducted), these organisms may revert to the typical bacterial form. Thus some microbiologists believe that the PPLO organisms are not independent types, but an unusual mutant of some more orthodox bacterium.

SUMMARY. The viruses and the rickettsiae are smaller than the bacteria, obligately parasitic, but still retain sufficient individuality to be considered living organisms. Their presence is usually noted by pathological manifestations in the host, but recent work suggests that their activity is typified by lysogeny in the bacteriophages. The viruses are extremely specific in their association with host cells. Their primary constituent is nucleic acid, which carries the code that directs the cell to replicate the virus. The larger viruses contain additional constituents, and the rickettsia have almost a complete array of the enzymes necessary for independent life.

11

Factors affecting Growth and Death

Of the factors regulating growth and death of microbial cultures some are inherent in the organisms, themselves, and others may be ascribed to the specific physical and chemical environment.

The Organism. Even under optimum conditions the rate of growth of different microorganisms varies considerably: Some organisms are inherently slow growers, while others grow more rapidly. On the other hand, environmental factors which accelerate growth may also accelerate the death processes. Under natural conditions any environment is occupied primarily by the organisms best suited for survival. Because of the ubiquitous occurrence of microbes, new groups are ready to move in as soon as the environment becomes unfavorable for the current occupant. In pure cultures, however, where contaminants are excluded, the effects of environmental factors have been worked out in considerable detail. If culture conditions are ideal for a number of types of organisms, the smaller will grow faster than the larger; for example, under conditions equally suitable for cultures of molds, yeast, and bacteria, the bacteria will outgrow the yeasts, and the yeasts will outgrow the molds. Organisms preferring high temperatures grow more rapidly than those preferring low temperatures. Organisms that build all their cell constituents from simple carbon and nitrogen compounds grow more slowly than those that require a medium containing more complex organic materials and use partially preformed building blocks.

Food. Organisms need food for building blocks and for energy. Exhaustion of the food supply is an ultimate factor limiting microbial activity, since the amount of food regulates microbial growth. In this situation the **law of the minimum** operates; if a bacterium needs a certain vitamin for growth, it will stop growing when the supply of that vitamin is exhausted, even though the broth may still contain large amounts of sugar and peptones (Fig. 11.1). The amount and kind of food available determines the types of organisms that will thrive and the rate and extent of their growth. In waters or soil where organic matter is in short supply, **autotrophic** organisms thrive by utilizing gaseous CO_2 as a source of carbon for building cell materials. Such organisms need as a source of energy an oxidizable inorganic material such as hydrogen sulfide, ammonia, hydrogen gas, or iron in the ferrous state. Or the organisms, depending on CO_2 as a source of carbon, may contain photosynthetic pigments and secure energy from sunlight. With the exception of algae, most microbes are **heterotrophic,** using organic carbon compounds for both energy and building blocks. Some are omnivorous, using a wide variety of compounds ranging from the large molecules of starch and protein to two-carbon compounds such as alcohols. Many molds and the bacteria of the genus *Pseudomonas* are examples of organisms having a wide range of carbon substrates. Other microbes may be limited to relatively few sugars as sources of

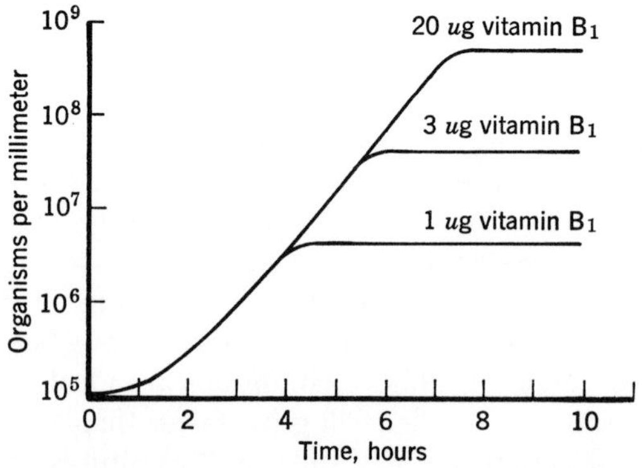

Fig. 11.1. The growth curves of three bacterial cultures with excess of all required nutrients except vitamin B_1. The culture with one microgram (μg) of the vitamin grows just as rapidly as the other cultures until the vitamin content of the broth is exhausted; then it enters the maximum stationary phase.

carbon. Nitrogen nutrition is equally diverse; some organisms can build proteins from ammonia or nitrate while others must have preformed proteinaceous material such as peptides or amino acids.

Moisture. Foods are transported into the microbial cell, and wastes are removed from the cell in water solution. Water also serves as a building material in cell synthesis. Oxygen generally is introduced into a biologically synthesized molecule by the addition of water (H_2O), followed by the removal of the two hydrogen atoms; these hydrogens are transferred to other molecules in the cell, and thus the hydrogen from water also becomes a part of the living organism and its products. A medium which is high in colloids will hold much of the water as **bound water,** that is, water which is tied to the colloid in such a way as to be unavailable for the microorganism. The addition of 10% agar to nutrient broth instead of the usual 1.5% gel will result in a medium on which most organisms will not flourish because much of the water is bound by the colloid, and little free water is available. Cereal products such as flour may contain as much as 12% total water, but microbial spoilage will not occur because of the low **free water** content. Yeasts require less moisture than bacteria, and molds can grow on even dryer materials.

The addition of dissolved materials affects the availability of moisture to the cells. The osmotic pressure of a solution is a measure of this availability. When a solution has an osmotic pressure equal to that inside the cell, it is said to be **isotonic** with the cell. A solution of 0.85% sodium chloride is isotonic with red blood cells and is sometimes used for suspending and diluting bacteria, although three times that value would be more nearly isotonic with bacteria. A **hypotonic** solution exerts an osmotic pressure much less than that inside the cells. When a cell is placed in a **hypertonic** solution (one of higher concentration of dissolved materials), water is drawn out of the cell, and the solute particles tend to pass into the cell to establish an equilibrium on both sides of the cell membrane. Since the living membrane is differentially permeable, the water moves out faster than the dissolved substance can move in. In highly concentrated solutions this water loss proceeds to such an extent that the protoplast shrinks away from the cell wall, and the cell dies (Fig. 11.2). This process is called **plasmolysis.** Organisms that live and grow best in high concentrations of dissolved substances are called **osmophiles;** a special subgroup is composed of organisms called **halophiles,** which grow preferentially in concentrated salt solutions. They are found in salt environments and are important spoilage organisms in salted foods.

If halophiles are removed from a salt solution and placed in dis-

(a)

(b)

(c)

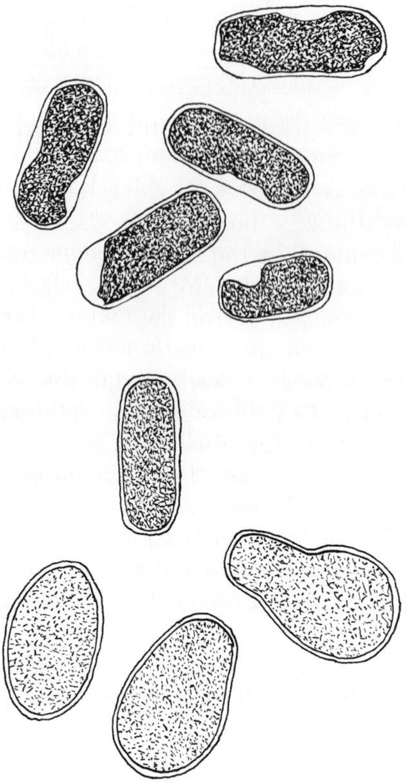

Fig. 11.2. Extreme changes in osmotic pressure affect bacterial cells in spite of the rigid cell wall. (*a*) Plasmolysis of cells transferred to a high salt or sugar concentration. (*b*) Normal cell. (*c*) Plasmoptysis is shown by swelling or even rupture of cells transferred from a high salt or sugar concentration to distilled water.

tilled water, the high salt concentration inside the cell causes a reverse of the plasmolysis phenomenon. Water entering the cell to equalize the osmotic pressure will distend the cell membrane and may cause it to burst; this is called **plasmoptysis.**

Bacteria, yeasts, and molds can endure great variation in osmotic pressure because of the corset-type action exhibited by the cell wall. When cell walls are weakened or removed by enzymic digestion or chemical poisoning, the cells take up water and expand until the cell membrane ruptures. Bacterial cells with the cell walls removed are called **protoplasts** or **spheroplasts.** Keeping them in a solution of 5% to 20% sucrose will prevent their bursting.

Water also participates in the death phase. More vigorous heating is required to kill organisms in dry material than in wet material; hence, the steam autoclave is a more efficient sterilizer than the hot-air oven. In fumigation, microbes are killed more readily if the air is humid. Pure ethyl alcohol does not kill bacteria nearly as rapidly as does a mixture composed of 70% alcohol and 30% water.

Temperature. Three points on the temperature scale, the minimum, optimum, and maximum temperatures, delineate the effect of temperature on microbial growth (Fig. 11.3). For some species the temperature range is very narrow; for example, the optimum temperature for growth of the gonococcus is about 35° C, with the minimum temperature a few degrees lower and the maximum of about 35.5° C. Other species may have a broad optimum temperature spectrum, the range between the maximum and the minimum extending over 40 centigrade degrees. The optimum temperature for an organism varies with the characteristic that is measured. Some organisms grow fastest at 40° C, produce the biggest crop of cells at 35° C, produce the most acid at 30° C, and form acid at the fastest rate at 45° C. Usually the total number of cells produced is the criterion for determining the optimum temperature; although in a practical problem such as penicillin fermentation, the optimum temperature is that at which the highest yield of penicillin is obtained in the shortest time.

Since biological reactions depend on the chemical activity of the cell, the temperature response of chemical reactions determines total cell activity (reaction rates approximately double with a rise in temperature of 10° C). Obviously biological reactions cannot proceed

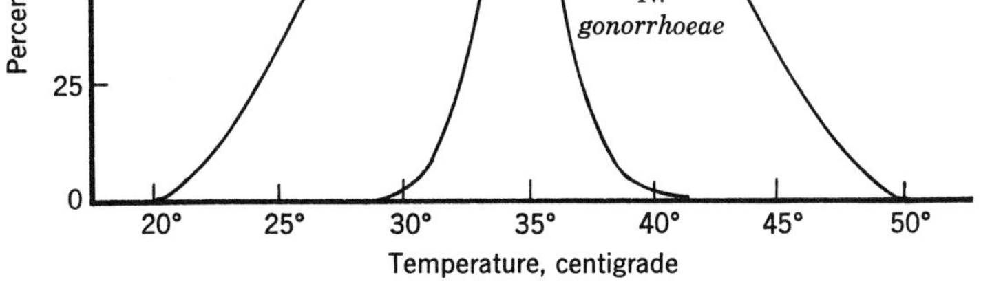

Fig. 11.3. The temperature range of some organisms show a broad optimum with a widely spread maximum and minimum. For other organisms it is extremely narrow.

when the cell water is frozen, nor can they operate if the temperature is raised to a point that cooks (denatures) the cell proteins. But between these values, the maximum and minimum temperatures are determined by the variation in the effect of temperature on the individual reactions which participate in cell growth. A change in temperature will increase or decrease the rate of some chemical reactions in the cell to a greater extent than others, effecting an excess of some cellular substances and, consequently, an insufficiency of others. Optimum growth occurs when the *best balance* is attained. Growth at temperatures higher than the optimum modifies the anthrax bacillus, destroying its ability to produce disease in animals and also its ability to form spores. Pigmentation and antibiotic production are also markedly influenced by incubation temperatures.

The **psychrophilic** or cold-loving group of microbes grow slowly, but they thrive at refrigerator temperatures (below 20°C) and make some growth at 0°C (Fig. 11.4). They take part in spoilage of refrigerated foods; however, they may produce desirable changes in the flavor and texture of beef as it ages in cold storage. The **mesophiles,** which thrive in the moderate temperatures, are the largest group and include all of the animal pathogens. The **thermophiles,** which thrive in high temperatures, are of economic importance in food-processing industries. Their growth in hot syrup may cause undesirable slimes in sugar factories; they are important spoilage organisms of canned foods. In the dairy industry, some species of thermophiles grow at pasteurization temperatures; in the production of Swiss cheese the milk is held at a high temperature to favor the growth of certain thermophiles that produce desirable flavors. Thermophiles thrive in hot springs and in the centers of piles of decomposing organic matter such as composts or manures. Some organisms are **obligate** thermophiles, requiring high temperatures for growth; others are **facultative** thermophiles able to grow at elevated temperatures but capable of growing in the mesophilic range. The adjectives obligate and facultative are also used to describe other microbial characteristics. The thermophiles are biological oddities because they grow best at temperatures which denature proteins (destroy protoplasm) and thrive under conditions generally regarded as incompatible with life. Constituents of thermophilic bacteria such as flagella and enzymes, which have been studied apart from the living organisms, are much more resistant to heat than are the analogous substances isolated from mesophilic species.

Increased temperature gives a steeper slope to the death phase of the bacterial growth curve. Even under very high temperatures the organisms do not all die at once, but the survivors follow the same type of exponential curve; that is, a straight line usually results when the logarithms of survivors are plotted against time. Many vegetative cells are killed by heating them for only 10 minutes at 55° C, and most are killed in less than a minute at 70° C. However, some mesophiles will survive long exposures to temperatures above the maximum for growth.

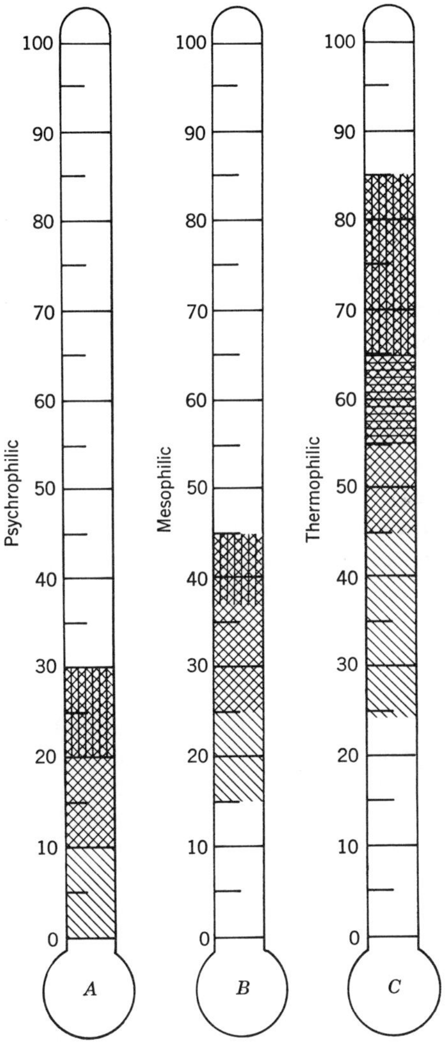

Fig. 11.4. The growth ranges of psychrophiles, mesophiles, and thermophiles are indicated on the centigrade thermometers. Convenient optimum temperatures to remember are: psychrophiles, 10° C; mesophiles, room temperature (25° C) or body temperature (37° C); and thermophiles, 50° C.

Such organisms are described as **thermoduric,** and they are found, among other places, in pasteurized beverages and on utensils washed with very hot water. But the heat resistance of thermoduric vegetative cells does not approach that usually exhibited by endospores. Some of the latter may be boiled for an hour or more without being killed. Hence, autoclaving is designed to deal with the heat resistance of spores. Resistance of spore proteins to the denaturing effect of heat probably results from their molecular arrangement which protects the reactive chemical groupings.

The lethal effect of heat on microorganisms depends on both temperature and time. The **thermal death point** is that temperature at which all bacteria in a culture are killed in ten minutes. However, all bacteria do not die at the same time; rather, the cells die off during the heating period. Thus the thermal death point merely tells us what temperature is necessary so that the last survivor will expire in ten minutes. Thermal death conditions must be carefully controlled since the species, numbers, physiological state of the organisms, and the nature of the suspending material affect the result.

The same restrictions apply to the **thermal death time,** a measure of the time required to kill a given species at a stated temperature. Typical thermal death times for vegetative bacteria are 30 minutes at 62°C or 30 seconds at 70°C.

Microbes can be killed by cold if frozen slowly so that ice crystals form in the cells and disrupt them. However, if frozen rapidly, microbes can be stored for years without significant killing. Bacteriologists preserve cultures by **lyophilization,** a process involving rapid freezing followed by evaporation of the ice under a vacuum.

Hydrogen Ion Concentration. The acidity or basicity of the medium in which microorganisms grow is determined by the concentration of hydrogen ions. The pH scale, by which this property is measured, runs from 0 to 14, the low values indicating acid and the high values, alkaline. Most organisms have an optimum pH for growth at or near neutrality, pH 7.0. Those pathogenic for man or animals have an optimum pH of about 7.26, the pH of blood. With few exceptions, the range for bacterial growth fits somewhere between pH 4 and pH 10; some organisms cover the entire range, whereas others are restricted to less than 1 pH unit (Fig. 11.5). Most fruit juices are too acid for bacteria, but yeasts and molds grow well in media as acid as pH 2 or 3. Plate counts of mold or yeast may be made without interference from bacteria by employing a medium adjusted to a low pH.

Many bacteria produce organic acids from sugar; these lower the pH to an unfavorable value before maximum growth is attained unless the medium contains effective **buffers**.

Buffers are substances which resist changes in pH, usually by accepting or releasing hydrogen ions. Phosphate, carbonate, acetate, and citrate are commonly used buffers in culture media. Amino acids and peptones are excellent buffers since they are amphoteric substances existing in solution both as weak acids and weak bases.

In the preparation of a culture medium the original pH is adjusted to a value optimum for the microorganism to be cultured. Colorimetric and potentiometric methods are employed for measuring pH. For the colorimetric procedure a series of dyes called indicators are used which change in color as the pH value changes; litmus and bromthymol blue are useful pH indicators. The latter is green at about pH 7.0, blue at more alkaline pH values, and yellow in acid solutions. The pH of a bacteriological medium is adjusted by adding the indicator and observing from the color whether it is too acid or too alkaline. The appropriate addition of acid or base is then made. Potentiometers are electronic devices employed in pH measurements to determine ionic transfer through a glass electrode.

Strong alkalies are incorporated into washing powders not only because of their cleansing action but

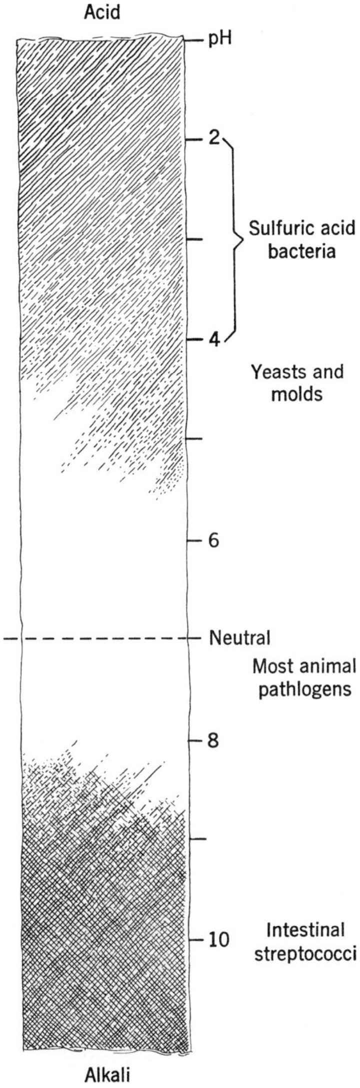

Fig. 11.5. One end of a piece of absorbent paper is dipped into acid, the other into alkali, and placed on an agar surface. A pH gradient is set up, and the optimum pH values showing growth of mixed populations range from pH 2 to pH 10.

also because they kill microorganisms. Strong acids are also powerful killing agents, but they are seldom used because of their corrosive action. Milder acids such as citric, acetic, and lactic have a preservative action and are employed for retarding microbial action in certain foods and beverages.

The Gaseous Environment. Although there are species of microorganisms involved in the production and utilization of methane, hydrogen, carbon monoxide, hydrogen sulfide, ammonia, and nitrogen gases, these are special instances and will be considered in other chapters. The bacteriologist generally considers the gaseous environment in terms of carbon dioxide and oxygen, since these gases affect the growth of all microorganisms.

Carbon dioxide (CO_2) is indispensable to all living cells, and, except in the early lag phase of growth, most microorganisms are able to produce all they require. For certain organisms, such as freshly isolated strains of the gonococcus or brucella, incubation of the inoculated medium under 10% CO_2 is necessary for growth. With other organisms, growth from a small inoculum is stimulated by an atmosphere enriched in CO_2. All organisms require special compounds made of four carbon atoms plus hydrogen and oxygen, as catalysts in their metabolism. These compounds are very reactive and are easily lost from the cell through use as structural materials. The organism has an effective means of replenishing these catalysts by attaching gaseous CO_2 to compounds containing three carbons—the common breakdown products of sugars and peptones. The addition of CO_2 to a three-carbon compound by heterotrophic organisms is called the **Wood-Werkman** reaction, and, although it was first discovered in bacteria, it probably occurs in all cells. An excess of CO_2 in the atmosphere inhibits some microorganisms. In some cases the inhibition is due to the lowering of the pH of the medium; in others it is considerably more complicated. With the autotrophs, CO_2 is required as their sole source of carbon.

Free oxygen was regarded as an essential for all life until Pasteur demonstrated that, although some microorganisms require it, other species not only grow without it but are actually poisoned by free oxygen. These organisms are called **anaerobes,** and the organisms requiring gaseous oxygen are called **aerobes.** Anaerobic life is similar to aerobic life, in that energy-yielding processes involve oxidations which occur by the addition of water to the molecule being oxidized, followed by the removal of hydrogen atoms. However, in aerobes, hydrogens are ultimately transferred to atmospheric oxygen to yield H_2O as the end product while oxygen is used up from the gaseous environment. In anaerobes, hydrogens are ultimately transferred to some other molecule and become a part of ethyl alcohol, lactic acid, ammonia, or other organic or inorganic end products. Some organisms are capable of both aerobic and anaerobic life; they are termed facultative and are distinguished from the obligate aerobes and anaerobes. Other organisms require gaseous oxygen but grow best at a concentration less than that which exists in air. Such organisms are called **microaerophilic.**

A medium containing such oxidized substances as nitrate or permanganate will fail to support the growth of anaerobic organisms even if oxygen is excluded. If a crystal of sodium sulfide or some other highly reducing substance is placed in the medium, anaerobic organisms will grow in the immediate vicinity of the crystal and microaerophilic organisms will grow at some slight distance, while aerobic organisms will not grow in the medium anywhere near the reducing substance (Fig. 11.6). The medium varies with the distance from the crystal, and the measurement of this variation is expressed as the oxidation-reduction (O-R or redox) potential (Fig. 11.7). In electrometric measurement a platinum electrode is placed in a culture medium saturated with oxygen at pH 7.0. The resulting reading is about 800 millivolts more positive than that given by a standard hydrogen electrode. If oxygen is excluded so that anaerobes will grow, the reading may be about -400 millivolts. By varying the amount of oxygen or the amount of reducing substance, intermediate values are obtained. There are colorimetric indicators which show the O-R potential; thus methylene blue is deep blue at about $+50$ millivolts and colorless at about -100 millivolts on the O-R scale.

Desirable O-R potentials are more easily obtained than are desirable pH values. Since the common procedures used in the preparation of culture media result in satisfactory values, adjustment is generally unnecessary. High potentials for aerobes are obtained by growing them on an agar surface, while low potentials for anaerobes are found at the bottom of a deep tube of agar. For optimum growth of aerobic organisms, the amount of oxygen required may be very large, and the medium must either be agitated or dispersed in shallow layers. To secure the low O-R potentials necessary for anaerobic growth, oxygen is excluded.

Anaerobic cultures are commonly prepared in deep tubes of medium with little surface exposed for the entrance of oxygen. The surface of a liquid medium may be covered with a layer of vaseline, or 0.1% agar may be added to a broth to reduce convection currents in the liquid, which aid in the penetration of oxygen. Heating the medium immediately before inoculation drives out the dissolved oxygen and lowers the O-R potential by causing reducing sugars and similar substances to react with and eliminate oxidized molecules in the medium. The O-R

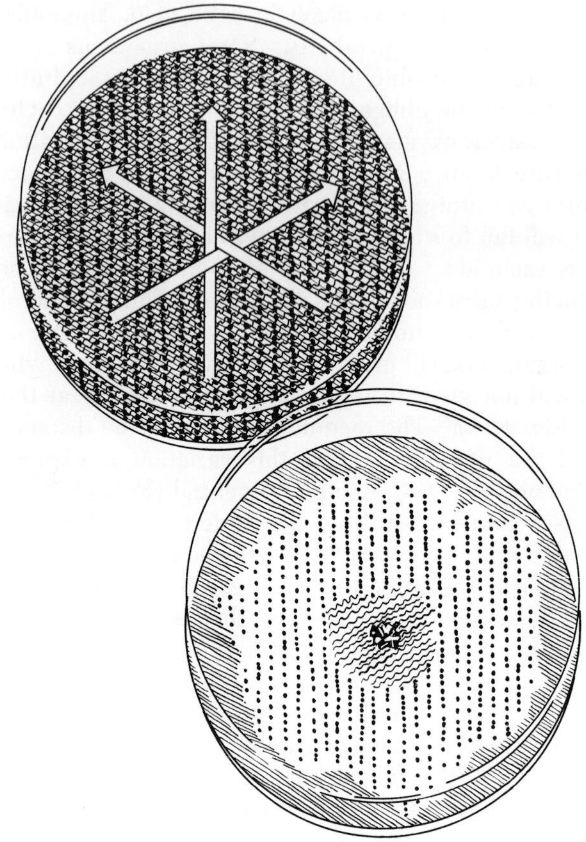

Fig. 11.6. On plates of nitrate agar, aerobes were streaked upward to the left; anaerobes were streaked upward to the right, and microaerophiles were streaked horizontally as indicated by the three arrows on the upper plate. If all had grown (which they would not) the plate would have appeared as indicated. When a crystal of the highly reducing substance, sodium sulfide, was placed in the center, the anaerobes (wavy lines) grew only near the crystal, the aerobes (straight lines) grew near the edge of the plate, and the microaerophiles grew in between. With a platinum electrode differences in oxidation-reduction potential can be measured in the three areas.

potential can be lowered even more if a highly reactive reducing chemical such as thioglycollate, reduced iron, or a piece of sterile, living, respiring animal or plant tissue is placed in the broth. Thus a reservoir of reduced substances is made available to react with any dissolved oxygen that may enter by diffusion. Diffusion of oxygen through agar, however, is reasonably slow, and tubes completely filled with agar will, with the exception of the upper inch, permit good growth and colony development of most anaerobes.

If anaerobes are to be grown in petri dishes, on the surface of agar slants, or in shallow broth tubes some provision must be made for removal of oxygen. Many ingenious procedures have been developed, but the following methods are those most commonly employed.

1. ***Evacuation.*** The cultures are placed in a vacuum jar and the air is removed by pumping. Care must be taken that the dissolved gases removed from the media do not form bubbles in the agar or cause the liquid media to boil, thus wetting the plugs. The air removed may be replaced with another gas such as hydrogen, nitrogen, or methane.

2. ***Chemical Removal of Oxygen.*** Quantitative removal of oxygen can be effected by placing a piece of phosphorus or a mixture of pyrogallol and strong alkali inside the container. The replacement of part of the air in the jar with hydrogen in the presence of a heated platinum catalyst results in the reaction of the hydrogen with the oxygen remaining in the jar.

3. ***Biological Removal of Oxygen.*** If moistened oats or other grains are placed in the bottom of a sealed culture container, the respiration of the oats together with that of the molds contaminating the grain rapidly removes gaseous oxygen and replaces it with CO_2. Any type of living tissue may be used in place of oats. Cultures of molds or other highly aerobic bacteria placed in a closed container with the anaerobic culture will accomplish the same result. The large numbers of anaerobes that develop in cultivated and seemingly well-aerated soil thrive because aerobic organisms in the soil use up the oxygen as rapidly as it diffuses into the spaces between the soil particles.

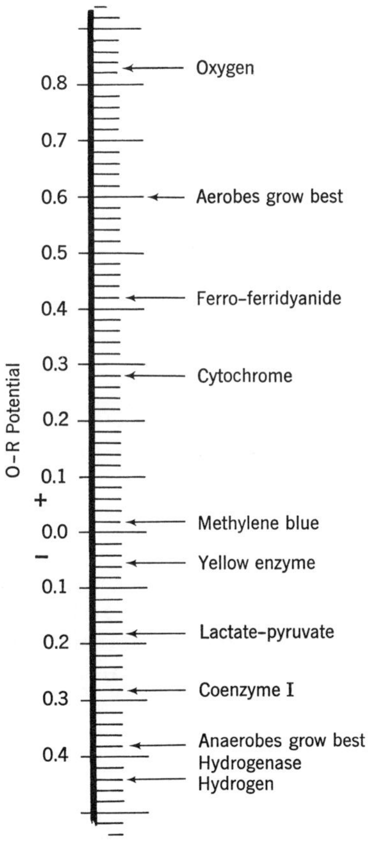

Fig. 11.7. At pH 7.0 the oxidation-reduction potential ranges from −0.4 to +0.8 volt. Methylene blue becomes colorless at values below 0. Some important biological chemicals are indicated at that potential where they exist as half oxidized and half reduced.

Surface Tension. Surface tension is a measure of the cohesive forces between molecules at the interface between liquid and air. The surface tension of water is about 72 dynes per centimeter at room temperature. Certain chemicals, such as salt, added to a medium will raise the surface tension slightly; others such as soaps lower the surface tension markedly. Gram-positive organisms generally prefer high surface tension. Gram-negative organisms, especially those capable of growing in the intestinal tract of animals, do very well in a medium with low surface tension. A medium with low surface tension favors the growth of intestinal bacteria by depressing or killing other forms. The tubercle bacilli carry a waxy surface coat and float on the surface of a medium. More vigorous growth is achieved in a medium containing a chemical which lowers the surface tension, because under such conditions the cells sink into the medium, are wetted on all sides, and thus present more surface for absorbing food materials and excreting wastes.

Hydrostatic Pressure. Variations in the atmospheric pressure of the earth's surface have no measurable effect on the life and death of microbes. Measurable killing does not occur until pressures of at least 5000 pounds per square inch are applied. However. microbes from ocean sediments often fail to grow when brought to the surface, as the pressure to which they are accustomed may exceed 12,000 pounds per square inch. These are **barophilic** organisms and can be cultured if the medium is incubated in a high pressure chamber.

Toxic Materials. The presence of toxic materials often has a predominant influence on the growth of microorganisms. These toxic materials may be such ordinary substances as mineral salts, vitamins, or amino acids if they are present in unusually high concentrations. Or they may be normal constituents of fresh milk, eggs, blood, soil, and natural waters. Even the broths prepared by the bacteriologist often contain chemicals inhibitory, or even lethal, to certain microorganisms. Some of these substances can be destroyed by heating or may be bound in an inactive form by the addition of an adsorptive colloid. Such addition of colloidal material to a culture medium will improve microbial growth by removing or neutralizing some toxic element rather than by supplying new food. Increased growth resulting from the addition of starch, protein suspensions, and extracts often results from adsorption of soluble inhibitory substances by the particulate material.

Some toxic materials are byproducts of microbial metabolism. Accumulated acids or alcohols formed from sugar by some organisms and the protein decomposition products from dead and dying organisms effectively inhibit microbial growth. When organisms produce hydrogen peroxide and do not form the peroxide-destroying enzyme, catalase, the curve of the death phase descends abruptly.

SUMMARY. The cells of plants, and especially of animals, live in an environment of their own making. Such living cells are subjected to only minor variations in temperature, concentration of nutrients, and inhibitors. Microbial cells live immersed in and at the mercy of the natural environment. Large variations exist in microbial response to the physical and chemical modifications brought to bear upon them. A knowledge of these factors permits the microbiologist to discourage those organisms which he finds undesirable to his purposes and to promote the growth of those which are useful to him.

12

Inhibiting and Killing Microorganisms

Man has developed many procedures to control and destroy microorganisms in order to protect himself, his animals, and his plants from disease and his food, clothing, and other equipment from microbiological deterioration. For this purpose he has used a wide variety of physical and chemical agents.

The destruction of all microorganisms in an environment is referred to as sterilization, and the term sterility implies freedom from seeds of reproduction. The removal of disease-producing organisms (disinfection) implies that the infectious material has been removed, but sterility has not necessarily been attained. Some people would restrict the term disinfectant to those chemicals used in destroying bacteria on nonliving materials. Antiseptics are milder agents and are applied to the living body. Some chemicals are used in high concentrations for disinfection and in lower concentrations for antisepsis. A chemical taken or injected into the living body for the purpose of inhibiting or destroying microbial infections in cells or tissues is called a **chemotherapeutic agent**.

Agents that kill bacteria are called **bactericidal agents**. If they merely inhibit bacterial growth, they are referred to as **bacteriostatic agents**: **Bacteriostasis** is a synonym for bacterial inhibition. **Fungicides** kill fungi, and **viricides** kill viruses. The term **germicide** is the more inclusive term.

Nine factors markedly affect any attempt to kill or inhibit organisms.

1. Intensity or concentration and time of exposure. Time and intensity are intimately bound together in any sterilization process; low concentrations require longer exposure times and *vice-versa.* Penicillin in a massive dose may cure syphilis in one day; a lower dose rate must be continued for weeks to achieve the same response. A still lower rate may require infinite time; that is, it will fail to destroy the microorganism causing the disease. At very low intensities or concentrations many useful antibacterial agents will actually stimulate the growth of the same organisms which higher concentrations will inhibit and still higher concentrations will kill (Fig. 12.1).

2. Number of microorganisms or the **contamination load.** Dying microorganisms generally exhibit a straight-line death curve when the logarithms of the numbers of survivors are plotted against time. A death-phase curve starting with high numbers will, therefore, take longer to descend to the bottom of the graph than will a curve of identical slope that starts lower down on the graph (Fig. 12.2). A resis-

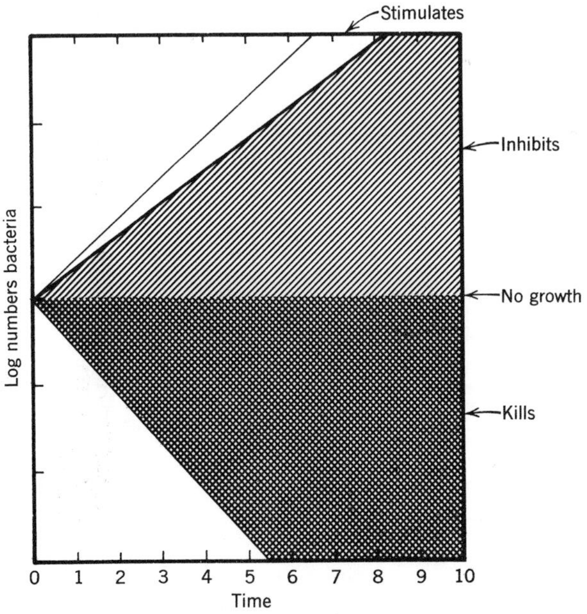

Fig. 12.1. An infinite number of curves can be obtained with a single antibacterial chemical used at varying concentrations. Very low concentrations have no effect; a slight increase results in stimulation. Further increase in concentration will give a decreased growth until a level is reached where killing occurs. The rate of killing is a function of the concentration.

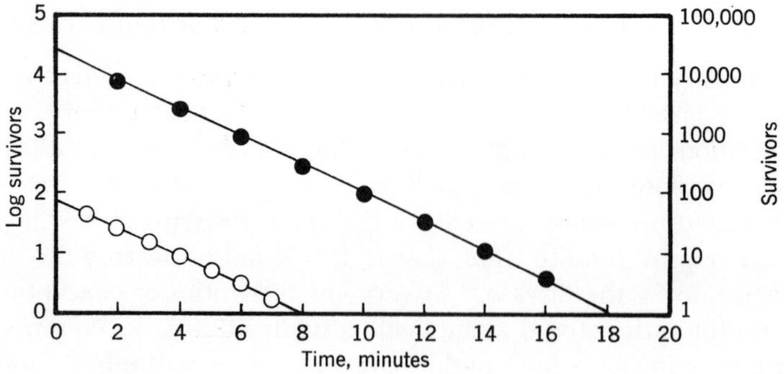

Fig. 12.2. Death rate of bacteria where the same disinfectant was applied at two levels of contamination. The curves are parallel, so the lower curve reaches the bottom of the graph 10 minutes before the upper one.

tant variant (or in mixed populations, a resistant species) is more apt to be present if the inoculum, or the initial load of contaminants, is large (Fig. 12.3).

3. Type of microorganism. While certain types of chemicals are toxic to all living things, most of the useful inhibitory agents act selectively. Some are excellent against fungi and useless against bacteria;

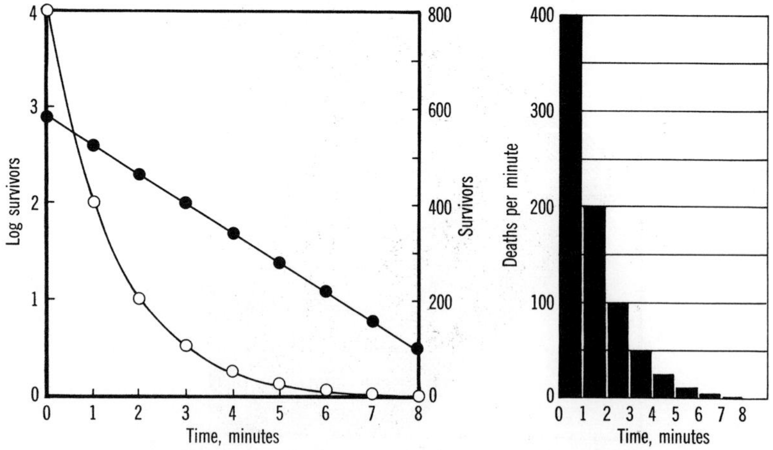

Fig. 12.3. In a typical disinfection experiment, a straight line usually results when the logarithms of the survivors are plotted against the time of exposure to the killing agent. If logarithms are not used, the curved line results. In microbiology it is usually impossible to count dead organisms, but if we could, the bar graph on the right would show a typical result.

some destroy or inhibit bacteria but fail against viruses; some are more effective against gram-positive than gram-negative bacteria. In general, spore formation, capsule formation, and acid fastness help the organism to resist killing but do not deter growth inhibition.

4. State of the culture. Even a single culture will vary in its reaction to antibacterial agencies. A synchronized culture is usually most sensitive to killing while the nuclei are dividing. In ordinary cultures sensitivity varies in different phases of the growth curve with greatest sensitivity often occurring in the early log phase and greatest resistance in the maximum stationary phase.

5. Moisture. Wet organisms are more easily killed than dry organisms.

6. Extraneous material. Usually microorganisms suspended in pure water are easiest to kill. Dissolved and suspended solids protect them from immediate contact with the antibacterial agent. Extraneous material such as blood or pus may absorb or otherwise react with the disinfectant, thus wasting it and lowering its effective concentration.

7. pH. Acidity and basicity affect most antibacterial activities. Cells are usually most resistant at neutrality and become more sensitive in both acid and alkaline substances. On the other hand, streptomycin and sulfonamides are less active at acid pH values, while phenol and chlorine are less active under alkaline conditions.

8. Temperature. In general, antibacterial agents are more effective at higher temperatures.

9. Antidotes. In addition to nonspecific interference by extraneous materials, certain specific antidotes in the medium can often restrict the damage done to the microbe by a killing agent, or interfere with the action of an inhibiting agent. The human body contains antidotes which may revive microorganisms "killed" by mercurial disinfectants. An infected lesion involving tissue breakdown (necrosis) contains enough of the vitamin, para-aminobenzoic acid (the antidote for sulfonamides), to render those drugs completely ineffective as inhibitors. When the bacteriologist attempts to isolate a microorganism from the blood or tissue of a patient under penicillin treatment, the antidote in this case, penicillinase, must be present in the broth or agar.

With microorganisms, "death" is defined as inability to reproduce, that is, to produce a colony on a plate, to make a tube of broth turbid, or to produce an infection in susceptible tissue. But the type of recovery medium used and the antidotes it contains may influence the "death" condition. A chemically treated polio virus may appear dead when tested for growth in a culture flask of monkey kidney tissue, but might still produce an infection in the brain of a living monkey.

TEST METHODS FOR ANTIMICROBIAL ACTION

Bacteriostatic Action. While no single method of studying antibacterial action can be used with all agents, two methods are widely used to study bacteriostatic action. (1) Measured portions of the bacteriostatic agent in concentrations ranging from zero to the highest practical concentration are added to several tubes of broth. These are inoculated with the test organism. After incubation that tube which contains just enough of the antiseptic or disinfectant to prevent visible growth contains the **minimum inhibitory concentration.** Such experiments compare different substances in order to determine which is superior as a bacteriostatic agent. (2) Nutrient agar plates are heavily seeded with the test organism, and a small piece of blotter paper soaked with varying amounts of the test chemical is placed on each plate. After incubation the plates will be covered by growths of the test organism except for clear zones around the blotting paper. The width of the inhibition zone is a measure of the inhibiting ability of the chemical concentration (Fig. 12.4).

Most bacteriostatic agents encounter individual organisms in the test culture that have a **heritable** resistance to the inhibitory action and will grow in the presence of concentrations which completely inhibit the rest of the population. Under normal growth conditions these few (usually one in a million or less) resistant mutants remain as an insignificant part of the normal population. But an inhibitor, concentrated sufficiently to restrict the normal organisms, will not affect the resistant mutants. After growth is complete all the microorganisms in the resulting culture will be resistant to that concentration of inhibitor. If the inhibitor is a drug such as penicillin or sulfonamide, the culture is said to be **drug resistant.** By transfer to media containing still higher inhibitor concentrations, the organisms become tolerant to very high levels. The individual organisms in the culture are not modified, but rather a selection of rare, more resistant mutants develops from the already partially resistant population. Fortunately, drug resistance is a very specific phenomenon; a population of microorganisms resistant to one agent such as sulfonamide is still as sensitive to penicillin as the normal or wild type.

Several practical consequences result from these considerations of resistance to inhibitors.

1. A massive infection is more likely to contain drug resistant organisms than a limited one containing fewer organisms.
2. Partially resistant groups of organisms are likely to contain individuals that are completely or highly resistant. Inadequate treatment

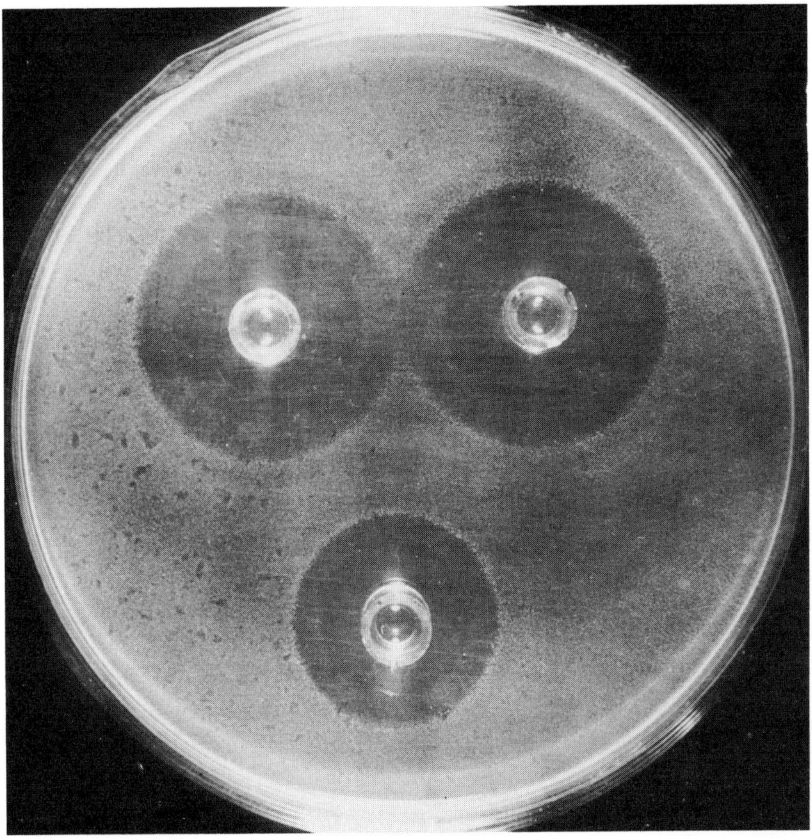

Fig. 12.4. An assay plate where the bacteriostatic chemical in three different dilutions is placed in small glass cups on the surface of an agar plate, whose surface is heavily seeded with bacteria. Near the cups the bacteria are dead; toward the outer edges of the clear zones there is only partial inhibition, and at the edge, a zone of stimulation is evident. Disks of blotting paper soaked in the chemical are convenient substitutes for the glass cylinders.

with small amounts of inhibitors can produce such partially resistant populations.

3. In hospitals and in other areas where inhibitors are used, the microorganisms found are more likely to be partially resistant or highly resistant than the same types of microorganisms found in other areas.

4. The use of combinations of inhibitors of different types minimizes the resistance problem.

Bactericidal Tests. Experiments determining the slope of bacterial death curves determine the basic principles of bactericidal action and provide maximum information about the killing process. When a standardized inoculum of the test organism is subjected to the killing agent and samples withdrawn at measured time intervals, plate counts determine the numbers of survivors. When data are plotted showing the relationship of the survivors to the time, a death curve is revealed for the total population; the slope of the curve is a measure of the killing. Repeated experiments with modifications in pH, inoculum size, type of organism, concentration, and all the other factors governing disinfectant action reveal the effectiveness of the killing agent in comparison with others already tested.

Disinfectants are most practically tested under conditions simulating those under which the agent will actually be used. For example, the infected skin from a mouse is painted with the test antiseptic; bits of skin are surgically removed and inserted in the abdominal cavity. If the antiseptic is ineffective, the mouse will succumb to the infection; if effective, he will survive and his wounds will heal. The efficiency of chemicals used to sanitize drinking glasses may be tested by placing typical organisms from the mouth or skin on glass beads. The time and the concentration of disinfectant required for sterilization of the glass surfaces measure the usefulness of the substance as a sanitizing agent.

The **phenol coefficient test** determines the amount of a disinfectant required to kill organisms in 10 but not in 5 minutes and compares this with the amount of phenol required for the same effect (Fig. 12.5).

Phenol Coefficient Test

	37°C		
	5 min	10 min	15 min
S. aureus			
Phenol:			
1– 80	+	–	–
1– 90	+	+	–
1–100	+	+	+
S. typhosa			
1–140	+	–	–
1–160	+	+	–
1–180	+	+	+

Fig. 12.5. *Staphylococcus aureus* is usually killed in 10 minutes but not in 5 minutes by a 1–80 dilution of phenol. *Salmonella typhosa* is more sensitive. This is the control part of the phenol coefficient test and similar information is obtained for the chemical that is to be compared with phenol.

Carefully standardized to inoculum size, temperature, etc., this test employs both gram-positive organisms, *Staphylococcus aureus,* and a gram-negative organism, *Salmonella typhosa.* The **phenol coefficient,** therefore, is a number which relates the effectiveness of the disinfectant to that of phenol; a compound is said to have a phenol coefficient of five if it takes only one-fifth of the concentration to do as well as phenol in the test described.

MAJOR APPLICATIONS OF DISINFECTANTS AND ANTISEPTICS

Thousands of chemical compounds have been promoted for use as disinfectants and antiseptics. Chlorine is used to kill bacteria in drinking water, in wash waters in food and dairy industries, in swimming pools, and even in treated sewage. Chlorine is an extremely active germicide; 0.1 part per million is adequate for rapid killing of vegetative bacteria in fairly pure water. It is general protoplasmic poison oxidizing, and thus destroying, essential protoplasmic components in all types of cells. It reacts so vigorously with any organic material that its killing action is largely dissipated in highly impure water; considerable killing might still be obtained by greatly increasing the concentration. Chlorine leaves no toxic residue because it is converted to chloride, which is a normal harmless constituent of all foods containing salt.

For sanitizing desk tops, mop waters, toilet bowls, and hospital and laboratory equipment, phenol and the related cresols are highly effective. This group, which includes the pine tar and coal tar distillates, destroys all types of organisms, and extraneous organic matter does not interfere with disinfection to the same extent as with chlorine action. These substances leave an active toxic residue on the desk top or other treated surface. Soaps and detergents are effective for the same purposes, especially when supplemented with an alkali.

High detergent concentrations react with and denature many protoplasmic constituents, but when used in limited concentrations, the initial damage to the microorganism appears in the cell membrane. Death results from leakage of protoplasmic constituents through the membrane damaged by the detergent-type chemical. Gram-positive organisms are killed by lower concentrations of detergents than are gram-negative organisms.

For removing and killing microorganisms on the surface of the skin some physicians use only soap and water; germicidal soaps as well as alcohol, iodine, or mercurials are commonly used. These substances may provide preventive treatment of minor skin injuries and may be used to disinfect medical and dental instruments when heat sterilization is not available. Ethyl and propyl alcohol are effective skin degerming agents and properly used are effective for thermometers and other hospital equipment; such substances as thymol and salicylic acid may be dissolved in the alcohols to increase their germicidal efficiency. Iodine, one of our most effective antiseptics, is usually used as a **tincture** which means it is dissolved in alcohol. As iodine is highly irritating to mucous membranes and certain sensitive skins, less irritating formulations have been developed. Mercurial compounds are sold under trade names such as Mercurochrome, Merthiolate, and Metaphen. While they have powerful bacteriostatic action, their bactericidal action is only moderate. Mercury compounds leave a toxic residue which is desirable for some purposes but not for others. Like other heavy metals they react with the sulfhydryl (–SH) groups of enzyme proteins and stop biological processes. Thus they are nonspecific, that is, toxic not only to all types of microorganisms but to all living forms. A germicidal silver preparation is widely used in treating infections of the eye; for many years state laws have required its application to the eyes of newborn infants to prevent congenital gonococcal infections. The ability of very small amounts of silver and a few other metals to inhibit microorganisms is designated as **oligodynamic** action.

The prevention of deterioration utilizes the greatest tonnage of antibacterial agents. Wood posts, poles, piling, and railroad ties can be preserved from fungal and bacterial deterioration for periods exceeding twenty years if treated with creosote, a distillate from tars. Also effective are copper salts and pentachlorophenol (penta) and its chemical relatives (Fig. 12.6). "Penta" is a comparatively insoluble material retained by wood for long periods of time. For use as an antibacterial agent copper is bound in insoluble salts. "Penta" and copper prep-

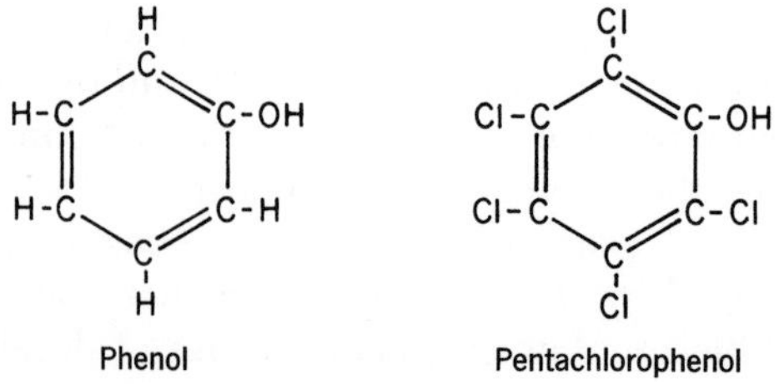

Fig. 12.6. Pentachlorophenol is used where a highly active and long lasting inhibitor is required. It is too insoluble to give the rapid killing exhibited by phenol.

arations are employed to protect rope and tent fabric from antibacterial action and to preserve paints; most paints also contain zinc salts, and the modern water-soluble paints usually need some active preservative to prevent spoilage in the can. Paper not used for food cartons can be impregnated with mercurials such as phenyl mercuric nitrate, but often "penta" or related compounds are employed.

Formulations of copper and of sulfur have been used for hundreds of years to inhibit the microbial attack on growing plants. They are especially effective against fungal infections. Hundreds of organic compounds with higher antimicrobial activity have been prepared, but their usefullness depends on several factors: completeness of spread and coverage over the leaf surface, the persistence on the leaf through rain and wind, and the cost. **Chelating compounds,** which tie up the nutritive mineral elements in chelate complexes and render the minerals unavailable for microbial growth, have diverse uses from seed disinfection to inhibition of growth in water cooling towers. Oxine (8-hydroxy quinoline) is an example.

Edible chemicals are sometimes added to foods to inhibit microbial growth. Salts, sugar, spices, and the edible organic acids (such as found in vinegar, sour milk, fruit juices, and cheese) inhibit the action of many microorganisms and therefore are acceptable food preservatives. Of course, most food is preserved by some physical means which leaves no toxic residue. The most important of these physical procedures are drying (cereals, cookies, etc.), heating in a closed container (canning), and refrigeration. In one instance, in refrigeration, a chemical inhibitor is used as a supplementary preservative. Uncooked chicken is dipped into a solution of the antibiotic, aureomycin (also called chlorotetracycline). Psychrophilic growth is thus inhibited, allowing the chicken to be refrigerated for a longer period without evidence of spoilage. Since all chicken is cooked before eating, and since cooking destroys the aureomycin, this type of additive has been approved by the U.S. Food and Drug Administration. Inhibitors such as benzoate are permitted in some foods which constitute only a minute part of the diet.

The gases used to any extent for disinfection and sterilization are formaldehyde and ethylene oxide. Formaldehyde, though in use for many years, is highly irritating, and the odor lingers even after prolonged airing. Ethylene oxide has much greater penetrating power and will kill the spores as well as the vegetative cells of all types of bacteria. Almost any material can be sterilized at room temperature if it is placed in a tight container, the air removed with a vacuum pump, and the container filled with ethylene oxide. Usually materials are sterilized overnight, but four hours will suffice. Pieces of human arteries to be used in surgical transplants, surgical bandages, and bulk foodstuffs, such as spices, are a few of the materials that have been sterilized in this way. Ethylene oxide reacts with chemical groups on bacterial proteins in an irreversible manner.

CHEMOTHERAPY

Chemotherapy involves the treatment of internal disease by chemicals which have a specific and toxic effect upon the microorganisms causing the disease, without seriously poisoning the patient. Antiseptics that are used externally—on the skin or even on the mucous membranes of the throat—are not regarded as chemotherapeutic agents. Although these agents may be useful when applied topically, chemotherapy implies systemic treatment, that is, circulation of the drug throughout the body following injection or ingestion. Chemotherapy of malaria with quinine has an ancient history; Paul Ehrlich first used the term to describe his use of arsenic compounds in the treatment of syphilis.

Today the useful chemotherapeutic agents include sulfonamides (compounds related to sulfanilamide), antibiotics, several iodine-containing compounds used for amebic dysentery, atabrine and related compounds used for malaria, and the antituberculosis drugs, para-aminosalicylic acid and isonicotinic hydrazide.

The Sulfonamides. After Ehrlich's success, almost 30 years elapsed before Domagk's discovery in 1935 of the therapeutic value of the sulfanilamide-containing dye, prontosil. This discovery ushered in the active phase of the use of chemotherapy in bacterial disease. Within 5 years over 5000 sulfanilamide-like compounds has been synthesized by chemists and tested by microbiologists. The better compounds of this group are especially useful in the treatment of respiratory, intestinal, and urinary infections. During the research efforts on the new sulfonamides, a vast store of useful information was gathered on the absorption, distribution, persistence of high levels in the blood, and excretion of drugs. Slight modifications in the sulfonamide molecule do not interfere with its antibacterial activity but prevent its forming damaging crystals in the kidneys. Some sulfonamides concentrate in the bladder and thus are useful in urinary infections; others are removed from the bloodstream by kidney action more slowly and consequently have a sustained action on bloodstream infections

Sulfonamides—chemical analogues (only slightly different in chemical structure) of the vitamin, para-aminobenzoic acid—proved to be successful because they interfered competitively with the microbe's ability to use the vitamin. An intensive campaign was launched by chemists to synthesize similar inhibitors for other vitamins. While understanding of the chemical reactions in living things has been increased tremendously by these efforts, only a few compounds have been uncovered. When other vitamins were modified, as the chemical structure of para-aminobenzoic acid is modified to yield sulfonamides (Fig. 12.7), the resulting compounds were not useful for one or another of the following reasons: (1) The concentrations of the real vitamin in the blood were sufficiently high to overwhelm the competitive action of the analogues. (2) Analogues interfered too much with the action of the vitamin in the tissue cells and thus damaged the patient as much, or more than, the infectious agent. (3) Analogues did not circulate freely in the blood and tissues where they were needed. (4) Analogues were no better than the sulfonamides or other drugs already available.

The **antibacterial spectrum** is the range of bacterial types against which a drug is active. Sulfonamides have a relatively narrow spectrum when used under practical conditions. The useful spectrum of isonicotinic hydrazide is limited to the bacterium causing tuberculosis. The vitamin niacin, though similar to this drug in chemical structure, does not serve as an antidote to the inhibitory action of the drug.

The Antibiotics. Antibiotics have been defined as relatively complex chemical substances of microbial origin which display antimicrobial activity. The simple organic acids or alcohols produced by fermentation exert antimicrobial action but are not regarded as antibiotics. Some idea of the impact of antibiotics on our lives can be gained from drug statistics; ten years after their appearance, antibiotics accounted for over half of the dollar-volume total of American drug sales. Surgical

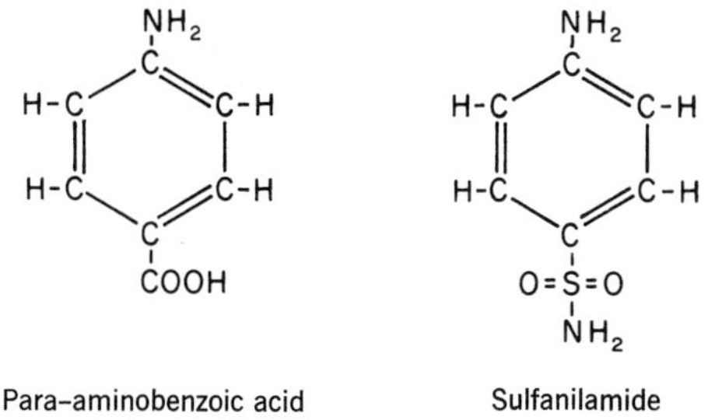

Fig. 12.7. The chemotherapeutic agent, sulfanilamide, differs from the vitamin, para-aminobenzoic acid, in chemical structure. The carboxyl group (COOH) of the latter is replaced by a sulfonamide group (SO_2NH_2).

procedures, which were formerly fraught with danger because of infection, are now routine, and the death rate from infectious disease of bacterial origin has declined dramatically.

In aging cultures most microorganisms excrete toxic products as a result of normal metabolism. Also toxic excretions may be produced by a metabolism disbalanced by a modified environment or by autolysis of aged cells. When toxic substances are released into the medium before growth is halted by lack of food, those forms survive which are resistant to their own inhibitory excretions. The loss of complex materials by excretion might then be advantageous to the resistant microorganism, since the excreted products will inhibit competing organisms. Antibiotics are produced by microorganisms whose normal habitat is the soil where competition between the various forms is keen. Molds of the genus *Penicillium*, actinomycetes of the genus *Streptomyces*, and bacteria of the genus *Bacillus* produce practically all of the antibiotics now in commercial use.

The story of penicillin begins with the observation by Fleming in 1929 that a disease-producing staphylococcus would not grow in the region of a petri plate which bordered on a colony of a contaminating green mold. Fleming isolated the green fungus, identified it as a *Penicillium*, and showed that the broth in which it had grown contained a bacterial inhibitor which he named penicillin. After the mold was filtered from the culture broth, the filtrate was not toxic to animals. Though Fleming suggested its use as a therapeutic agent, research languished for almost 12 years until science and technology advanced sufficiently to implement the discovery.

In commercial production of penicillin a selected high-yielding mutant of *Penicillium chrysogenum* is grown on a liquid medium under vigorous aeration. The medium contains corn-steep liquor (a waste product of whiskey production), sugar, and mineral salts, as well as organic chemicals which the mold makes with some difficulty, or at least at a slower rate. When these chemicals are present in the medium, more penicillin is produced because then the rate is no longer dependent on the slow chemical reactions. Slight modifications in the penicillin molecule may result from different types of additives, the strain of mold, or the degree of aeration. Penicillin G and penicillin V are the most useful variants; the latter is stable in the presence of stomach acid and can be taken by mouth. Generally penicillin is so easily destroyed by heat, moisture, acid, alkali, and aging that its inhibitory activity is probably useless to the *Penicillium* when it is growing in its natural environment. *Penicillium* molds are usually restricted in nature to those environments too dry or too acid for bacterial competitors.

The **therapeutic index** of an antibiotic is computed by dividing the largest dose that can be administered without showing severe toxic reactions in the patient by the lowest dose necessary to destroy the infection. If this ratio is large, an excess dosage of the drug insures curative effects and still allows a large margin of safety. Penicillin possesses an extremely favorable therapeutic index, but some patients develop severe allergic-type reactions to it upon repeated exposure.

The action of penicillin is directed against cell-wall synthesis (Fig. 12.8). Its antibacterial spectrum includes the organisms of syphilis, gonorrhea, and most of the thick-walled gram-positive bacteria, with the exception of the tubercle bacillus. It is inactive, or much less active, against thin-walled gram-negative bacteria and completely inactive against animal cells and pleuropneumonia-like (PPLO) organisms (these have no cell walls), and against plant cells (these have cell walls of cellulose).

The enzyme penicillinase, which destroys penicillin, is produced in strains that are naturally resistant, or in resistant mutants that develop from sensitive strains. A resistant organism may restrict the drug from penetrating to the sensitive part of the cell; it might bypass the inhibited reaction, or it might employ a modified process in which the drug is a less effective inhibitor.

The potency of penicillin broths were originally measured in units;

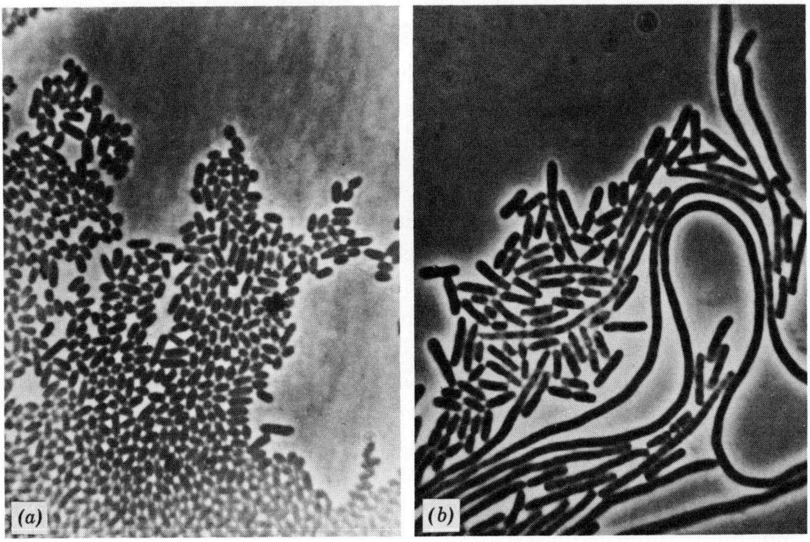

Fig. 12.8. (*a*) Microscopic appearance of a normal culture of *E. coli*. (*b*) The same strain but growing in the presence of a small amount of penicillin, which inhibits cell wall formation.

one unit of penicillin is that amount which, when placed in 50 milliliters of broth, just inhibits Fleming's strain of *Staphylococcus*. The present unit, the international unit or I.U., is the activity of 0.6 microgram of penicillin G. Although today penicillin is extracted from the mold broth, purified, crystallized, and weighed, the unit is still used as the measure of potency; one gram of pure material contains almost 2 million units.

Following the introduction of penicillin, a systematic search for antibiotic-producing soil microorganisms was undertaken, which still continues. Of the hundreds of thousands of strains tested only a small fraction produced active antibacterial substances, and of these all but a few had to be discarded since the products were too toxic to animals, too unstable, or not as good as others already available.

Five commercially successful broad-spectrum antibiotics produced from actinomycetes of the genus *Streptomyces* warrant our attention. Streptomycin is obtained from *Streptomyces griseus*, and its useful spectrum includes the tubercle bacillus and many gram-negative organisms. Though more stable than penicillin, it is much more toxic. Chemists have been able to decrease its toxicity by attaching hydrogen atoms to the molecule, thus converting it to dihydrostreptomycin. In the treatment of tuberculosis it is often used in conjunction with isonicotinic hydrazide and para-aminosalicylic acid to minimize the opportunity for development of resistant strains. Streptomycin appears to interfere with the action of ribosomes in the bacterial cell.

Chloramphenicol (also called chloromycetin) is a broad-spectrum antibiotic produced by *Streptomyces venezuelae*. Having a much simpler chemical structure than any of the other major antibiotics, it can be produced inexpensively by chemical synthesis rather than by fermentation. It has a broad spectrum of activity including gram-positive and gram-negative bacteria, rickettsiae, and even a few of the large viruses. Allergic reactions to it are rare, but in a very few sensitive individuals it has produced a severe blood disorder. Chloromycetin appears to exert its action by inhibiting protein synthesis.

The tetracyclines are much more complex chemical structures consisting, as the name implies, of 4 attached rings, each made of 6 carbon atoms along with additional side groups. Chlorotetracycline (also called aureomycin), produced by *Streptomyces aureofaciens*, has a chlorine attached to the tetracycline structure. Oxytetracycline (also called terramycin), produced by *Streptomyces rimosus*, has an additional oxygen on the tetracycline. Tetracycline itself, which is slightly more stable than the two derivatives, can be produced by chemical modification of aureomycin or by fermentation using a selected strain of *Streptomyces*. It is sold under a number of trade names including *Tetracyn* and *Achromycin*. The use of several terms for the same antibiotic is unfortunate. When a new drug is discovered, it is given a name such as penicillin, streptomycin, chloromycetin, aureomycin, or terramycin. In the case of the first two drugs the name became firmly established before the chemical structure was known; the latter three were named according to their chemical structure: chloramphenicol, chlorotetracycline, and oxytetracycline. Later trade names for the drugs may appear.

All the tetracyclines have low toxicity for animals and broad spectrums of activity including rickettsiae and the larger viruses. Organisms resistant to any one of the tetracyclines are also resistant to the others, suggesting an identical mechanism of action, which is as yet unknown.

Three **polypeptide**-type antibiotics produced by bacteria of the genus *Bacillus* are usually mixtures of several substances and have found limited use in medicine. Relatively toxic when given by injection, they are more commonly used for local application to infected lesions and to the nose and throat. Almost any strain of the genus *Bacillus* will produce these substances, but only three are available commercially. **Tyrothricin** is produced by *Bacillus brevis;* **bacitracin** is produced by *Bacillus licheniformis;* and a group known as the **polymyxins** is produced by *Bacillus polymyxa.* Though high toxicity restricts their use, they have been occasionally successful in systemic treatment where other antibiotics have failed. Most of them function by interfering with the cell membrane of the microorganisms; they usually are lytic for the red blood cells in the animal body.

Though a number of other antibiotics currently occupy a minor role in this field, none threaten to replace penicillin, streptomycin, chloramphenicol, and the three tetracyclines. Experience with antibiotics has generally determined the choice for treatment of an infection; for example, for tuberculosis, streptomycin; for syphilis, penicillin. In other cases the decision depends on the personal preference of the physician and the effectiveness of promotion by the manufacturer. In stubborn or unusual infections the isolated organism is subjected to sensitivity tests (Fig. 12.9) to determine the drug most likely to be successful.

Growth Stimulation. Antibiotics are included in modern feeds for young poultry and livestock. A few grams per ton of feed increases the rate of growth of young animals up to 50%. The mechanism of this stimulation is not known, but it has been explained as:

1. removal of certain intestinal bacteria that interfere with absorption of vitamins;
2. curing of chronic or subclinical infections.

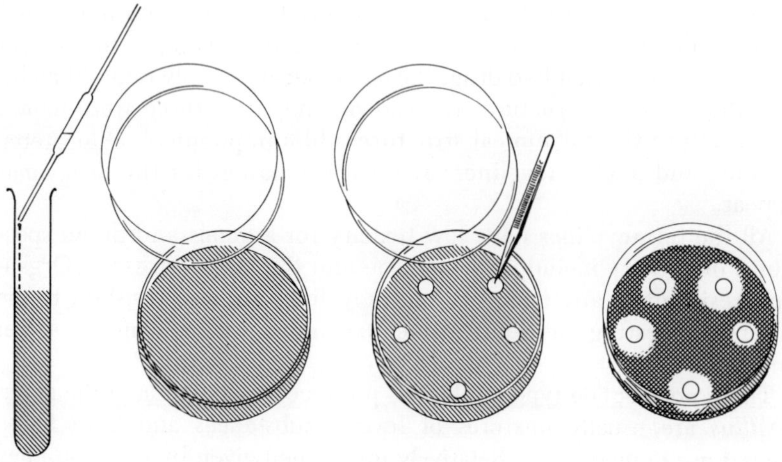

Fig. 12.9. Sensitivity to antibiotics. (*a*) The organism isolated from the patient is inoculated into melted blood agar. (*b*) This is poured into a plate and permitted to harden. (*c*) Disks impregnated with the different antibiotics are placed on the plate. (*d*) After incubation the most effective antibiotic for that particular organism is evident.

PHYSICAL METHODS

Microorganisms may be destroyed, inhibited, or removed without the addition of chemical substances which may leave a residue by (1) heat, (2) cold, (3) desiccation, (4) radiations, (5) ultrasonic waves, and (6) filtration. The first three of these have been discussed in earlier chapters.

Radiation, a physical phenomenon in which energy travels through space, is of two types: **Corpuscular radiations** consist of streams of various kinds of atomic or subatomic particles which can strike against other substances and transfer their kinetic energy. The electrons, which constitute one type of corpuscular radiation, are easily produced in a vacuum by heating a metal; such a process occurs in a cathode-ray tube. Positively charged particles, **positrons,** are emitted by certain radioactive elements or produced by stripping with the Van de Graaff generator. Electrons and positrons are easily controlled since they can be directed by magnets. **Radioactive substances** are those undergoing nuclear changes and thus emitting electrons or alpha particles with energies of the order of a few million electron volts. Best known of the radioactive substances is radium, but actually there are about 50 different types of radioactive atomic nuclei which occur naturally, and more than 1000 different types of nuclei have been produced artificially as a result of nuclear collisions. Radioactive substances are unstable in that they give off particles such as electrons or positrons. Some produce protons, deuterons, or alpha particles, the latter of which is the nucleus of the helium atom stripped of its electrons. Radium continually disintegrates, giving off alpha particles and electrons. An intense beam of neutrons, produced by collisions between the nuclei of atoms, can be obtained by opening a port through the shielding that normally surrounds the nuclear reactor or pile.

Self-propagating electric or magnetic disturbances which affect the internal structure of matter and dissipate material energy are called **electro-magnetic radiations.** These include radio waves, light waves, and X rays. Sonic vibrations, a type of sound wave, require the presence of air or other substances and are not classified as radiation. Their application to microbiology is restricted to the breaking up of cells for laboratory study.

Ultraviolet Light. Microorganisms on surfaces exposed to sunlight are destroyed more effectively than can be accounted for either by the heat or the drying which results. The germicidal action of the visible rays of the sun is relatively small compared with the antibacterial action of the ultraviolet range of the spectrum. While much of the ultraviolet light emanating from the sun is screened out by the atmosphere, of the considerable amount which reaches the earth the most highly bactericidal wavelengths are found in the area of 2600 angstrom units (Fig. 12.10). An angstrom unit (Å) is 0.1 of a millimicron, or 0.0001 of a micron. The germicidal range is from 2100 to 3000 Å. Since the human eye can detect light at about 3900 Å and above, the germicidal rays are invisible to the human eye. The emission spectrum of mercury yields a strong band in the area of 2600 Å, and, consequently, a mercury-vapor lamp is an excellent source of ultraviolet light. Ultraviolet rays, weak in penetrating power, do not pass through ordinary glass. However, they do penetrate a few layers of cells and, therefore, can penetrate a microorganism. They pass through thin layers of pure water, but any cloudiness in the liquid screens out the germicidal rays. The success of ultraviolet light in the treatment of acne probably does not reside in its germicidal power but in its irritating action on the skin cells, which results in greater circulation.

The nucleic acids, found in high concentrations in microorganisms and constituting the essential materials of the nucleus, absorb ultraviolet light very strongly. The wavelengths most strongly absorbed are almost identical to those with the highest germicidal activity. Since only absorbed radiations can bring about changes, the death of micro-

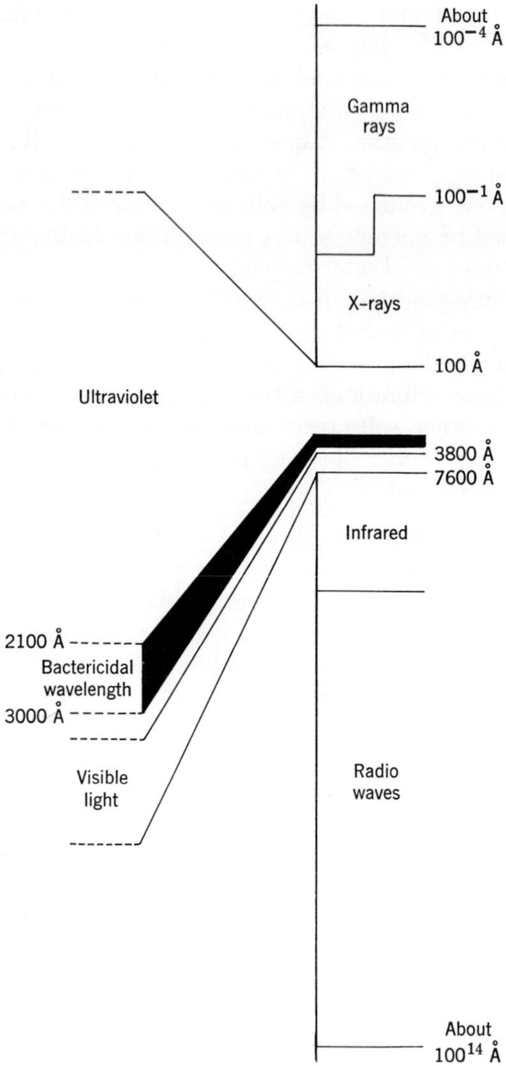

Fig. 12.10. Electromagnetic waves are measured in angstrom units (Å). Gamma rays and X rays have some antimicrobial action but the wavelengths usually used in microbiology occupy a very narrow region in the ultraviolet zone.

organisms probably results from a chemical modification in the nucleic acid. Ultraviolet light produces mutations in genetic material; when a microorganism receives only that amount of ultraviolet light which will kill it, the destructive action may affect the nucleic acid in the genetic apparatus of the microbes. The ultraviolet light has produced a lethal mutation. These radiations also coagulate proteins and produce hydrogen peroxide, which is in itself a powerful killing agent. Hydrogen peroxide will react with certain organic components in the cell to produce organic peroxides which are strongly germicidal and quite persistent.

Ultraviolet light is used effectively for destroying bacteria in air and on exposed surfaces. Ultraviolet lamps are used in hospitals, in microbiological laboratories, especially where dangerous pathogens are used, and in drug manufacturing where aseptic packaging precautions are required.

When organisms killed by ultraviolet light are immediately exposed to visible light, many of the cells will revive. **Photoreactivation** is this process by which visible light serves as an antidote for ultraviolet; however, this process is effective only in very special situations. Excessive exposure to visible light will kill bacteria if a dye is present in the medium which will absorb the visible rays. This effect is called **photodynamic action** or **photodynamic sensitization.** Killing probably results from the formation of peroxides in the medium by the interaction of the light and the dye.

Ionizing Radiations. Ionizing radiations have shorter wavelengths than ultraviolet light. Soft X rays, hard X rays, gamma rays, and cosmic rays are the best known of this group. They are often classified relative to their source, such as cathode rays or roentgen rays. Ionizing radiations are those which have sufficient energy to ionize water molecules. The absorption of a single electron is sufficient to cause the death of a bacterium, probably by the release of a shower of ions following the track of the electron through the cell.

The expense of using ionizing radiations to kill was formerly thought to render any extensive application impractical. However, as byproducts of the development of atomic energy, sources of high energy radiations are available and are being applied on a limited scale in the food industry.

Filtration. In the purification of water, sedimentation and filtration remove the major part of the contaminating microbial populations. Filtration also purifies air as in air-conditioning equipment or in the growth of aerobic organisms in industry where a great volume of air must be freed of contaminants before it is pumped through the fermenter. Antibiotics may be freed from contaminants by passing a concentrated solution through a bacterial filter.

Air filters of cotton, glass wool, or other fibers are firmly packed into a tube through which air is passed. Laboratory filters for liquids are made of porcelain, sintered glass, paper pulp, or cellophane membranes. Drinking water filters are beds of sand, crushed rock, or lignite.

SUMMARY. Microbiology developed as a science only after the microbiologist was able to destroy all organisms in his test tube except those which he chose to maintain. The destruction of unwanted microbes has been one of the most serious challenges to the ingenuity of this science. The development of chemotherapy extends the selective action of chemical inhibitors to the interior of the living animal where the chemicals used are destructive to the microbe but tolerated by the host. Less dramatic, but no less effective, are the procedures developed for the control of microbes in the environment which permit the sick and the well to live in association. A beginning has been made in the problem of understanding the mechanisms of death.

13

Physiology of Microorganisms

Microorganisms are organized living units which grow, consume food, reproduce, and finally die. These processes are influenced by the external environment of the cell and by the microbiologist's study methods such as the development of cultures in broth and the formation of colonies on agar. Microbial physiology studies the processes and functions of microbes. Though this chapter is slanted toward bacteria, the principles discussed are relevant to all microbiology and even all of biology.

Just as the cell is the basic structural unit of bacteria as well as of plants and animals, so certain basic physiological processes proceed in all organisms, giving them those properties we describe under the term "living." Much of our knowledge of the cellular biochemistry and physiology of animals and plants is derived from studies on bacteria by scientists who have had little interest in the bacteria themselves. The outstanding characteristic of microorganisms is their tremendous biochemical activity, which is almost solely responsible for their importance in industrial processes, in the soil, and in disease.

At the cellular and biochemical level, any fundamental property found in higher animals and plants will have its counterpart somewhere among the microorganisms, often with several modifications. For example, the many steps in the process by which lactic acid is made from sugar in the cells of muscle, liver, and brain are well known; among the microorganisms, some bacteria carry out this process in precisely the same manner. Other microorganisms, however, produce the same lactic acid from the same sugar in a completely different manner. This diversity of processes among the microbes is explained by evolutionary theory. Numerous procedures may be adequate for life at the microbial level, but the processes that survived in the evolutionary development of higher animals and plants are more limited. Higher animals and plants have great uniformity of cellular environment. The microbial cell is naked and unprotected in a highly variable environment; the development of complex structures in plants results in the plant cells being bathed in a sap of fairly uniform composition; the animal cell is exposed to an environment that is even more strictly regulated in pH, osmotic pressure, chemical composition, and often in temperature.

Microbes are referred to as "simple" forms of life because they lack such complicated plant and animal structures as tissues and organs. However, the microbial cell, itself, is certainly no less complex than any individual cell of a multicellular organism. The single microbial cell contains all the elements necessary for independent existence.

Physiologically, the microorganism consists of **structural parts** such as walls and membranes, **reactor molecules** called enzymes, and a nuclear **director apparatus** or code, which is an arrangement of genes (Fig. 13.1). The genes determine the characteristics of an organism; each microorganism may have up to 100,000 genes acquired originally by some remote ancestor. These control heredity and thus determine whether the organism will be a staphylococcus, a tubercle bacillus, a mold, or a rickettsia. Prior to cell division the genes in an individual microbe double, and then the cell splits by a complex and precise procedure which insures that each daughter nucleus gets exactly the same complement of genes as the parent.

The other function of the genes, more pertinent to this chapter, is to supervise the affairs of the cell. Each gene directs the cell to produce one or more reactor molecules or **enzymes.** The enzymes catalyze chemical reactions involved in such life processes as nutrition, growth, energy utilization, multiplication, and even death. In its simplest form a living system must have three fundamental parts: a code, a translating mechanism to transfer information, and a reactor which acts in response to the transferred information. This picture of a living cell finds a simple analogy in the phonograph, where the code is on the record or tape, and the pick-up arm translates and carries the information to the sound-producing device. Science is only beginning to learn about the translating device in living cells; it is probably com-

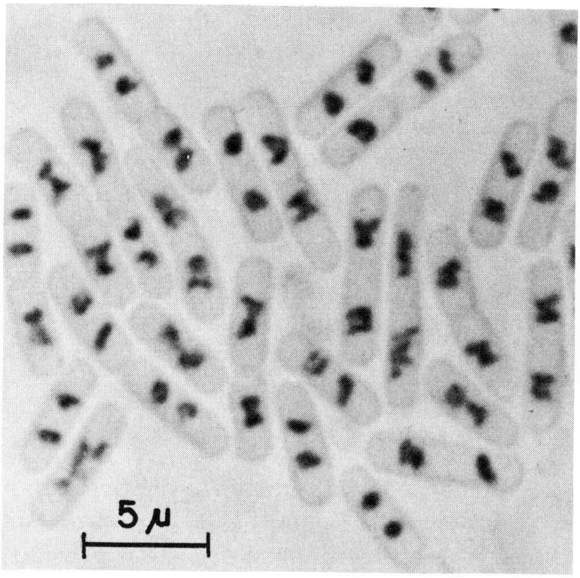

Fig. 13.1. The log-phase cells were stained with a nuclear stain which reveals where the DNA is concentrated. The nuclear bodies divide prior to cell division. Whether the nuclear material is curdled into this shape by the fixing and staining process or whether this represents the true shape of the nuclear material is disputed. *Photo by C. F. Robinow, courtesy Academic Press.*

posed of ribonucleic acid (RNA). More is known about the code, which is composed of deoxyribonucleic acid (DNA). Since the genes cannot be seen, knowledge of their presence and, in fact, their very existence is inferred from a study of the reactor mechanisms, the enzymes functioning under their direction.

ENZYMES

Nature of Enzymes. Enzymes are organic catalysts produced by the living cell. In the cell sap they form colloidal suspensions which are quite sensitive (labile) to deleterious influences. A substantial part of the protein of cells consists of enzymes. Some enzymes are pure proteins; others are proteins attached to a nonprotein component known as a **prosthetic group** or associated more loosely with a nonprotein **coenzyme.** The protein part of these associations is the **apoenzyme.** A large number of enzymes have been purified, and many have been isolated in crystalline form and their characteristics studied by the methods of the protein chemists. Like other proteins they have high molecular weights and are denatured by heat and certain chemical agents.

Enzymal Action. Enzymes working as catalysts permit the organism to complete its reactions rapidly and at moderate temperatures, approximately neutral pH, and low concentration of substrate. The chemist can carry out the same reactions in the test tube in a reasonable time only by resorting to high temperatures, strong acids or bases, and concentrated solutions. Though the enzymal mechanism of action is not completely understood, it does proceed in at least two distinct steps. First the enzyme reacts with the substrate to produce a complex consisting of a firmly bound combination of the two:

$$\text{Enzyme} + \text{substrate} \rightarrow \text{enzyme-substrate complex.}$$

The existence of such a complex during enzyme action has been demonstrated for a variety of enzymes. The enzyme-substrate complex may break down to give a new compound, which is the product of the reaction, and the enzyme is recovered unchanged, thus:

$$\text{Enzyme-substrate complex} \rightarrow \text{enzyme} + \text{product.}$$

In this way one enzyme molecule can catalyze the conversion of thousands of substrate molecules into product molecules without becoming depleted. The reactions are reversible; under suitable conditions the enzyme may react with the product and, after forming the complex, may yield the original substrate. The active part of the enzyme protein which reacts with the substrate may be sulfhydryl (SH), amino (NH_2), hydroxyl (OH), or carboxyl (COOH) groups on the protein. Also, the prosthetic group attached to the protein has active components capable of combining with the substrate. Many of the coenzymes are composed either wholly or in part of substances commonly known as vitamins.

Factors Affecting Enzyme Action. The activity of enzymes is determined by a variety of factors:

1. Enzymes are specific for certain substrates; for example, an enzyme which will act on cellulose will not act on protein. This specificity is not absolute, for in some instances closely related substances are acted upon by a single enzyme.

2. Enzymes exhibit a definite maximum, minimum, and optimum temperature. In fact, the relationship of microorganisms to temperature depends on the effect of temperature on the correlated, functioning enzymes of the cells. Two factors are involved; one is the increase in chemical reaction rates with increased temperatures. Thus enzyme

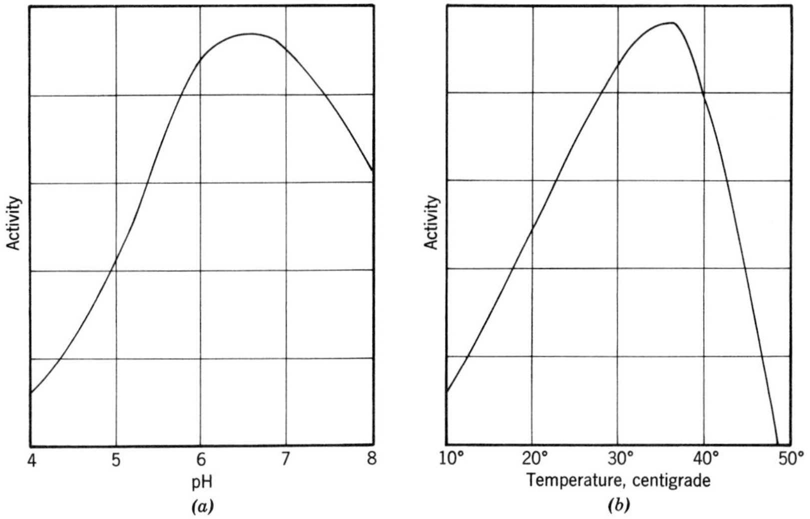

Fig. 13.2. Every enzyme shows minimum, optimum, and maximum points when activity is measured at varying (*a*) pH levels and (*b*) temperatures. These studies were made with a capsule-digesting enzyme from a soil bacterium.

reaction rates increase as the temperature rises, until that range is approached where the enzyme is partially destroyed by heat. Above that point the activity of the enzyme drops sharply (Fig. 13.2).

3. Activity of enzymes is influenced by the pH of the solution. Again, a maximum, optimum, and minimum are observed, although the pH inside a cell need not always be that of the medium. An organism's enzymes are protected to some degree by the semipermeable cytoplasmic membrane. The concentration of the active form of an enzyme may be altered by pH changes. In addition, the substrate may also be capable of ionization and, as the pH changes, yield more or less that form subject to attack by an enzyme. pH may also affect the metal cofactors or activators. At high pH values magnesium ions form an insoluble, and therefore inactive, hydroxide. The combined actions of these effects define optimum, maximum, and minimum pH values for enzyme action.

4. The activity of an enzyme is proportional to its concentration (Fig. 13.3).

5. The activity of an enzyme is affected by the substrate concentration. At very low substrate concentrations the reaction is slowed or stopped, since the product can convert to substrate as fast as the forward reaction occurs. As the substrate concentration is increased so is the rate, because the molecules of enzyme encounter substrate mole-

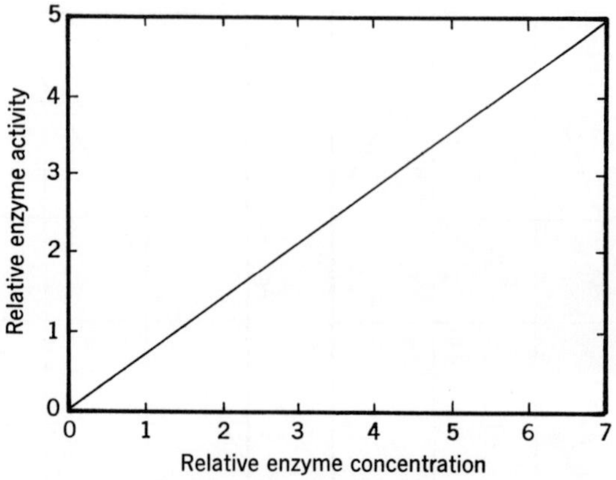

Fig. 13.3. The activity of an enzyme is proportional to its concentration.

cules more frequently and react with them. With concentration increase, sufficient substrate molecules are present to contact every free enzyme molecule. At such concentration of substrate all of the enzyme is, at every moment, actively engaged. Further increase in substrate concentration will have no effect on the rate of the reaction.

6. The amount of activity is affected by the time permitted for reaction. There is a definite relationship between temperature and time, especially at high temperatures, where tremendous enzymatic action may occur in very short times, but because of destruction of the enzymes, the average activity over longer time intervals may be very low.

7. Activity of enzymes is influenced by the presence of dissolved salts. A certain salt concentration is essential for maintaining the colloidal state, but salts of the toxic heavy metals (mercury, silver, lead) may form inactive complexes with enzyme proteins.

Classification. Representatives of most enzymes encountered in biology are produced by microorganisms, and every organism contains hundreds of enzymes. Of course, every microorganism does not have all these enzymes, and its reactions depend on which enzymes are present. Physiological reactions which aid us in classifying bacteria are usually qualitative tests for the presence of specific enzymes. An anaerobic organism is deficient in certain enzymes found in the aerobe which permit the latter to utilize oxygen. Since such characteristics are inherited, the ultimate control of enzyme formation resides in the genetic apparatus, and anaerobes are deficient in the genes controlling the formation of the enzymes necessary for life in oxygen.

A certain minimum number of enzymes must be present at all times to maintain life, regardless of the composition of the medium. Enzymes that are always present are termed **constitutive** enzymes; **inducible** enzymes (also called **adaptive** enzymes) appear only when microorganisms are grown on a medium containing the substrate for that enzyme. For example, some microorganisms never produce the enzyme which ferments the sugar, galactose; others produce the enzyme only when that sugar is present in the medium. If galactose is absent from the medium during growth but later is added to the grown culture, no fermentation takes place for about an hour, during which time galactose "induces" the enzyme formation. Obviously the gene controlling the formation of the galactose-fermenting enzyme is present all the time, but the enzyme is formed only when "induced" by a substrate that interferes with a repressor gene. In spite of the minute size of the bacterial cell, it is capable of using a wide variety of substrates; to do this it maintains repressors for enzyme formation which must be released before the needed enzyme can be produced.

Most enzymes are produced by the organism and retained in the cell. They are called **intracellular** or **endoenzymes** to distinguish them from those elaborated into the medium, the **extracellular** or **exoenzymes.** The extracellular enzymes digest large molecules in the medium into smaller fragments which can be transported into the cell: gelatinase, cellulase, and amylase are examples. Starch will not pass through the cell membrane; the only organisms which can use starch for food are those producing the extracellular enzyme, amylase, which breaks the large starch molecule down to the relatively small, diffusible molecules of the sugar, maltose. When bacterial cells are filtered from broth in which they have grown, the exoenzymes remain in the broth filtrate.

In the naming of enzymes the suffix, *-ase,* is attached either to the name of the substrate being attacked or to the name of the reaction taking place. The latter method is generally used for groups of enzymes, for example, **hydrolases** are the group of enzymes that catalyze the splitting of a molecule by hydrolysis: thus the name implies the addition of water. Specific enzymes such as **urease** by the addition of water split urea to CO_2 and NH_3; lipase similarly splits lipid or fats. Since fats belong to that class of chemical compounds known as esters, lipase is also called an **esterase.** Some enzymes have retained their classical names such as rennin, trypsin, and ptyalin.

Physiologically, enzymes may be grouped according to five major activities: (1) *splitting,* (2) *adding,* (3) *isomerizing,* (4) *transferring,* and (5) *oxidizing.* The **splitting** enzymes include the extracellular amylase, gelatinase, etc., as well as intracellular enzymes which split sugar and protein molecules into fragments containing only one, two, or three carbon atoms. Such fragments are added to other fragments through the catalytic action of **adding** enzymes to build large molecules needed for constructing new cell material or cell products.

Some molecules are **isomerized** (parts of the molecule are shifted around, but the size or composition is not changed) in order to render them more susceptible to further enzymatic activity. The **transferring** enzymes may shift molecular parts from one molecule to another; an amino (NH_2) group on an abundant amino acid may be transferred to complete another amino acid which is in short supply.

Oxidizing enzymes carry out oxidations and reductions in the cell. Oxidation is accomplished by (1) removing electrons; ferrous iron, found in the prosthetic group of many oxidizing enzymes, is oxidized to the ferric form:

$$Fe^{2+} \leftrightarrows Fe^{3+} + 1 \text{ electron}$$

(2) removing hydrogen atoms, as in the oxidation of many organic molecules. Actually, in this process an electron is also removed, but the hydrogen ion combines with it to make a hydrogen atom. In aerobes, pairs of electrons unite with oxygen and a pair of hydrogen ions to form water. In anaerobes the electrons with their accompanying hydrogens are finally attached to some molecule other than oxygen. (3) adding oxygen directly to the molecule being oxidized. This is not the normal procedure of the oxidizing enzymes and occurs in few biological systems. Usually extra oxygen in an enzymatic product is introduced by the addition of water and followed by removal of the two hydrogens by oxidizing enzymes. When oxidizing enzymes produce the reverse reaction (electrons or hydrogen atoms are put on a molecule rather than removed from it), the process is called **reduction**.

The microbial cell is not merely a sack containing endoenzymes distributed as a random mixture in the cell sap; rather, the cell has a definite geography of enzyme distribution. Those enzymes involved in respiration are associated with the cell membrane; those involved in protein synthesis are associated with ribosomes. We may anticipate that other associations will be discovered; for example, the several enzymes involved in making a vitamin are probably bound in a complex.

IMPORTANCE OF ENZYMES IN MICROBIOLOGY

Correlated enzyme activity offers the best explanation yet available for life processes. Enzyme action accounts for the destructive activities of microbes, the procedures by which they produce disease, and their formation of useful products.

After studying the morphology of the microorganism (which is itself a result of enzyme activity), the taxonomist studies physiological characteristics, reflections of the complement of enzymes. Of course, he cannot study them all; usually about a dozen is sufficient. He classifies the microorganism by checking those enzymes which in simple tests demonstrate the disappearance of substrate or the formation of products.

Bacterial and fungal enzymes are produced in industry for use in such diverse processes as tanning of fine leathers, clarification of fruit juice, and conversion of starch to sugar. Penicillinase is used to destroy penicillin in blood cultures from penicillin-treated patients.

MICROBIAL NUTRITION

The catalyzing reactions of enzymes are involved in two basic problems of microbial metabolism—energy and building blocks. For many purposes in microbiology the success of a medium is judged by the rate of growth of the cultured organism. Physiology deals with the manner in which each constituent in the medium serves the living cell.

Sources of Elements for Cell Material. Microbial cells like those of higher animals and plants are constructed from distinctive chemical elements. Those mineral elements found in minor amounts include iron, magnesium, manganese, calcium, potassium, copper, cobalt, zinc, and molybdenum. A few other trace-mineral elements are secured from the medium in the form of soluble salts; however, they are not proven parts of the living cell. The major elements making up the cell substance are carbon, hydrogen, oxygen, nitrogen, sulfur, and phosphorus. Phosphorus and usually sulfur are also utilized as the soluble phosphate or sulfate salts. Hydrogen and oxygen are obtained readily from water. Microorganisms are so versatile that few forms of carbon and nitrogen naturally occurring on this earth cannot be utilized by some species.

Autotrophic organisms use carbon dioxide as their sole or principal source of carbon. The algae and a few bacterial forms are autotrophs. Most microorganisms are **heterotrophic** and use organic substances as their main source of carbon. The heterotrophs exhibit a wide spectrum of nutritional requirements. Many grow in a medium containing salts of the necessary minerals (including phosphate and sulfate) with sugar as the carbon source and ammonia (NH_3) as the nitrogen source.

From these, some organisms are able to synthesize all the proteins, carbohydrates, fats, and vitamins of which the living cell is composed. Instead of ammonia, others may require ten or more amino acids and a dozen or more preformed growth factors or vitamins.

Media containing all of the materials necessary for growth have not been devised for some organisms; such organisms which grow only on other living cells are called **obligate parasites.** The nutritional complexity of microorganisms ranges between the extremes represented by the obligate parasites on one hand and the autotrophs on the other. Some autotrophs require, in addition to the basal medium, a single vitamin. The pus-forming staphylococcus of the skin can grow in a medium containing sugar, mineral salts, eight of the amino acids, and three of the vitamins.

Analyses of the different nutritional groups indicate that all microorganisms contain the same complex chemical substances; those requiring vitamins or other special substances in the medium simply are unable to synthesize these materials for themselves. Biosynthetically, the autotrophic organisms are the most complex. They must contain not only enzymes to synthesize everything made by heterotrophs but also the additional substances which heterotrophs obtain, prefabricated from the medium.

The heterotrophs utilize a wide variety of organic materials. Some exceedingly versatile soil organisms can use over 100 different compounds as sources of carbon. Other more specific microbes are restricted to one or a few sugars, to cellulose, to alcohol, or to illuminating gas.

The organic food material brought into the heterotrophic bacterial cell is broken down into small molecules containing one, two, or three carbon atoms. Specific adding, transferring, isomerizing, and oxidizing enzymes incorporate the food material with nitrogen, sulfur, phosphorus, and other mineral elements to produce new cell material. Scientists now understand most of the biosynthetic steps involved in the conversion of sugar and simple nitrogen compounds into the complex molecules of the cell. When readily utilizable carbon compounds are present in high concentrations, the cell may synthesize large amounts of capsular material, fat, or other storage products. Since biosynthesis requires energy, biosynthetic reactions must be coupled with energy-yielding reactions in the cell. Heterotrophic organisms secure this energy from oxidizing organic matter, while autotrophic organisms secure the energy from oxidizing inorganic substances or from trapping sunlight. The autotrophs have the more complicated systems since they must synthesize all of their carbon-containing substances from CO_2.

SOURCES OF ENERGY

Photosynthesis. The green and the purple pigmented bacteria use light as a source of part or all of their energy. Those autotrophic bacteria that are photosynthetic and independent of organic matter are termed photolithotrophic, which implies feeding by light and minerals (Fig. 13.4). The rest of the photosynthetic bacteria require organic matter; these are photoorganotrophic. Photosynthesis involves splitting of electrons from the chlorophyll and attachment to a coenzyme together with a hydrogen ion. The resulting hydrogen atom serves as fuel for the cell, but the electron removed from the chlorophyll must be replaced. The algae and higher plants secure the electron by splitting water and thus releasing oxygen gas. The photosynthetic bacteria employ a more cumbersome method.

Bacterial and green plant photosyntheses differ in three important ways. First, in bacterial photosynthesis oxygen gas is never produced; in fact, green and purple bacteria are usually obligate anaerobes. Second, photolithotrophs use hydrogen sulfide and photoorganotrophs use organic matter to secure electrons. The algae and green plants can substitute water for this purpose. Third, the active pigments differ chemically, and therefore the bacterial chlorophyll absorbs longer wavelengths of light. Consequently, the photosynthetic bacteria can grow deeper in pond water than the algae, since they are able to use wavelengths of light that pass through the pond scum. All of these bacteria contain a green pigment, chlorophyll, but have in addition red, orange, and brown pigments that sometimes mask the green color.

The CO_2 taken up during photosynthesis is added to organic molecules in the cell. The hydrogen atoms produced in photosynthesis by the action of light on chlorophyll reduce the combined CO_2 to a stable organic molecule, which can be used for building blocks. The organic molecules now contain part of the energy captured from the light, energy that will be released when heterotrophic organisms break up the molecules.

Anaerobic Heterotrophs. During breakdown reactions, molecules characteristically release chemical-bond energy. Living cells secure this energy by shifting the chemical bonds and rearranging the molecules. While isomerizing, splitting, adding, and transferring enzymes may participate in the process, the energy-release step is dependent primarily on oxidizing and reducing enzymes. Energy release through oxidation can occur aerobically or anaerobically.

In industrial terminology fermentation designates any change in

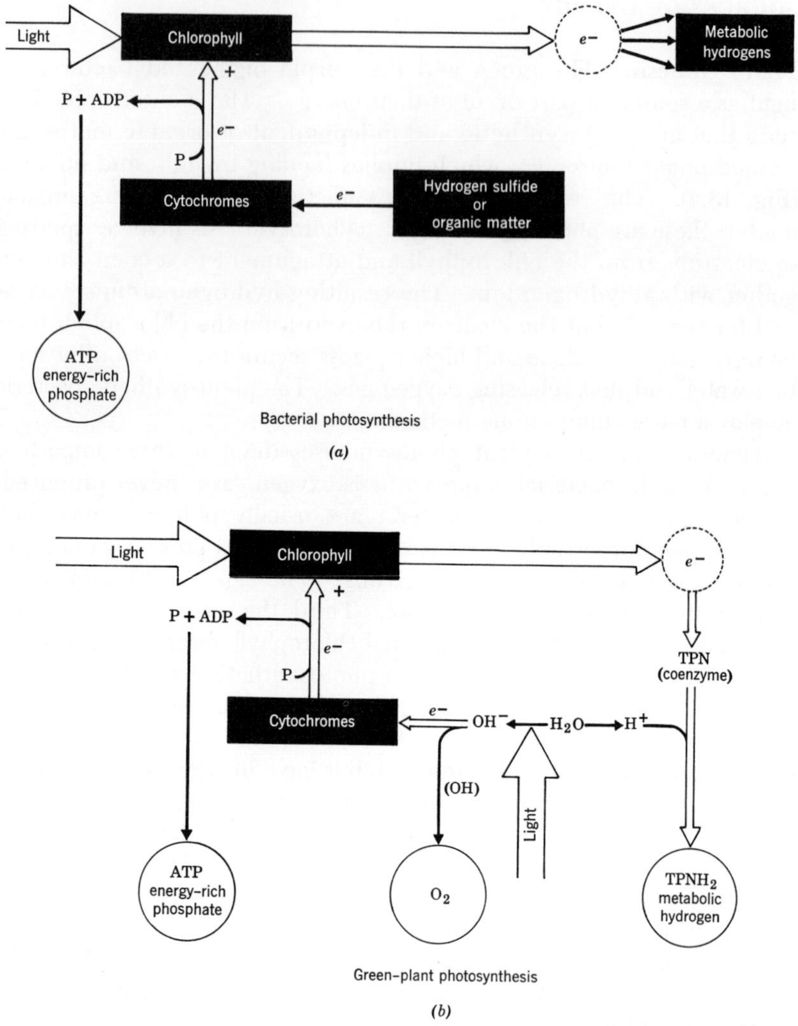

Fig. 13.4. A concept of photosynthesis. (*a*) In photosynthetic bacteria the light displaces an electron (e^-) from chlorophyll. Electrons can unite with hydrogen ions (H^+) to form the metabolic hydrogens (as reduced TPN or DPN) needed to reduce CO_2 to carbohydrate. The electron is replaced in the chlorophyll from hydrogen sulfide (in photolithotrophs) or organic matter (in photoorganotrophs). This electron passes through the cytochrome-enzyme system and in doing so generates an energy-rich phosphate bond. (*b*) In algae and other green plants the electron displaced from the chlorophyll is replaced by one secured from splitting a water molecule. If light is needed to split the water molecule is not certain. But the OH radical, having given up the electron, combines with itself to release gaseous oxygen thus: $4\ OH \rightarrow 2\ H_2O + O_2$. As with the bacterial photosynthesis, the electron removed from the chlorophyll unites with a hydrogen ion to yield metabolic hydrogens, which serve to drive forward the synthetic activities of the cell.

organic matter produced by microorganisms. Strictly, fermentation is the energy release from organic molecules under anaerobic conditions. A yeast ferments one molecule of a simple sugar ($C_6H_{12}O_6$) to produce two molecules of alcohol (C_2H_6O) and two molecules of carbon dioxide (CO_2). The total number of carbons, hydrogens, and oxygens in the alcohol and the CO_2 is exactly that found in the original sugar. Fewer calories of energy remain in the alcohol and CO_2 than the original sugar contained. The microbe has extracted some of the energy. A consideration of the structural formulas show how the process involves oxidations and reductions even though oxygen from the air does not participate (Fig. 13.5).

Some of the carbon atoms in the products contain more oxygen and less hydrogen than the corresponding atoms in the glucose from which they came: These atoms have been oxidized with the release of energy, and the hydrogens have been placed on other carbon atoms. Although the equation shows a single step, the process actually requires a number of distinct steps each involving an isomerizing, splitting, adding, transferring, or oxidizing enzyme. Some of the bond energy is lost as heat. The rest is transferred to **energy-rich** phosphate bonds by special coenzymes. These energy-rich phosphate bonds are energy packets of a convenient size for use in the energy-requiring reactions of biosynthesis.

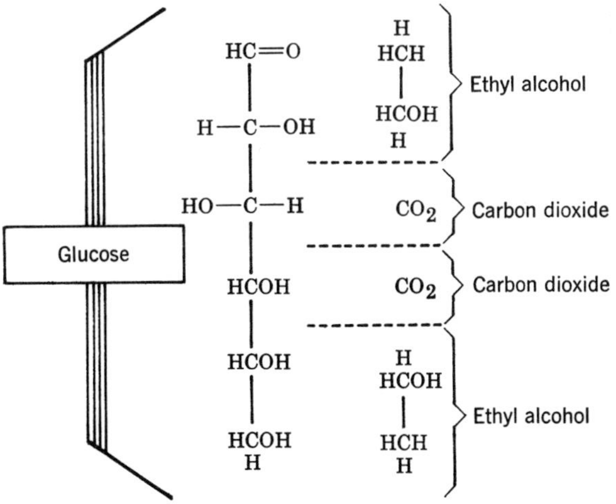

Fig. 13.5. The 6-carbon glucose molecule is split into four pieces in the alcohol fermentation. The hydrogens are removed from those carbons that end up as CO_2 and are accepted by those fragments that end up as ethyl alcohol. These oxidations and reductions net the cell energy sufficient to make two energy-rich phosphate bonds. The ethyl alcohols still contain most of the chemical bond energy which could be released to the cell by aerobic mechanisms.

The term **intermediary metabolism** summarizes the enzyme reactions going on in conversion of sugar to end products. Some of the steps serve a double purpose in yielding fragments readily used by the biosynthetic enzymes. Ethyl alcohol and carbon dioxide are fermentation end products of most yeasts and a few bacteria. Instead, or in addition, other bacteria may yield lactic acid, formic acid, acetic acid, propionic acid, butyric acid, acetone, butyl alcohol, isopropyl alcohol, acetoin, and hydrogen gas. When proteinaceous material is fermented, ammonia and hydrogen sulfide are produced in addition to acids and alcohols. The important feature of the fermentation process is that a large part of the organic compound which was oxidized must remain in the medium to accept the hydrogen. Since only a small part of the energy of an organic compound is extracted by this process, the anaerobic organism must work over tremendous amounts of material and leave large amounts of fermentation products in the medium. A microorganism may ferment its own weight in sugar in less than the time for one cell division.

Some anaerobic organisms are able to oxidize organic compounds and transfer the hydrogen to inorganic compounds such as nitrate or sulfate. When inorganic substances other than oxygen are employed as the final hydrogen acceptors, the process is called **anaerobic respiration.** Nitrate is reduced to nitrite, ammonia, or nitrogen gas, and sulfate is reduced to hydrogen sulfide. These processes are termed nitrate reduction and sulfate reduction.

Aerobic Heterotrophs. The term **respiration** describes the aerobic energy-yielding process in which oxygen gas participates. Hydrogens (and electrons) removed from the substrate are transferred to atmospheric oxygen through a series of enzymes and coenzymes. Each pair of hydrogens transported in this way in the aerobic system may yield up to three energy-rich phosphate bonds. In contrast, the anaerobic system yields only one energy-rich bond when a pair of hydrogens is taken from one molecule and transferred to another. In addition to greater energy yield for each pair of hydrogens in the aerobic system, the entire molecule can be oxidized, since none need be left in the medium to accept hydrogens (Fig. 13.6). At least twenty different enzymes of all the functional types are involved in this process, which includes adding water, removing and transferring hydrogens, splitting out carbons in the form of CO_2, and producing energy-rich phosphate bonds. The relative efficiency of the two processes is well demonstrated in yeast, one of the many faculative microorganisms. Aerobically, a large amount of yeast is produced from respiration of a small amount of sugar or other organic food; anaerobically, a smaller number

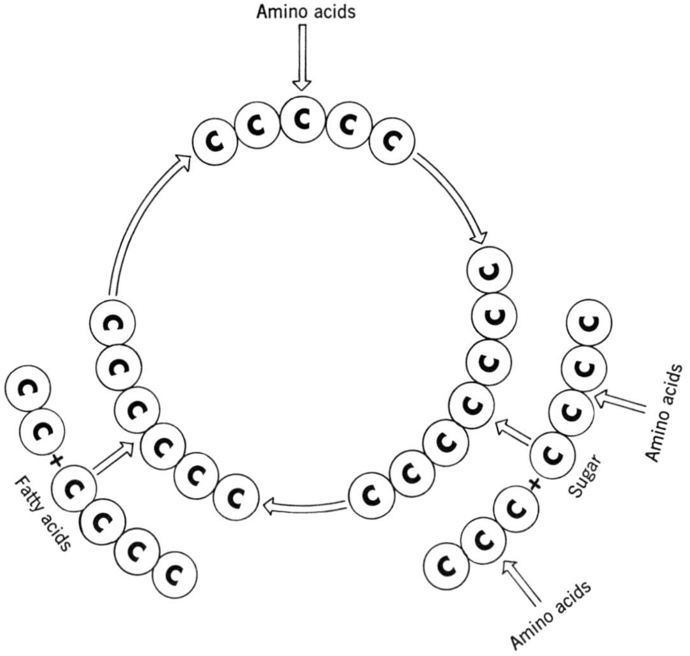

Fig. 13.6. The entry to the citric acid cycle. 3-carbon fragments (C_3) from sugar or amino acids unite with a 4-carbon fragment (C_4) to yield C_7. This is broken down one carbon at a time to C_6 and C_5 and C_4. Fats enter the cycle by first being broken down to C_2; sugars may be broken first to C_2 and some amino acids yield C_5 directly. The citric acid cycle enzymes add water and split off hydrogens and CO_2 until the organic fragments are dissipated.

of cells is produced from the fermentation of prodigious quantities of sugar.

The ideal aerobic system found in higher animal tissue and many aerobic microorganisms oxidizes an organic compound completely, extracting all available energy and converting all of the carbons to CO_2. Many aerobic microorganisms have less than perfect enzyme systems and carry out incomplete oxidations. Such aerobic organisms may oxidize a sugar partially and return to the medium such acids as gluconic, acetic, citric, and oxalic. For example, vinegar bacteria are aerobic organisms useful to man because they produce acetic acid by incomplete oxidation of alcohol. Other microbes oxidize other substances incompletely.

Energy from Respiration of Inorganic Substrates. Autotrophic microorganisms that are unable to use light as an energy source must oxidize inorganic substances to secure the energy needed to build their organic structures entirely from CO_2. These bacteria have been termed **chemolithotrophic.** While their numbers are not large, they carry out certain very important steps in the cycles of the elements. These include the oxidation of inorganic sulfur compounds, the oxidation of inorganic nitrogen compounds, the oxidation of hydrogen gas, and the oxidation of the reduced forms of iron and manganese.

In the oxidation of ammonia certain species produce nitrite ($—NO_2$) or nitrous acid (HNO_2). Other species oxidize the nitrite to nitrate or nitric acid (HNO_3). These energy processes are similar to those used by heterotrophic organisms (chemoorganotrophs) in the oxidation of organic materials. Hydrogen atoms are removed by enzyme systems and are transferred to oxygen with the release of energy; at the same time CO_2 is taken up by the autotroph, built into a more complex carbon compound, and stabilized by reduction with hydrogen atoms.

Some sulfur autotrophs start with hydrogen sulfide, others with sulfur itself, and still others with thiosulfate. The end product is sulfuric acid (H_2SO_4), the most oxidized form of sulfur. The hydrogen bacteria convert gaseous hydrogen into metabolic hydrogens and transfer them to oxygen gas, securing energy from the process. The iron bacteria oxidize soluble ferrous ions (Fe^{2+}) to ferric (Fe^{3+}) ions. This oxidation is also accomplished by the removal of hydrogen:

$$\underset{\text{ferrous hydroxide}}{Fe(OH)_2} + \underset{\text{water}}{H_2O} - \underset{\text{hydrogen}}{H} = \underset{\text{ferric hydroxide}}{Fe(OH)_3}$$

SUMMARY. The cell has no fuel but hydrogen. The green and the purple bacteria use light energy and chlorophyll to secure hydrogen. The heterotrophic organisms split hydrogens from organic molecules, and the chemoautotrophs take hydrogens from inorganic molecules. Anaerobically, hydrogens are transferred to some organic or inorganic hydrogen acceptor which then appears in the medium as the product of the fermentation or anaerobic respiration; a relatively small amount of energy is thus yielded to the cell. Aerobically, the hydrogens are transferred to oxygen, yielding much larger quantities of energy. Some of the energy is dissipated as heat; the rest is used by coupling energy-yielding with energy-consuming reactions. Energy-rich phosphate bonds are important intermediate steps. Energy is also stored by the organism in the chemical bonds of the molecules making up the fats, carbohydrates, and proteins of its structure.

14

Sexuality and Genetics in Bacteria

The study of bacterial genetics has supplied a better understanding of the operation of genetics on the molecular level. However, bacterial genetics is a fairly new science. With the development of pure culture methods, especially by Koch and his associates, the concept of **monomorphism** (the stability of single types) became so firmly established that variability of bacterial form was derisively ascribed to culture contamination, or possibly to degeneration of the cells of a pure culture. Eventually the doctrine of strict monomorphism died out and was succeeded by what has become an extremely active and productive field of research—the recognition and investigation of true heritable, or genetic, variation.

Genetic studies on higher organisms have revealed much about the cytology and mechanics of inheritance. Despite the relative deficiency of cytological data for microorganisms such as are available for the higher plants and animals, the genetic terminology and interpretations of observed phenomena as seen in the higher forms have been largely transferred to the field of bacterial genetics. New terms have been invented to describe situations that occur only with the microbes or that can be studied more exhaustively and precisely with these organisms.

Genetic and cytological studies on plants and animals have established that genes, located along the thread-like chromosomes in the cell nucleus, are the determiners of heritable characters (Fig.14.1). When a cell divides, the chromosomes also divide, and an identical set of genes goes to each daughter cell. Unless one or more of the genes changes, the two cells will be identical in all respects. If one of the

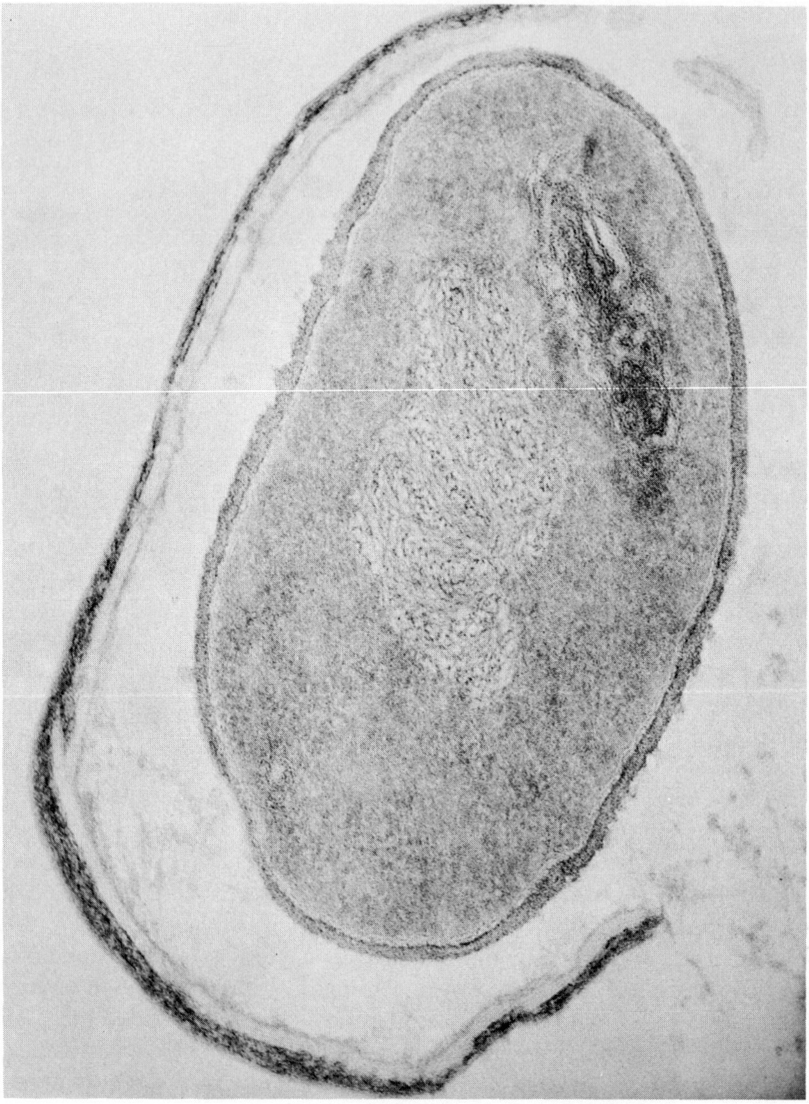

Fig. 14.1. The coiled nuclear thread is visible in this electron micrograph of a thin section of a germinating spore of *Bacillus subtilis*. *Photo courtesy C. F. Robinow.*

genes changes, or mutates, the character governed by the changed gene is different from the comparable character in the "wild type" (the cell with the unchanged gene).

Each chromosome carries a number of genes, and since chromosomes are usually transmitted as a unit, the genes of any single chromosome likewise are transferred as a unit and are spoken of as linked genes. In the cells of higher organisms the sex cells carry a single chromosome representative of each linkage group. Such cells are called **haploid**. When fertilization takes place the number of chromosomes is doubled, and two homologous chromosomes represent each linkage group. Such a cell is termed **diploid**. If there are more than two homologous chromosomes in a nucleus, the cell is a **polyploid**. Polyploidy can be induced by certain chemicals.

In diploid organisms each chromosome, and likewise each gene, is paired. A gene located at a particular site in one chromosome is matched by a corresponding gene at a similar location in the homologous chromosome. Frequently, the members of a gene pair produce differing effects. Such genes are called **alleles**. If one dominates, covering detectable effects of the other member of the pair, the gene is said to be **dominant**. The opposite number of the pair is called **recessive**. If the gene pairs are identical, the cell is said to be **homozygous**. A cell containing a dominant and a recessive gene is **heterozygous**. Since most bacteria are haploid, they ordinarily behave as homozygous cells, although a haploid cell with two nuclei can behave as if it were a heterozygous diploid if any homologous genes of the two nuclei are unlike in effects produced.

Chromosomes consist of nucleoproteins—protein plus deoxyribosenucleic acid (DNA). DNA does occur in bacterial cells in chromatinic bodies, the functional equivalents of nuclei. Reports of mitosis in bacterial cells have not been universally accepted, and cytological evidence of bacterial chromosomes is moot, although the genetic evidence definitely demonstrates true heredity-governing units that have an orderly arrangement and are precisely proportioned between the two daughter nuclei on cell division.

The sum total of the gene composition of an individual gives the **genotype**. This is the heritable condition. The morphological appearance and physiological behavior of a genotype in response to the influence of environment gives the **phenotype**. Thus, difference in skin pigmentation is controlled by genes (genotypic difference), but the actual skin color will greatly depend on the extent of exposure to sunlight (phenotypic difference). Phenotypic differences are termed modifications, or adaptations. The idea that phenotypic differences can be transmitted has been very attractive, at times, to inadequately trained individuals, but the idea does not survive the test of scientific analysis. Genotypically motile bacteria may lose their flagella and become nonmotile when grown in broth containing 0.1% phenol. They may be repeatedly transferred in such a medium wherein for months or even years they possess no flagella; but when transferred to suitable phenol-free medium they develop flagella and resume motility. Such acquired characters (nongenetic changes) are not inherited.

MUTATIONS

The genotypes resulting from the division of a cell are duplicates in morphology and physiology of the parent cell within the limits imposed by the environment. In a very low percentage of cases a gene may change, or mutate. The mutant genes give rise to new genotypes. If the mutation occurs in a diploid cell and is recessive, it may not be detected for several generations. In uninucleate haploid organisms a mutant gene expresses itself promptly.

Mutations may occur spontaneously and may be induced experimentally. Spontaneous mutations are those for which no definite cause is known; probably factors such as cosmic rays and chemicals produced during growth influence mutations. The rate of mutation is usually expressed as the rate per bacterium per cell division. The spontaneous rate is fairly constant for any one gene, but it varies among different genes as can be illustrated by citing a few of the rates which have been determined, such as sulfathiazole resistance for *Staphylococcus aureus*, 1×10^{-9} and penicillin resistance, 1×10^{-7}, and streptomycin resistance (1000 micrograms) of *Escherichia coli*, 1×10^{-10} (Fig. 14.2).

Mutations of all types occur constantly in a bacterial population. For example, drug-resistant mutants are appearing in populations that have never contacted the drug. In ordinary media such mutant organisms are outgrown by the wild type population; only when the drug is present and the wild type is inhibited do the mutants dominate the population. The spontaneous occurrence of mutants, prior to contact with the selecting environment, can be demonstrated by the indirect-selection test using **replica plates.** In this procedure the colonies are transferred en masse to other dishes by the use of a velvet covered wood or metal disc. The fabric is pressed gently onto the surface of the culture, and the threads of the fabric pile pick up numerous organisms from each colony. The velvet is stamped on several sterile plates containing different kinds of selective media designed to select mutants from the wild type population. The colonies which grow, develop in

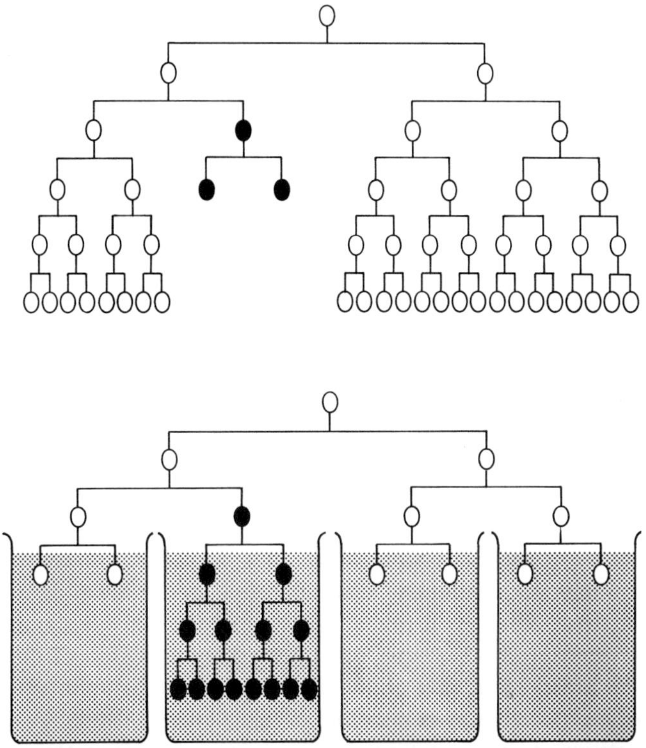

Fig. 14.2. A mutation (black dots) occurs in the bacterial colony in the top diagram. Under usual circumstances the mutant divides more slowly than wild type (open circles), are soon overgrown, and make only an insignificant contribution to the total population. In the bottom diagram the cells are placed in a selective environment, e.g., in broth containing a drug. Therein the wild type do not grow at all, and the mutants dominate the final population.

the same arrangement on the stamped plates as on the original culture, and thus their origin can be determined. Mutants that appear can be identified on the original plate, and every transfer from such colonies yields mutants, while transfers from other colonies yield nonmutants. This replica-plate method is one of many techniques developed for the rapid detection and identification of mutants.

Mutation rates are increased by exposing the population to radiations (ultraviolet rays and X rays) or to such chemical substances as peroxide, mustard gas, formaldehyde, nitrous acid, acriflavine, manganous chloride, and caffeine. The majority of the mutagenic agents cause death as well as mutation; some scientists hold that such killing constitutes lethal mutations. The survivors will mutate at a much higher rate than will untreated cells. Such mutants are called induced mutants, and proper application of mutagenic agents can increase the mutation rates 1000 times or more.

The detection of mutants in a culture, even when present in very small numbers (e.g., one mutant per 10^8 parent cells), is a fairly simple matter when a very large proportion of the culture can be plated on a medium sufficiently selective to allow only the mutant cells to form colonies. For example, drug resistant mutants may be selected from a culture plated on a medium containing a quantity of the inhibitory drug sufficient to prevent growth of the sensitive parent cells; mutants capable of synthesizing an amino acid needed by the parent culture may be selected on a medium deficient in this amino acid. The detection of antigenic mutants, though more difficult, has been accomplished by repeated single cell isolations and by cultivation in media containing antiserum, where an observable colony difference results between parent and mutant types.

If an organism varies in response to an environment, the change is often spoken of as adaptation or training. Training is usually a procedure for selecting mutants. Cultivation of an organism on a concentration of drug which will inhibit growth of the parent strain usually results in a culture that is drug resistant. The individuals in the resistant culture are descendents of one or a few resistant mutants present in the wild-type population at the time of inoculation. Resistance to high concentrations of drugs may require several mutations within the same organism. In such cases, a low level of drug selects a population of mutants resistant to that level; transfer to a higher drug concentration selects mutants of these mutants which are more highly resistant. Observation of this phenomenon led early microbiologists to assume mistakenly that the population was being trained or adapted to the higher drug level. Since mutations to drug resistance can occur in the body of an infected individual, the importance of an adequate initial dosage of the chemotherapeutic agent is obvious. The microbe can also make phenotypic accommodation to the environment but will assume the original type when it is returned to the original environment.

The types of bacterial mutations are numerous and varied. They include the following characteristics.

1. ***Color Variation.*** Since pigmentation is affected by environment, standard conditions are essential in the study of color mutants. But when a culture shows a sudden inherited change in pigment production, that gene controlling this trait has probably mutated, and an enzyme involved in the synthesis of the pigment is absent or modified.

2. ***Cell Morphology.*** The appearance of nonmotile mutants of motile species, variations in cell size, and loss of the ability to form

capsules or spores are representative changes in cell morphology that result from mutations. One of the very important manifestations of this type of mutation is seen in the O and H variation in colonies. Colonies of motile *Proteus vulgaris* spread to cover the surface of a moist solid medium in a form suggestive of the film produced by breathing on glass. Nonmotile variants remain as discrete colonies. These two colony types were designated as H (Hauch = breath) and O (ohne Hauch. Ohne = without). The terminology has been adopted as laboratory shorthand, and is used to describe flagellar antigens (H) and cell body (somatic) antigens (O) regardless of variation.

3. ***Colony Morphology.*** Differences in cell wall constituents, capsules, and chaining result in differences among colonies of the *Salmonella-Shigella* groups, which are now designated as smooth and rough (S and R). The normal parent form on solid medium gives convex, smooth, glossy colonies with a smooth margin. The variant colony has an irregular margin and is dull and rough in appearance. The smooth type gives a diffuse growth in broth and is stable in normal salt solution. The rough type shows a granular growth in broth and forms clumps in salt solution (Fig. 14.3). S cultures tend to yield R mutants, which usually overgrow the wild type as the culture ages. Apparently, the S organisms excrete substances into the medium which are toxic to themselves but not to the R mutants that arise spontaneously in the culture.

In addition to S and R colonies some organisms may show mucoid (M) colonies; sometimes small L colonies appear in which the cells are irregular in shape and size and lack well defined boundaries.

4. ***Antigenic Variation.*** The body or O anitgens of a bacterial group can be divided into a number of different components (antigens) present in mosaics and in layers. Cells with a complement of surface antigens give S type colonies. A mutant develops that no longer produces the surface antigens, and the next layer, which has been masked previously, is revealed and can manifest itself. The cell is roughly similar to an onion; peeling off one layer (antigen surface) reveals another layer. For example, the encapsulated pneumococcus cells show a variety of antigenic types, depending on the chemical nature of the capsule. A loss of the capsule reveals a body antigen (O), which is the same for all antigenic types.

Variation in H antigen is commonly referred to as phase variation. Many of the species of motile enteric bacteria are diphasic; that is, the flagella may assume two antigenic types, each of which is an antigenic mosaic, or mixture of antigens. Originally, these were termed the specific and nonspecific phases but are now designated as phase 1 and phase 2. A culture in one phase is capable of giving rise to de-

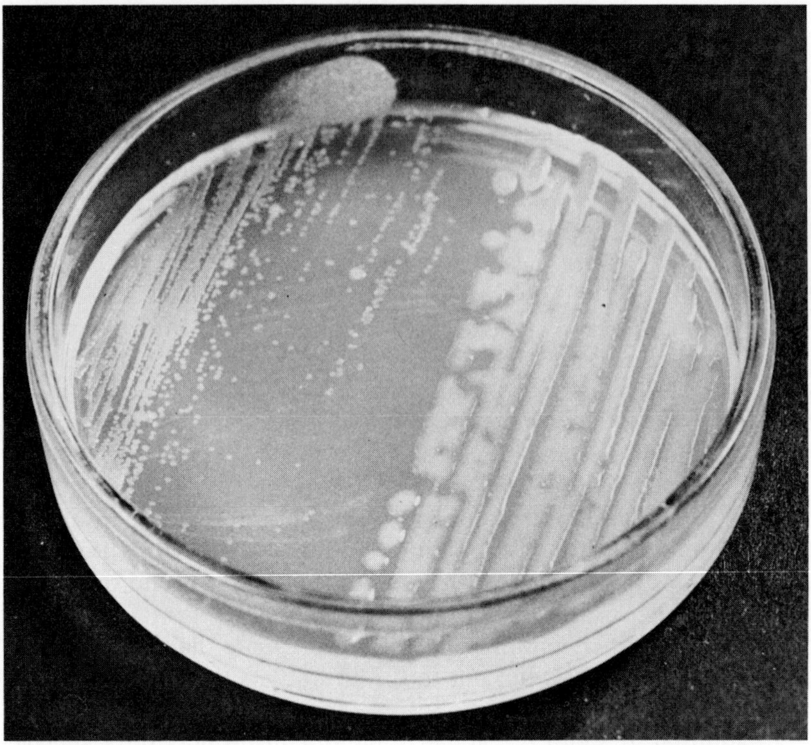

Fig. 14.3. A wild-type culture of *Azotobacter agilis* (right) and a rough mutant isolated from it (left) are streaked on the same plate.

scendants in the other phase. The individual cells may have flagella of either phase but not of both, as can be established by streaking and testing individual colonies. A single phase is maintained by a culture from a "pure" colony for a time, after which phase variation occurs, and the culture contains both phases.

5. ***Virulence and Toxigenicity.*** For most pathogenic organisms the virulent form is the S or M form. A change from S to R, or M to R, is accompanied by a reduction in virulence, even complete loss. Variation resulting in a loss of the capacity to produce toxin by toxigenic bacteria appears to be dependent of S–R variation.

6. ***Fermentation Mutants.*** Differences in the ability to ferment lactose by a strain of *Escherichia coli*, termed *coli-mutabile*, were described by Massini in 1907, although observations of fermentation differences within a strain antedate this report. Cultures of coli-mutabile streaked on a differential lactose medium may show only nonlactose

fermenting colonies (lac$^-$) for several days, after which lac$^+$ papillae appear on the surface of the colony. Subcultures from the lac$^+$ papillae are prompt fermenters of lactose. Isolates from the lac$^-$ portion of the colony repeat the pattern of the parent strain. Mutants that have gained or lost the ability to ferment other sugars are easily obtained and are useful tools for genetic studies.

7. ***Biochemical Mutants.*** In the process of mutation some organisms gain or lose a nutritional requirement. Organisms which require additional growth factors, or amino acids, not required by the parent strain (wild type) are called **auxotrophs**. A biotinless auxotroph (biotin$^-$ strain) is a mutant strain that needs the vitamin, biotin, added to the minimal medium on which the wild type (biotin$^+$ strain) would grow; a methionineless auxotroph (meth$^-$ strain) requires methionine added to a medium adequate for the wild type (meth$^+$ strain). These have been especially useful in studies of genetic exchange.

8. ***Drug-fast Mutants.*** The development of drug fastness (drug resistance), particularly to antibiotics and sulfa drugs, has become a problem of obvious major interest to clinicians as well as to bacterial geneticists.

9. ***Phage-resistant Mutants.*** Organisms become resistant to phages usually by an inherited modification of the cell wall which prevents entrance of the phage into the bacteria.

GENETIC EXCHANGE

The rapid growth and large population of bacteria make them useful subjects for studying mutations. The amount of variation possible by mutation alone is probably sufficient to insure the fitness of bacteria to a changing environment. Yet, since most fundamental processes found in higher plants and animals appear in some form in the bacteria, the exchange of genetic material between individuals would be expected in the bacteria. The sexual activities of all higher plants and animals permit the production of individuals with new combinations of genes. Actually, no less than four methods of bacterial genetic exchange occur between closely related bacteria whose DNA is chemically similar, allowing fragments from one strain to be incorporated into the other (Fig. 14.4). Usually mutant strains of the same species of bacteria are employed in genetic-exchange experiments, but gene exchange can sometimes take place between bacteria that had been classified as different species or even as different genera. For example, the DNA's from *Shigella* and *Escherichia* are so similar in chemical composition,

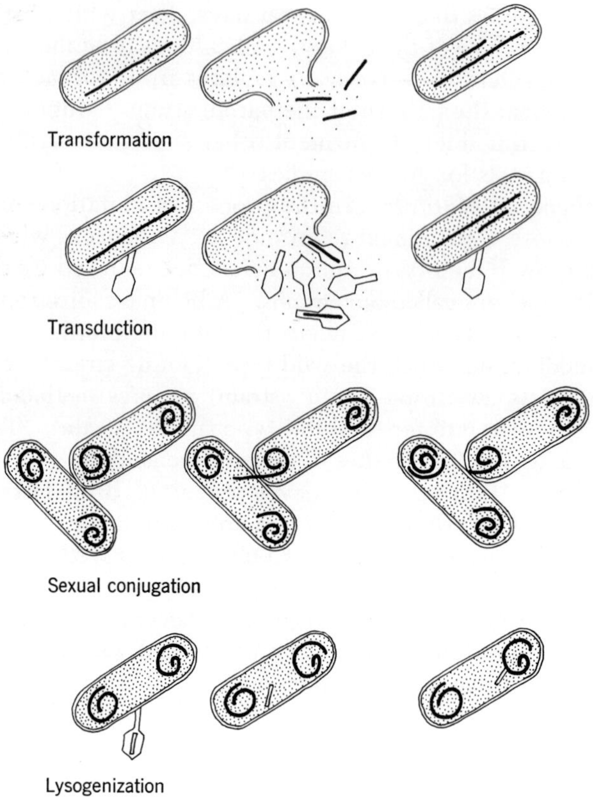

Fig. 14.4. Four methods of exchange of genetic material in bacteria are shown diagramatically.

and consequently in melting point, that genetic exchange takes place between them; any new modification of the bacterial classification scheme will have to take this into account.

Transformation. The simplest method of genetic exchange, and therefore the most primitive evolutionary development in the direction of sexuality, is called transformation; DNA from one strain of bacteria is fed to a second. If the second organism incorporates a mutant gene from the DNA of the first organism, this difference will become a stable inherited trait in the progeny of the second organism. Usually only a single gene is introduced by a single transformation. Much of the early experimentation in transformation was done with *Diplococcus pneumoniae*, wherein the antigenic type of the capsule was transformed from one culture to another (Fig. 14.5). Since this fundamental work, many different characters have been transmitted from a donor strain to a recipient strain by DNA extracted from the donor bacteria. Furthermore, transformation has been discovered in a variety of other bacterial species. The transformation phenomenon offered the first convincing evidence that pure nucleic acid carries the genetic information in the heredity apparatus of the cell.

Lysogenization. New combinations of genes may be acquired during the formation of lysogenic strains of bacteria. Lysogenization leads to a stable association between the bacterium and the bacteriophage. In old cultures the phage may become induced and destroy some of the bacterial cells, thus releasing free phage. Otherwise the phage may be difficult to detect since it exists as a marker on the bacterial chromosome in a state termed **prophage.** In this condition it renders the bacterial cell immune to attack by phages of a similar type. The immunity

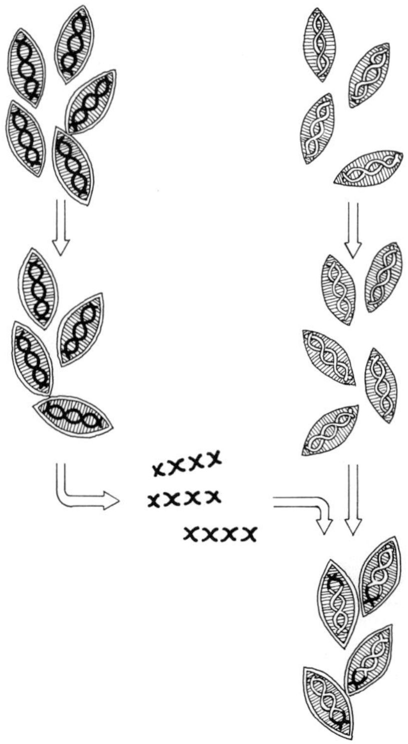

Fig. 14.5. Transformation involves chemical or mechanical extraction of the DNA from one culture and feeding it to another culture where it may be incorporated. In this case the capsule formation is controlled by the DNA.

persists in the progeny of the bacteria as long as the prophage remains attached to, and reproduces with, the bacterial genetic structure. Some bacteria acquire other genetic characteristics associated with the process of lysogenization, for example, the production of toxin by the diphtheria bacillus. The information which directs the bacterium to give a new response is probably a part of the phage DNA. In this second method of genetic exchange only those characteristics are transferred whose code is inscribed in the phage DNA.

Transduction. The third method of transfer of genetic characters is the accidental incorporation of small random pieces of bacterial DNA in the phage particles. When such phages invade another bacterial strain, the chromosomal fragments from the original bacterium are introduced. The size of the chromosomal fragment is limited by the small size of the phage particle; usually only one gene is transferred, although occasionally several genes located close together on the bacterial chromosome may be included. Unlike lysogenization (where every bacterium entered by the phage acquires the new hereditary properties), only one bacteriophage particle per million transduces any given character. Each phage may include some bacterial DNA, but since the bacterial chromosome is so large relative to the phage particle, there is only a one in a million chance that the included piece will carry the bacterial gene under study. Only certain temperate phages can transduce, and the recipient bacteria are not necessarily lysogenized by the transduction process. Of course, if the recipient bacteria are lysed by the transducing phage, the effect of the incorporated genetic material could not be observed. Transformation depends on the diffusion of DNA into the recipient cell; in transduction the DNA is carried into the cell by a phage.

Sexual Recombination. In the fourth method of genetic exchange in bacteria, the DNA is passed directly from one cell to another. When certain strains of *Escherichia coli* are mixed, fusion tubes form between individuals of the two strains, and the chromosomal thread of a nucleus of one of the organisms (called the donor male, F^+ or Hfr strain) passes through the tube into the other (the recipient female, or F^- strain). After a period up to ninety minutes, the fusion tubes break and the cells separate. If the cells are then isolated into pure cultures and permitted to grow, the descendants may be observed. Those of the male cell will not have changed in their inherited traits, while the descendants of the female cells will exhibit genetic characteristics inherited from both the male and the female strains. If the male was phage resistant and the female was streptomycin resistant, the progeny of the female line will contain some bacteria resistant to both phage and streptomycin and also some resistant to neither.

The bacterial genes of an F^- strain are probably arranged in a linear order on a closed or circular chromosome. Each cell of the male (F^+) strain contains a few units of the sex factor F (also called fertility factor)—a piece of DNA in the cytoplasm unattached to the circular chromosome. During conjugation with F^- bacteria, a unit of the F factor is passed to the F^- cell; that is, maleness in bacteria is contagious. During growth on unfavorable media some cells may lose their F factor, and F^- strains can be isolated readily from F^+ strains. At the time of conjugation in a few organisms of the F^+ strain, the F factor in the male strain may attach itself to the circular chromosome and the chromosome breaks at the attachment point. Instead of the F factor passing through the conjugation tube, the chromosomal thread with the F factor on the trailing end passes into the F^- cell. This sexual recombination occurs at an extremely low rate. In some F^+ strains the F factor is always attached to the chromosome, and the circular arrangement of the chromosome is permanently broken. These high-frequency recombining (Hfr) strains transfer genetic material to almost all of the F^- cells which they contact.

While sexual recombination may occur with other organisms, practically all of the experiments have been carried out with a single strain of *Escherichia coli, E. coli K12.* The nuclei of male cells have replicated before a chromosome is transferred to the F^- recipient, so the male cell, following conjugation, is still complete and viable. The male chromosome is fragile and usually breaks before the entire chromosome enters the female; yet the transferred proportion of the entire genetic makeup of the male contains hundreds of times as many genes as are involved in any single event of transformation or transduction. Unlike higher animals and plants, the bacterial chromosome has not been seen, even under the electron microscope. The preceding picture has been developed as an explanation of the experimental results.

Dozens of mutant strains of both the Hfr and F^- strains have been studied, and various recombinations of these have been obtained. The relative location on the chromosome of the genes controlling various bacterial traits have been determined, and maps showing gene locations have been drawn. Such procedures have relied on analogy to the determination of the linkage groups in fruit flies, corn, etc., by classical genetic studies.

Genetic analysis is based on the fact that when individuals differing in several hereditary characters are crossed, the progeny contain a reassortment of genes. The assumption is made that when the Hfr chromosomal segment enters the F^- cell, it lines up beside that portion of the F^- chromosome bearing the corresponding genes. When the new chromosomes are synthesized, preparatory to cell division, some information is taken from each of the parental structures. When genes are close together, a switch-over probably will not occur when the chromosome copy is being made for the daughter cells. The frequency of such "switch-overs" is a function of the distance between the genes, and studies of these distances aid in mapping gene location. Because of the ease in handling bacteria, great numbers of observations can be made, and details on short chromosomal segments can be studied, which would not be resolved in recombination studies using higher animals and plants. For example, the lactose-fermentation region of the chromosome can be resolved in *E. coli* into three distinct parts; one controls the synthesis of the enzyme, lactase; one determines the enzyme as inducible or constitutive; one controls the penetration of lactose into the cell. Many other elucidations of the fine structure of the genetic apparatus have resulted from studies with bacterial recombination.

A second method for mapping the bacterial chromosome involves measuring the time required for penetration. When an Hfr culture is mixed with an F^- strain carrying many mutant genes, conjugation occurs, and the penetration of the Hfr chromosome begins. If every few minutes thereafter aliquots of the conjugating cells are removed and shaken violently to break the conjugation tubes, analysis of the genetic constitution of the progeny will reveal the time of penetration of each gene (Fig. 14.6). With one Hfr strain the threonine-synthesizing gene (Th) enters at 8 minutes, the lactose-fermenting gene (lac) at 18 minutes, the streptomycin-resistance gene (Sr) at 90 minutes, and the vitamin B_1 gene (B_1) at 115 minutes. Therefore, Th is located on the chromosome 10 units (minutes) from lac, 82 units from Sr, and 107 units from B_1.

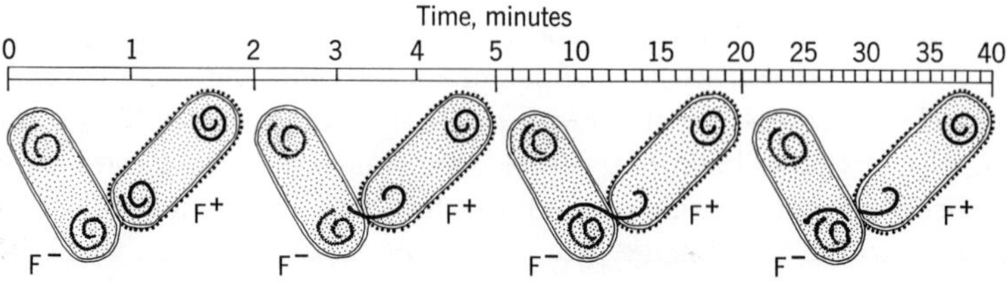

Fig. 14.6. The location of various genes along the bacterial chromosome can be mapped by interupting the mating process by vigorous shaking and then determining which genes had been transferred.

Sexduction. Occasionally the F marker in an Hfr strain becomes detached from the chromosome, thus producing an F^+ strain. A small piece of bacterial chromosome may break off in the detachment process, remaining attached to the F particle and multiplying with it in the bacterial cytoplasm. When a conjugation tube is formed between this unusual F^+ cell and an F^- cell, the F factor carries the piece of bacterial chromosome into the F^- cell. This process is called F -duction or sexduction and is very similar to transduction except that the carrier is an F particle rather than a phage.

SUMMARY. In bacteria as in higher animals and plants, errors in the replication of DNA, called mutations, introduce the variability necessary for survival and development in a changing environment. Bacteria have haploid nuclei, but the cell usually contains two or more nuclei and, therefore, two or more copies of the genetic code. The code is a linear arrangement of genes which directs the activities of the cell and divides prior to cell division. New combinations of mutant and wild-type genes arise as a result of genetic exchange. In bacteria at least four methods of genetic exchange exist plus lysogenization. Bacterial viruses (also called bacteriophages) are pieces of genetic material, which may become integrated into the genetic apparatus and, in this lysogenic state, multiply as prophage. Thus they may modify the behavior of the cell.

15

Microorganisms as Disease Producers

Health and disease are complex states which are subject to much variation among individuals. In general, health implies that all parts of the body are functioning in a satisfactory manner. Recognizable departure from normal function is regarded as disease. A condition of malfunction resulting from some constitutional or physiological defect or from a mechanical or chemical injury is restricted to the affected individual. Disease caused by an agent which can be transmitted from an affected individual to one who is not affected is termed **infectious** or transmissible. If it is spread by contact, it may be spoken of as **contagious.**

Evidence from skeletal remains indicates that diseases have afflicted man since prehistoric times. However, the concept that disease results from natural causes is relatively modern. Primitive peoples interpreted the natural as supernatural and regarded disease as an invasion of the body by a devil. The Greek physician, Hippocrates (460–370 B.C.), broke with this **demonic** theory and fathered the **humoral** theory of disease causation which persisted for hundreds of years.

The epidemics of the Middle Ages led some observers to assume that the cause of the disease was a living agent. As the idea of a **contagium vivum,** or a living causal agent for contagious diseases, began to crystallize, the development of the microscope and the discovery of bacteria provided a solid basis for the new theory. Here were organisms not previously known which could be implicated in disease; thus the germ theory was born. The concern of early experimentation with the origin, rather than the significance of microorganisms, delayed development of the germ theory.

The similarity between the fermentation process and the progress of infectious disease had long been noted. When Pasteur established the biological nature of fermentation, the germ theory of disease received strong support. Lister, a Scottish surgeon, reasoned that microorganisms caused the septic conditions which so frequently followed surgery. By operating under a spray of phenol solution and using antiseptic dressings for surgical wounds, he dramatically reduced postoperative sepsis. His stature was such that his acceptance of the germ theory greatly influenced other members of the medical profession to accept the theory.

Additional support was provided by the success of Pasteur in controlling pebrine. In studying this disease of silkworms, which threatened the silk industry in France, Pasteur found microscopic bodies in diseased worms, not present in healthy worms. Reasoning correctly that these bodies caused the disease, he instituted successful control measures directed toward the living agent.

Though many investigators had noted microorganisms in various disease studies, the relationship of the organisms to the disease was unclear. It had been claimed that anthrax could be transmitted by blood free of the rod-shaped bodies commonly found in material obtained from diseased animals. Robert Koch, a German physician grew the rod-shaped organism in pure culture from pieces of spleen of animals suffering from anthrax (Fig. 15.1). He showed that the organism was able to cause anthrax in susceptible animals and that the disease could be transmitted from animal to animal. Furthermore, the disease was distinct; it could not be initiated by other similar rod-shaped bacteria. Koch's rapid progress in methods for isolation and study of bacteria ushered in the golden age of discovery in bacteriology. Over a short period of years the bacterial causes of many diseases were established.

Koch's Laws of Disease, or Koch's Postulates, set down the conditions which must be met for proof that a particular organism is the cause of a given disease.

1. The organism must be found in every case of the disease, and should agree in distribution with the lesions observed.
2. The organism must be isolated and maintained in pure culture outside the body of the infected animal.
3. The introduction of the pure culture into a susceptible animal should reproduce the disease.

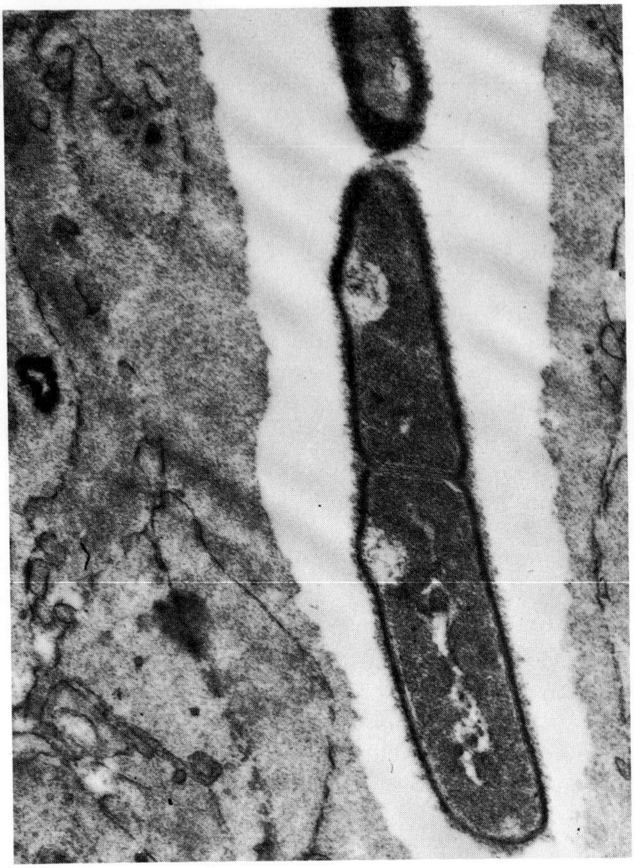

Fig. 15.1. Electron micrograph of a thin slice of the spleen of a mouse infected with anthrax. The pathogen, *Bacillus anthracis*, is in the intercellular space of the tissue. *Photo by Roth, Lewis, and Williams: J. Bact., LXXX, 722, 1960.*

4. The experimentally-produced disease should agree in characteristics with the naturally occurring disease and should yield the organism.

Not all diseases, however, can be made to fit Koch's laws. An organism associated with leprosy may be demonstrated in lesions of the disease, yet it will not grow on laboratory media or produce the disease when transferred to experimental animals or human volunteers.

The principles embodied in Koch's laws are not limited to infectious disease but are equally applicable to proof of a cause-and-effect relationship between an organism and a physiological or biochemical process. For example, they can be adapted to prove the relationship of *Azotobacter* to nitrogen fixation or of yeast to alcoholic fermentation.

Most bacteria are saprophytic, obtaining their nutritive needs from nonliving sources. The remainder exists in ecological relationships ranging from the simplest sort of loose independent association between two living organisms to an obligate intracellular habitat of one member of the association. This sort of relationship is termed parasitism, and the members are termed parasite and host, respectively. If the members are so well adapted to each other that the association is relatively inconsequential with neither member showing evidence of harm or special benefit, the association is termed **commensalism.** If, however, the relationship between the two is still in a state of evolution toward a biological balance and the association results in injury or disease to the host, the parasite is said to be pathogenic. Almost all pathogenic bacteria are parasitic. One notable exception is *Clostridium botulinum,* an obligate saprophyte that grows in food and produces a poison which is later absorbed from the digestive tract.

It is but a short step from parasitism or commensalism to pathogenicity, in which the organisms cause infection by invasion and growth in the host. Some parasites commonly live as commensals, but under suitable conditions can invade and cause infection. Such organisms are termed **opportunists.** As they are practically always present, they can take advantage of any opportunity to invade.

Though the terms *pathogenicity* and *virulence* are frequently used synonymously, a subtle distinction exists between them. Pathogenicity properly describes the capacity of a group or species of microorganisms to produce disease. Virulence, the relative pathogenicity of a particular culture of an organism, depends primarily on (1) the organism's ability to invade and grow, and (2) its capacity to produce poisons. Almost all gradations and combinations of these two characteristics occur among microorganisms.

Some species of microorganism which are ordinarily saprophytic may mutate to become virulent. Furthermore, some cultures of ordinarily pathogenic groups are not virulent. Disease production is a complex affair and results when, and only when, the host and the organism meet under conditions which favor disease. If an organism has higher virulence, or a host shows lower resistance than usual, an ordinarily inconsequential association between host and organism results in disease.

Lack of balance between host and pathogen is not sufficient to result in disease. An adequate number of pathogenic organisms must be present in an environment permitting contact with the host and subsequent growth. The number of cells of any pathogen necessary to start an infection varies. In some cases the number is almost always high; in other cases only a few are necessary.

Some pathogenic types are fairly exacting as to the site of their entry; others are able to cause an infection from any of several portals of

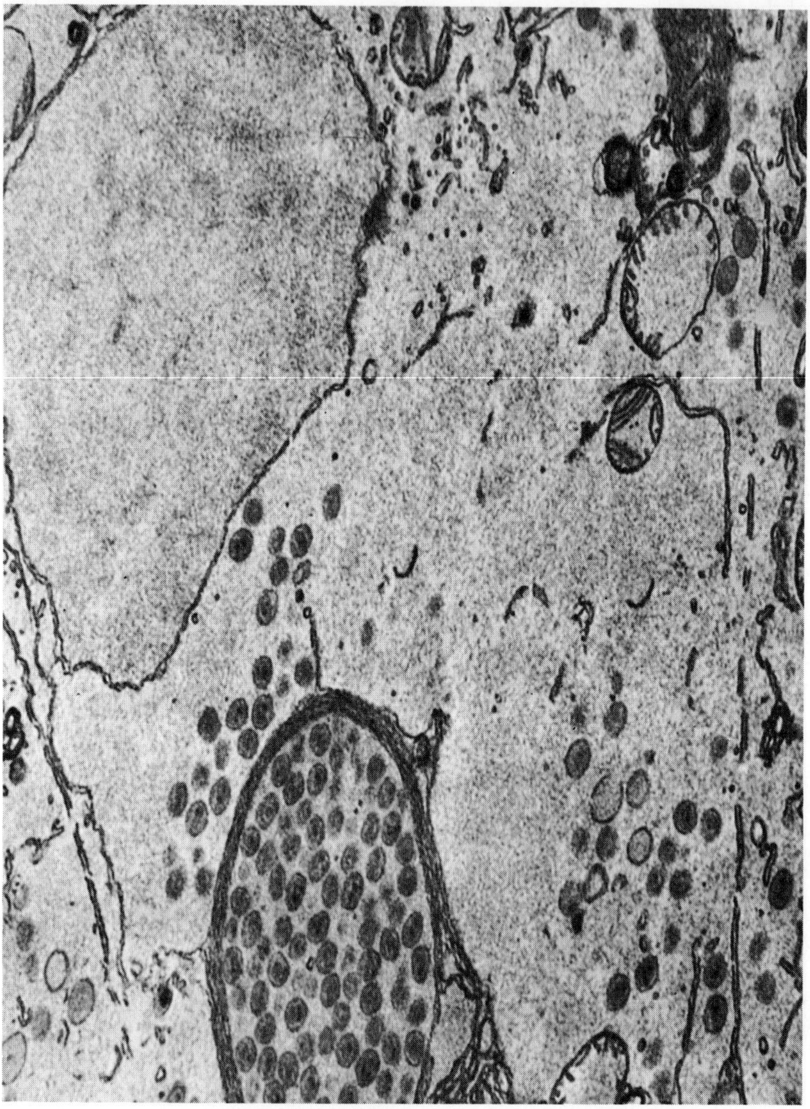

Fig. 15.2. Electron micrograph of vaccinia (smallpox) virus showing localization in tissue cells. *Photo by Norton McDuffie, Univ. of Texas.*

entry. However, one avenue will almost certainly be the most favorable.

Respiratory diseases. The portal of entry is most frequently the respiratory tract. Infection follows inhalation of an airborne pathogen. Examples are measles, smallpox, (Fig. 15.2) and pulmonary tuberculosis.

Gastro-intestinal diseases. Infection follows the ingestion of contaminated food, water, or milk. Examples are dysentery and Q fever.

Urogenital or venereal diseases. Infection results from sexual contact. Examples are gonorrhea and syphilis.

Traumatic diseases. The organisms invade through breaks in the skin or mucous membrane, or are implanted by bloodsucking insects or arthropods. Examples are staphylococcal infection, tetanus, anthrax, rabies, and yellow fever.

Congenital diseases. Infection is transferred through the placenta. It is only necessary that the mother be infected and that the disease be transmissible to the fetus. Examples include syphilis and measles.

Under special circumstances some representative of a group may invade through other portals or perhaps through some portal which cannot be clearly recognized.

HOW MICROORGANISMS CAUSE DISEASE

Each case of disease is an individual matter. Degree or severity is determined by the conditions of resistance of the host and by the virulence of the pathogen at the time of contact. There are, however, two common mechanisms of disease production.

1. Microorganisms may produce disease **by mechanical means.** Heavy growth of the organisms interferes with the functions of certain tissues or vessels.

In some diseases of plants the water-conducting vessels become plugged by massive bacterial growth or by gums formed as a result of the bacterial injury so that the plant wilts and dies. In whooping cough, bacterial growth interferes with the action of the cilia of the respiratory tract so that they are unable to sweep out accumulations of mucus.

2. Microorganisms may produce disease **by chemical means.** Two types of poisons are most commonly involved: (a) **exotoxins,** or true toxins, which are formed by the organism and exist in the surrounding environment while the cells which formed them are still alive and intact; and (b) **endotoxins,** or intracellular toxic substances, which are liberated only after the cell dies and disintegrates. Exotoxins and endotoxins are distinct in composition and in the nature of the symptoms caused by each (Table 15.1).

Table 15.1. Toxic Reactions

	Location	Symptoms	Potency	Antitoxin Production	Heat Sensitivity	Alterability
Exotoxins	Extracellular	Muscle spasms Nerve poison	Highly toxic	Effective	Destroyed by mild heat (high)	Altered by formaldehyde (toxoidable)
Endotoxins	Intracellular	Fever Headaches	Toxic only in large doses	Relatively ineffective	Heat-stable (low)	Unalterable (nontoxoidable)

In addition to their capacity for toxin production, many pathogenic microorganisms produce accessory chemical substances which aid in breaking down the defenses of the invaded host. Such aids to pathogenicity include **leucocidin,** a poison to white blood cells, and **hemolysin,** a poison for red blood cells. Some pathogens produce enzymes harmful to the host. One of these, **coagulase,** causes the formation of coagulated-blood fibrin at the site of infection and reduces circulation in the infected area. Another enzyme, **hyaluronidase,** causes the breakdown of hyaluronic acid, one of the cementing substances which holds body cells together. The spread of the microorganism through the tissues is thus facilitated. Bacteria with capsules are often more resistant to body defenses than those without capsules; hence the presence of a capsule seems to increase pathogenicity and virulence.

HOW THE HOST DEFENDS AGAINST DISEASE

Three defense mechanisms may protect an individual exposed to an infectious organism. These include both nonspecific factors, which are operative against any invading organism, and specific factors, which are operative against a particular organism.

The first defense is the **body covering.** In general, pathogenic organisms must enter the body tissues before harmful effects can be produced. Very few are able to pass through the intact skin. Likewise the mucous membrane is an effective barrier against most pathogens. The protective action of these mechanical barriers is aided by tears, which tend to wash organisms from the eyes; by the hairs of the nostrils, which act collectively as a filter; by the acidity of the gastric juice; and by other body secretions such as mucus which traps invading microbes and in which they are ejected or excreted.

The second defense is the **body phagocytes.** These protective cells destroy microorganisms by ingesting and digesting them. There are two general types of phagocytes: **free** forms, which include the white blood cells and "wandering" macrophages, and **fixed** forms, which are found in abundance in the lymph nodes, spleen, liver, bone marrow, and connective tissue. The phagocytes are sometimes called "scavenger cells" because of their capacity to remove foreign material from the body. Unfortunately, conditions are not always entirely favorable for phagocytic activity. Some pathogens escape these protective cells and must be dealt with by other means.

The first two defenses are nonspecific, operating against any organism. The third defensive mechanism, **immunity,** consists of those properties of the host which confer specific resistance. Immunity implies relative or absolute resistance to infection by a specific pathogen. **Natural immunity** is that state of resistance which is possessed as a heritage, rather than as a consequence of previous contact with the infectious organism. One individual may possess a natural immunity to a disease to which others are susceptible. In any extensive outbreak of an infectious disease a few persons do not become infected, although they have been freely exposed. Some species do not develop a disease to which another species is susceptible. Certain diseases occur spontaneously only in man, or in one or very few animal species: Man does not develop hog cholera; rats are not subject to the diphtheria of human beings. Or immunity may be racial, in which one race of a species is more resistant than another race of the same species; for example, the wild mouse is quite resistant to pneumococcal infection, although the white mouse is highly susceptible.

Acquired immunity is the development of resistance by susceptible individuals. It is of two types: **active immunity** and **passive immunity.** Active immunity develops as a result of the activity of the body cells of the individual who becomes immune; he is active in producing his own immune state. Passive immunity is obtained by the transfer of immune substance which was developed by another. The body cells of the passively immunized person do not participate in the production of the immune state. The body becomes immune by the introduction of antibodies which were produced actively by another. For this reason, passive immunity is frequently spoken of as secondary immunity; and active immunity, as primary immunity. In general, the protection from passive immunity is of short duration, while that from active immunity is longer lasting. On the other hand, protection by passive immunization results immediately after transfer of immune substance, while protection by active immunization develops more slowly.

Either active or passive immunity can be acquired naturally or artificially. Active immunity may be acquired naturally as a result of recovery from a disease. Also, repeated exposure to organisms in

Fig. 15.3. A purified preparation of polio virus as seen in a shadowed electron micrograph. *Photo courtesy Virus Lab, Univ. of Calif., Berkeley.*

numbers too small to cause an infection (subclinical infection) will result in the development of a natural immunity.

Immunity can be induced artifically in several ways:

1. Living, attenuated organisms of reduced virulence may be inoculated. Various methods of attenuating pathogenic microorganisms have been described, and several practical immunizing procedures with attenuated organisms are extensively used. The best known example involves the use of vaccinia virus for immunization against smallpox.

2. Dead organisms may be inoculated. Millions of persons have been immunized against typhoid fever by the use of a suspension of killed typhoid cells. The Salk vaccine for prophylaxis against poliomyelitis consists of killed virus (Fig. 15.3).

3. For those diseases in which the symptoms are caused by an exotoxin, toxoid may be inoculated. The toxoid is a toxin so modified as to lose its poisonous qualities but retain its prophylactic power. Toxoids are inoculated as a prophylactic against tetanus and diphtheria.

4. A combination of active and passive immunization may be employed. Infective and protective materials are injected at the same time. This procedure is used in preventing hog cholera. The animal to be immunized is given a protective dose of hyperimmune serum, and simultaneously a small dose of infected blood. The immune serum protects against disease from the infectious material, but it does not prevent stimulation of the body cells for production of antibody.

Passive immunity likewise may be acquired naturally or artificially. Natural passive immunity can be acquired by transfer of protective substance from mother to child by the fetal circulation. An infant is born with the same immunities as the mother. Artificial immunization by the passive transfer of immune substance may be prophylactic or it may be therapeutic. Prophylactically, tetanus antitoxin can be used to protect a previously nonimmunized person against tetanus following injury. Large doses of specific antitoxin are employed therapeutically in treatment of diphtheria and tetanus.

SUMMARY. A pathogenic organism can cause disease only when it is able to survive the three defenses and establish itself in tissue favorable for its growth in sufficient numbers.

16

Antigens and Antibodies

An understanding of the phenomenon of immunity requires a knowledge of antigen-antibody reactions. The science which deals in these reactions is called **serology**. An important part of serology, **immunology**, deals with those serological reactions involved in resistance to infection.

Some infectious diseases are treated by an injection of the serum (the liquid part of the blood after clotting) from a recovered case. Such treatment often affords temporary protection against the specific disease in otherwise susceptible individuals. A protective factor in the serum of the recovered case is thus transferred from one person to another. This factor cannot be demonstrated in the serum of a "normal" person, but has developed as a result of infection. Such a factor is termed **antibody**. The substance which stimulates the body to produce antibody is designated **antigen** (antibody generator).

For many observations of immune reactions there are no readily apparent explanations. Furthermore, workers in this field are not always in full agreement about all of the recorded phenomena. This discussion is restricted to fundamentals about which there is little difference in interpretation.

ANTIGENS

A **complete antigen** must possess two fundamental properties:

1. It must stimulate the body to produce antibodies.
2. It must react with the antibody in some demonstrable way.

An antigen is a protein which is soluble in the fluids of the body and foreign to the animal species to which it is added. In order to stimulate antibody production, it must reach the tissues of the body in an unaltered form. Protein taken by mouth loses its specific foreign-protein characteristics as a result of digestion in the alimentary tract. It reaches the tissues of the body as amino acids or other altered digested products of protein. Consequently, it no longer meets the requirements for antigenic behavior. Although most native proteins are antigenic, a few are not, simply because they are insoluble in the unaltered state. Silk is used as a surgical suture since this protein is insoluble and therefore does not provoke antibody formation.

Microbial Antigens. Antigens of microbial origin which exist outside of the cell are called **exocellular**. Antigens of this nature include the exotoxins and exoenzymes. Other antigens are part of the inner cell proteins and are called **intracellular**. The bacterial cell, which consists of a complex of many different proteins, also contains a complex of different antigens, which are carried as a unit so long as the cell membrane is intact. This multiplicity of antigens is termed the **antigenic mosaic**. Each individual protein of the mosaic acts independently and stimulates the production of specific antibody.

Human Blood Groups. Though the antigen must generally be foreign to the species to be immunized, blood cell proteins which are antigenic for some members of a given species may occur in other members of the same species. Such antigens are called **isoantigens**; and the corresponding antibodies, **isoantibodies**.

Blood groups of man are determined by two isoantigens of the red blood cells which are designated A and B. The naturally occurring homologous isoantibodies for these antigens are designated a and b, respectively. The distribution of these isoantigens and isoantibodies among the four major blood groups is shown in the following tabulation:

Group	*Isoantigen on Cell*	*Isoantibody in Serum*
O	none	ab
A	A	b
B	B	a
AB	AB	none

The discovery of these groups made possible the present safe and extensive use of blood transfusions. Blood from a donor must not have antigens homologous to the antibodies of the recipient. The isoantibody level of plasma, or gamma globulin, is sufficiently low to allow injection of these substances without regard to blood type. Dilution below reacting level occurs in the blood of the recipient.

Other antigens occur in blood cells; therefore, compatability tests of donor and recipient bloods are made to avoid transfusion accidents. One of these additional antigens is the heritable Rh factor, which occurs in about 85% of the Caucasians. Mating between an Rh positive male

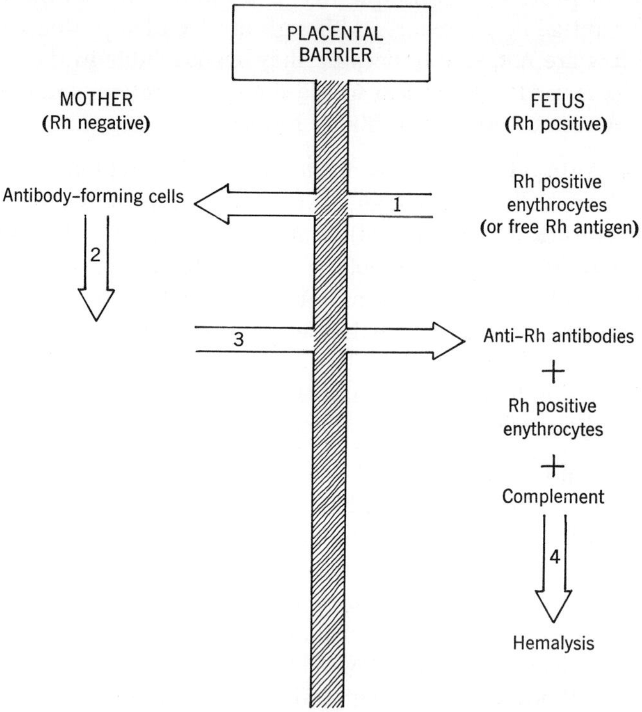

Fig. 16.1. The circulation of this Rh negative mother and her Rh positive child are separated by the placenta. Should some of the child's Rh positive red cells get into the mother's circulation (1), they would start the formation of antibodies against the Rh protein (2). These anti-Rh antibodies may diffuse back into the child (3), and react with the child's red blood cells causing them to lyse (4). Such a child may be still-borne or may be suffering from lack of red cells. Usually step 1 occurs late in pregnancy or at delivery; therefore step 4 is rarely reached during a first pregnancy, but rather in a subsequent pregnancy. Of course, step 2 (followed by steps 3 and 4) could result if the Rh negative woman received a blood transfusion properly typed as to the four major blood groups, but improperly typed as to Rh.

and an Rh negative female can result in a fetus with Rh positive blood cells. Repeated pregnancies of this type may cause **erythroblastosis fetalis;** if fetal blood accidentally enters the maternal circulation, Rh positive cells of the developing child stimulate the mother to produce homologous immune antibodies. In a later pregnancy these maternal anti-Rh antibodies may enter the fetal circulation causing destruction of fetal blood cells (Fig. 16.1).

ANTIBODIES

An antigen introduced into the body causes a change in the fluids and fixed tissues; they develop the capacity to react with the antigen in a manner different from their behavior before exposure to the antigen. This altered reactivity results from the presence of specific antibodies. For a long time antibodies could be described only in terms of their reactions. They are now recognized as altered blood proteins. Antibody activity seems to reside chiefly in the gamma globulin fraction of serum protein.

According to latest theories, antibody production is carried on by certain cells (plasma cells) which inherit the capacity to produce special types of globulin molecules (i.e., antibodies). The function of the antigen, then, is to seek out the cell type capable of producing its specific antibody and to cause these cells to form and release quantities of antibody. However, those cells which may produce antibodies reactive to an animal's own antigenic proteins are eliminated early in the animal's development (before birth). Thus antigenic response to constituents of its own tissues never occurs; that is, the animal body can distinguish chemical differences between "self" and "nonself." Recent evidence suggests that some pathological conditions, such as certain types of anemia, may be manifestations of immunological reactivity against autogenous antigens.

Antibody formation cannot ordinarily be detected for several days or weeks after an injection of antigen. Successive doses of antigens raise the antibody content to a higher level than could be achieved by a single injection (Fig. 16.2). If no further contact with the antigen occurs, antibodies begin to disappear or decrease. However, fresh injection of the antigen will usually result in a more rapid rise in antibody content than occurred with the initial injection. "Booster" doses of immunizing antigens are given from time to time after initial immunization to maintain protective antibody levels. In a few cases the secondary response may be brought about by the injection of a heterologous antigen. Since the body cells react as if in memory of their

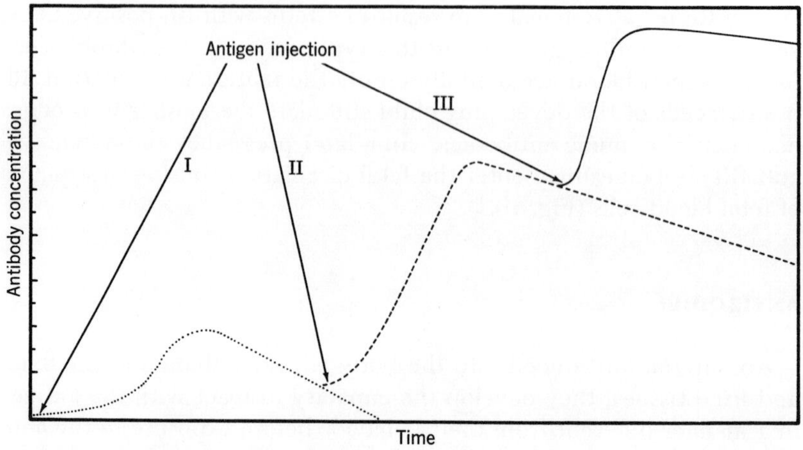

Fig. 16.2. Antibody formation occurs more quickly and to a higher level with succeeding injections of antigen. This also explains why a person, once immune, may not succumb to a later infection, even though his antibody titer has fallen almost to zero.

prior experience in the production of antibodies, this phenomenon has been termed the **anamnestic reaction.**

Complement. A third component, **complement,** may also take part in antigen-antibody reactions. This reaction complements certain reactions between cell antigens and their antibodies. Complement is a protein complex occurring in the blood serum of all normal individuals and varying in amount in different species and in individuals of the same species. Unlike antibody, it does not increase in quantity with immunization. It is heat labile and may be destroyed by 56°C treatment for 30 minutes. Though not specific for individual antigens, it is an essential participant in several types of immune reactions.

The reaction between antigen and homologous antibody is highly specific. The type and nature of the reaction is determined by the nature of the antigen and the environment in which the two reacting members are placed.

Toxin-Antitoxin Reaction. If the antigen is an exotoxin, the reaction with homologous antibody (antitoxin) neutralizes the toxicity. The reaction renders the exotoxin harmless as is demonstrated by inoculating the reaction mixture into a susceptible animal.

Precipitation Reaction. If an antigen in solution is brought into contact with its homologous antibody, a precipitate will form. The antibody in such a reaction is specifically referred to as a **precipitin.**

Agglutination Reaction. If the antigen consists of cells in suspension, the reaction with homologous antibody causes the cells to adhere to one another in clumps. This is called **agglutination,** and the antibody in this case is referred to as an **agglutinin** (Fig. 16.3).

Agglutination and precipitation (alterations in surface characteristics of protein molecules) are fundamental to many immune reactions. Basically, each results in a decrease in the dispersion of the antigen. The undispersed antigen may be less effective in production of pathologic effects; furthermore, the living body is capable of more efficient disposal of the antigen when it is assembled into the larger units resulting from agglutination or precipitation.

Lytic Reactions. If the antigen consists of cells which are subject to disintegration, a **lytic reaction** may result from combination of cellular antigen, homologous antibody, and complement. The lytic reaction results in a rupture or lysis of the cell; hence the antibody is referred to as a **lysin** (Fig. 16.4). The specific lysin for red blood cells, **hemolysin,** dissolves the cells if complement is present. Generally, gram-negative bacterial cells also undergo a similar breakdown in the presence of homologous antibody and complement. Clearly the antigen and antibody react prior to lysis, since the cells frequently agglutinate before they are broken down.

Complement-Fixation Reaction. Antigens not readily demonstrated by the above methods may sometimes be observed in a special reaction involving complement. Fundamentally the same as the lytic reaction, **complement fixation** is particularly useful when complement is bound by the antigen-antibody reaction, but the cellular antigen does not lyse. The addition of an indicator-lytic system produces a visible reaction.

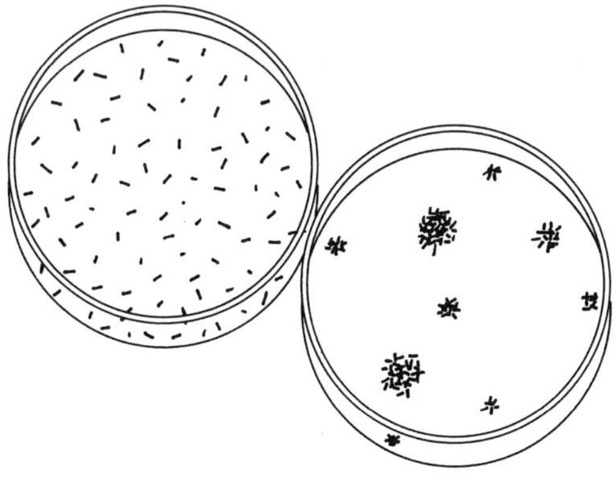

Fig. 16.3. The Widal test indicates the presence of typhoid antibodies in a patient's serum. The diagram to the left represents a dispersed culture of *Salmonella typhosa.* To the right, the agglutination of cells after mixing with serum indicates the presence of typhoid antibodies.

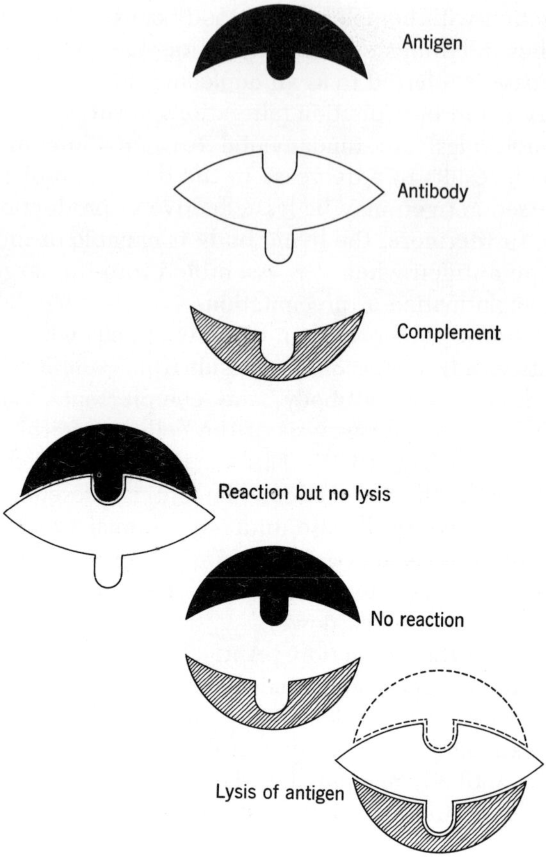

Fig. 16.4. The lytic reaction. Certain bacterial cells and red blood cells lyse when the specific antibody against them is present; however, this reaction will occur only in the presence of complement. Antibody alone or complement alone gives no lysis.

The most commonly used indicator system consists of a suspension of sheep red blood cells and the anti-sheep cell hemolysin. Several reactions constitute the fixation reactions (Fig. 16.5).

The Opsonocytophagic Reaction. This reaction measures the ability of white blood cells to phagocytize bacteria. Although phagocytosis will occur in the presence of complement, even if specific antibodies are absent, the efficiency of the activity is increased if antibody for the bacterial antigen is available. A heavy suspension of bacteria is mixed with freshly drawn blood; drops of the mixture are then placed on microslides and stained, allowing actual counts of the number of bac-

Fig. 16.5. (*a*) The Wasserman test is a complement fixation test. To tube 1 is added complement and syphilis antigen and the patient's serum. Since syphilis antibody is present in the patient's serum, antigen and antibody unite, "fixing" the complement as indicated on the right. After a few minutes tube 2, which contains sheep red blood cells and anti-sheep serum, is poured into tube 1. Since all the complement is fixed in the syphilis reaction, there is none left over for reacting with the sheep cell-sheep antibody combination; the sheep red blood cells do not lyse.

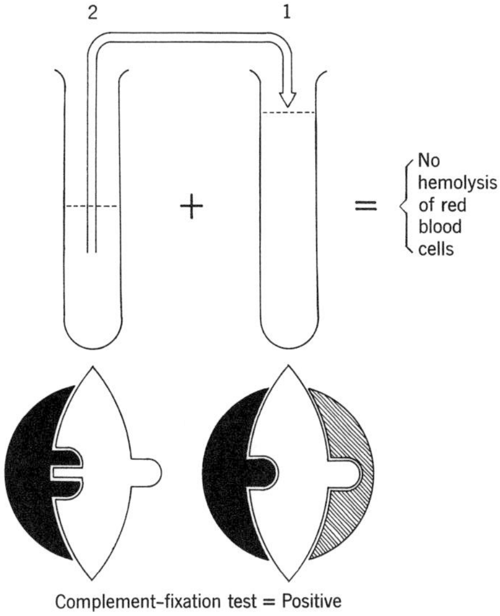

(*a*)

Fig. 16.5. (*b*) As in 16.5*a*, but no syphilis antibody is present in this patient's serum. Antibody is not fixed as in 16.5*a*, so it is left over to react with the sheep cells, and these lyse. The appearance of the tube changes from a turbid blood suspension to a clear red solution.

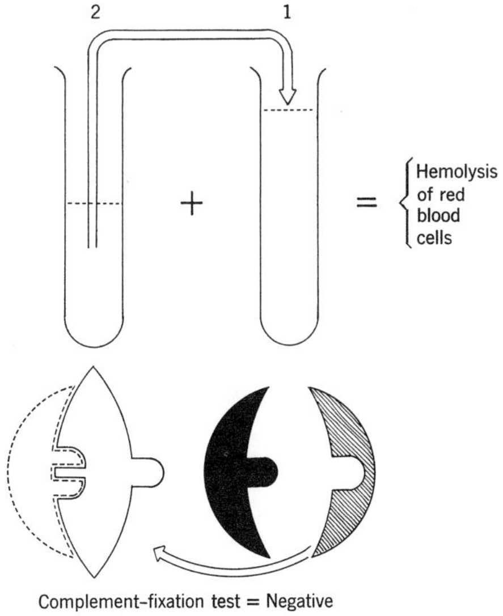

(*b*)

teria engulfed by the white blood cells. If the antibody, opsonin, is present, a large percentage of the bacterial population will appear inside the white blood cells. Opsonin also markedly enhances destruction of such phagocytized bacteria.

Special Immune Reactions. A number of the tests used for diagnostic purposes involve special manifestations of immune reactions. For example, antibodies against the spirochete of syphilis, *Treponema pallidum,* can be detected by means of an **immobilization** test. Living cultures of the spirochete remain motile in normal blood serum, but serum from a patient infected with the pathogen prevent active motility. An immune reaction which results in swelling of the capsule of *Diplococcus pneumoniae* in the presence of specific antiserum was long used to determine the specific antiserum required in the treatment of pneumococcal pneumonia. Certain viruses are readily adsorbed to the surface of red blood cells, which are then agglutinated. These so-called *virus-hemagglutination* reactions allow rapid assay of virus-containing fluids.

If an antibody preparation is reacted with a fluorescent dye to make a fluorescent antibody, it is possible to directly observe antibodies reacting with antigens. When antigens are mixed with homologous fluorescent antibody, the fluorescence can be seen attaching to the antigen (See Fig. 1.6).

Experimental data support the concept that one pure antigen stimulates the production of a single antibody, not of several. This highly specific relationship between antigen and antibody is known as the **unitarian hypothesis.** The various tests for antibody formation are not demonstrations of different antibodies, but simply represent variations in the nature of the antigen and antibody and the effects of the environment in which the reaction takes place.

Immune reactions may help to identify an unknown component. If the antigen is known, an unknown antibody can be identified. On the other hand, if the antibody is known, an unknown antigen can be identified. For example, the serum of a patient suffering from a febrile disease may be put to agglutination tests with a series of organisms which conceivably could be responsible for the symptoms. Agglutination occurring with one and not with others may determine both diagnosis and therapy.

Antigen-antibody reactions are not limited to diagnosis.. Precipitin tests are routinely used to identify unknown proteins from such materials as blood and meat. For example, a bloodstain suspected to be human blood can be identified by using the stain as antigen. The bloodstain antigen is mixed with serum from a rabbit previously injected with human blood. If precipitation occurs with this antihuman antiserum, the stain is identified as human blood. The same reaction has legal use in the enforcement of food laws. Horse meat, sold as beef, can be similarly identified by the precipitin test.

Table 16.1. Types of Immunity

Type	Source	Degree and Duration
ACTIVE	Antibodies are produced by the body as a result of stimulation by living, killed, or attenuated organisms (antigens). Immunity develops slowly and becomes effective in several weeks.	Usually complete and enduring.
(*a*) Natural	Antibody formation stimulated by presence of living organisms causing the disease.	Lifelong immunity is common.
(*b*) Artificial	Antigens composed of living, killed, or attenuated microorganisms or toxic or detoxified products, stimulate antibody production.	Solid protection for many years reinforced by "booster" inoculations.
PASSIVE	Antibodies produced by active immunization in one individual are transferred to another. Provides immediate but temporary protection.	Protection is of short duration.
(*a*) Natural	Transferred to young from an immune mother by placental transfer or colostrum.	Complete but temporary; may last up to 6 months.
(*b*) Artificial	Conferred by injection of serum from an immune animal or human to a susceptible individual. Used to provide immediate protection in cases of known exposure to infection or during epidemics.	Complete for 2 to 3 weeks.

From Pelczar and Reid: *Microbiology*, New York, McGraw-Hill Book Co., 1958.

Unfortunately, not all of the antigen-antibody reactions which occur in the body are beneficial. Under certain conditions, the reactions can cause severe damage in the host. The person experiencing such damage is considered to be **hypersensitive** to the antigen. Although hypersensitivity reactions vary considerably in the nature of their manifestations, all do follow a general pattern. The reactions occur after the individual has first been **sensitized** (immunized) by exposure to the antigen. A lapse of time is required for antibody formation to take place. Subsequent to this, exposure to fairly large amounts of the same antigen may result in adverse antigen-antibody reactions.

Many names are applied to hypersensitivity reactions, but the most familiar is **allergy**. Allergic responses vary from mild symptoms on the part of individuals who are unusually sensitive to pollens or certain foodstuffs to the serious disease, rheumatic fever, which follows a series of streptococcal infections.

SUMMARY. The ability to form antibodies is an evolutionary adaptation which assists in the recovery from infectious diseases. Immunity to further infection by the same agent may result. Increased facility with problems of antigens and antibodies have yielded a better understanding of their action. Medical problems, which were formerly insoluble, are handled easily as a result of microbiological research in this area. Unfortunately, some manipulations have created such problems as those encountered in drug allergies, in serum reactions, and in transfusion accidents.

17

Microbiology of Infectious Diseases of Man

With the possible exception of the algae, infectious-disease-producing microorganisms may be found among all the major groups. Indeed, even the algae though not infectious agents, are capable of adding allergens or lethal decomposition substances to drinking water during periods of algal decay and in this sense represent potentially harmful forms. Disease production is a dynamic phenomenon dependent on the highly variable resistance of the host as opposed to the lethal factors manifested by the parasite pathogen. Each case of an infectious disease is actually very different from every other case. Infectious diseases caused by one kind of microorganism may differ widely in symptomatology, average severity, modes of transmission, and portals of entry.

Vast numbers of different kinds of organisms produce disease, and the disease symptoms produced by microorganisms of the same species vary widely. This complexity suggests that a rational and systematic consideration of human infectious diseases is impossible. Certainly a consideration of all the infectious diseases of man, even in slight detail, is beyond the scope of this text. The following discussion concerns only some of the more common types, chosen to present prominent features of infectious diseases. These are the classic examples, and in actual practice the microbiologist, working closely with the physician, is often called upon to help diagnose and suggest methods for the cure of atypical cases which bear little resemblance to these classic textbook descriptions.

The infectious diseases are outlined broadly in five classes on the basis of their customary mode of transmission: **secretions of the respiratory tract, food and drink, direct contact, wound inoculation,** and **arthropod vectors.** The subheadings in the outline represent the general groups of microbial agents: **bacteria, fungi, viruses, rickettsiae,** and **protozoa.**

RESPIRATORY TRACT DISEASES

The respiratory diseases tend to appear in epidemic form, large numbers of susceptible persons succumbing in a short period of time. The number of cases usually rises during the fall and winter months as people tend to congregate in crowded, poorly ventilated areas. Forceful exhalation, which accompanies a cough or sneeze, sprays into the air a cloud of saliva together with the microorganisms present in the mouth and respiratory tract. The microorganisms remain air-borne on minute flakes of protein for a considerable period and are readily inhaled by others. Transmission may occur indirectly by **fomites**—articles such as handkerchiefs or eating utensils—which have been contaminated by the infected person. Control of respiratory diseases is best brought about by isolation of active cases and by disinfection of fomites.

BACTERIAL AGENTS

Diphtheria is an acute infection characterized by the formation of a patch or patches of a grayish membrane in the throat. The pathogen most frequently invades the body by way of droplets and becomes localized in the tonsils, throat, and nose. It elaborates, as a growth byproduct, an exotoxin which is one of the most powerful poisons known. The toxin causes damage to membranes lining the throat, which in turn results in the development of an inflammatory exudate consisting of red and white blood cells, fibrin, and diphtheria bacilli which coagulate to form a pseudomembrane. In untreated cases, the membrane may clog respiratory passages and cause suffocation. The toxin is absorbed locally and distributed throughout the body causing damage to cardiac muscle, liver, kidneys, adrenals, and cranial nerves.

The causative agent, *Corynebacterium diphtheriae,* is a nonmotile, nonsporeforming, weakly gram-positive, rod-shaped bacterium which shows considerable variation in form. Metachromatic granules are characteristic in young culture smears stained with aniline dyes. These organisms are aerobic and are most readily cultivated on coagulated blood-serum media. Enough potassium tellurite is frequently added to solid medium to inhibit contaminants in primary cultures and to give differential value to the medium. Colonies of the different types of diphtheria bacilli are easily distinguishable on a tellurite medium.

Though once one of the most dreaded of the childhood diseases, diphtheria is now of secondary importance. The active case can be cured by antitoxin from the blood of animals immunized with diphtheria toxoid. Recovery is followed by lasting immunity. Susceptible individuals can be immunized by inoculation with toxoid. As a result of widespread immunization of children, the disease has become quite rare.

The immune state can be detected by the Schick test, in which a small amount of toxin is injected into the skin. If antitoxin is present, the toxin is neutralized and no reaction occurs. If the body is deficient in antitoxin, a small area of inflammation develops. Since the artificially produced immunity of children is not usually reinforced by repeated exposure to the diphtheria bacillus, young adults frequently exhibit a positive Schick test, suggesting that diphtheria is now of greater potential danger to young adults than to children.

Whooping cough, or **pertussis,** is predominantly a disease of young children. It is caused by heavy growth on the mucous membrane of the larynx, trachea, and bronchi of *Bordetella pertussis,* a small, nonmotile, gram-negative, cocco-bacillus which grows slowly on special media.

Whooping cough begins much like an ordinary cold. The heavy growth of the organism interferes with the cilia, and toxins may paralyze action of cilia as they attempt to sweep out newly formed mucus. Irritation from the accumulation of mucus stimulates spasmodic coughing which ends with an inspiratory crowing sound, or whoop. The cough is relieved by expulsion of the plug of mucus. Death may result from a throat spasm which cuts off the air supply. No specific exotoxins have been isolated from the bacillus, although both the bacterial cells and culture filtrates have been found toxic to some laboratory animals.

The incidence of pertussis is highest among children under seven years of age, and the mortality is highest in infants under six months. Active immunization of infants, two to six months old, with a vaccine of killed organisms has greatly reduced incidence of the disease. Passive immunization with convalescent or hyperimmune serum is advocated for unprotected cases. Although the tetracycline antibiotics help eliminate the organisms, they do not relieve symptoms.

Laboratory diagnosis is rarely necessary in a disease with such pronounced clinical manifestations; however, confirmation of diagnosis can be made by isolation of the bacillus from sputum by the cough-plate method or by streaking nasal swabs on a pertussis medium of potato-glycerin agar enriched with blood.

Lobar pneumonia is an acute bacterial infection characterized by sudden onset with chill followed by fever, pain in the chest, and a productive cough. The lobes of the lungs accumulate fluid and exudate in the air spaces, rendering them nonfunctional.

The disease is most frequently caused by *Diplococcus pneumoniae.* The microorganisms occur typically in pairs or short chains. They are gram-positive, oval cells, which are nonmotile and typically encapsulated when isolated from animal exudates. They produce the alpha or green type of hemolysis on blood agar. Before chemotherapeutic agents were available, type specific antisera were used for therapy. The Quellung reaction, which involved an apparent swelling of the capsule in the presence of type-specific antiserum, was most commonly used for type determination (Fig. 17.1). Typing is not now generally practiced except in tracing the course of an epidemic.

The mortality rate for untreated cases is about 25%. Fatalities have been greatly reduced by antibiotic and chemotherapeutic treatment, yet the disease is still particularly serious for infants and the aged. Resistance is generally lowered by exposure to wet and cold, by physical and mental fatigue, and by alcoholism. Immunity of variable duration usually follows an attack. Active immunization of the general population is not considered practical because of the large numbers of different specific antigenic types.

The best method for prevention involves avoiding infection. Since the pneumococci may be found in the upper respiratory tract of healthy members of most communities throughout the world, isolation from infection is practically impossible. Epidemics in closed groups can be controlled by practicing good social hygiene, by avoiding close contact, and by chemoprophylaxis with sulfonamides or antibiotics. Occasionally worthwhile protection in such groups can be achieved by active immunization with type-specific vaccines.

Aside from their role as the primary cause of lobar pneumonia, the pneumococci are frequently the cause of other serious infections during or following pneumonia. They may cause pericarditis, otitis media, endocarditis, meningitis, arthritis, and other diseases. Lobar pneumonia is occasionally caused by other pathogenic inhabitants of the mouth, nose,

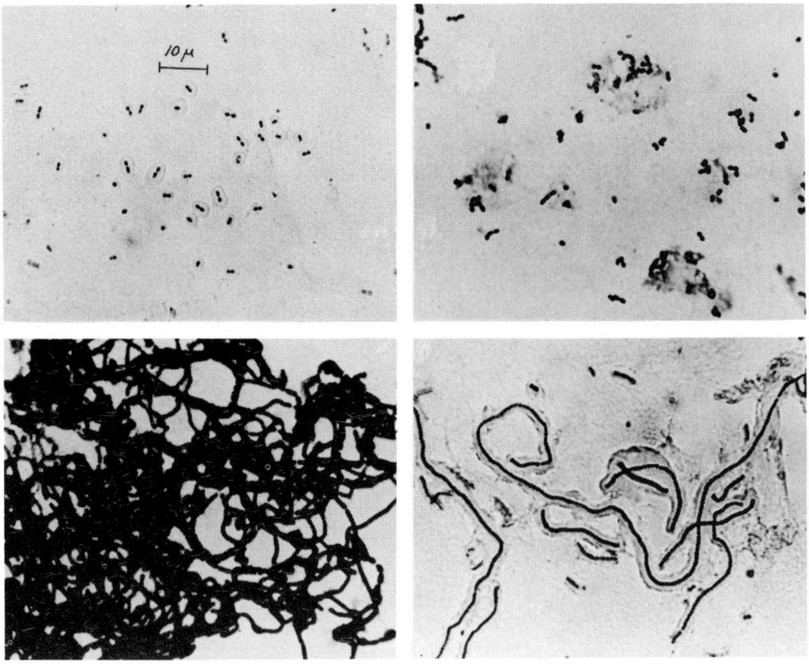

Fig. 17.1. The capsule swelling or Quellung reaction in *Diplococcus pheumonia* observed in a nonfilamentous strain (top) and a filamentous strain (bottom). The left picture of the top pair and the right picture of the bottom pair show the capsule swelling that occurs when a homologous antiserum is added. *Photos by Robert Austrian, courtesy* S.A.B. *LS-324.*

and throat, such as *Streptococcus pyogenes, Staphyloccus aureus, Hemophilus influenzae* (Fig. 17.2), or *Klebsiella pneumoniae.*

Measles, whooping cough, and influenza are often complicated by a secondary infection of the lungs in the form of a **bronchopneumonia.** The secondary pneumonia, though not always fatal, is particularly dangerous since the patient is usually much weakened by the previous disease. No single microorganism is responsible for all cases of secondary pneumonia, but the hemolytic streptococci, staphylococci, pneumococci, and *Hemophilus influenzae* are frequently designated as the infectious agents.

Streptococcal diseases are fairly easily diagnosed, as most of the streptococci found in the mouth and respiratory tract are capable of acting on blood-agar plates to cause recognizable changes. Members of the

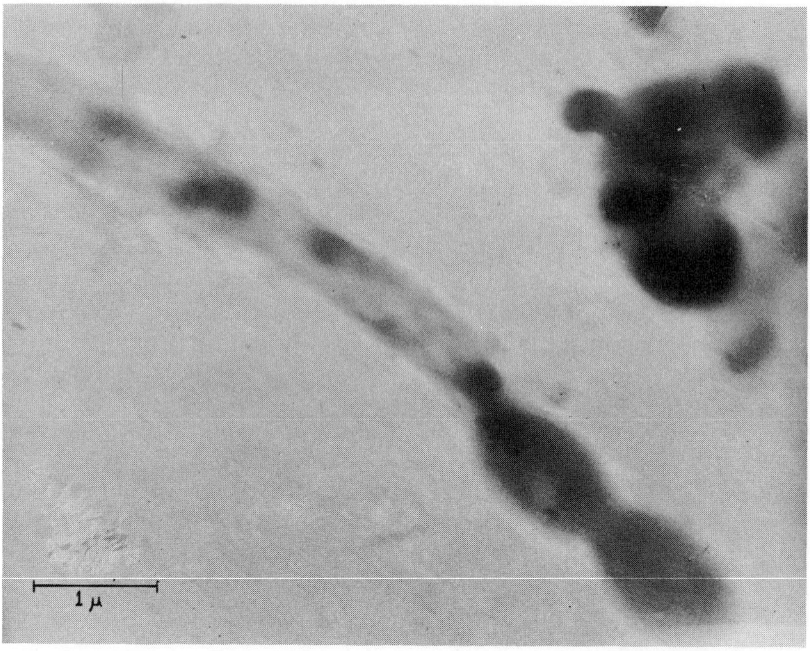

Fig. 17.2. An electron micrograph of *Hemophilus influenzae* showing coccobacillus as well as filamentous forms seen in old cultures grown on heated "chocolate" blood agar. *Photo by H. E. Morton and R. G. Picard, courtesy S.A.B. LS-99.*

pyogenes group produce a soluble enzyme, beta-hemolysin, which destroys red blood cells; colonies on blood agar are surrounded by colorless areas. The pyogenes group is thus designated **beta-hemolytic.** Incomplete breakdown of the red blood cells resulting in a zone of greenish tinge around the colonies of the **viridans** group is termed **alpha-hemolysis.** Upon initial isolation, stained cells are ovoid and occur in diploid arrangement. The organisms are gram-positive.

The streptococci are classified in serologic groups by testing for specific carbohydrates in the cellular bodies. Grouping (as in group A, B etc.) is based on a precipitin test using group-specific antisera from rabbits and extracts from pure cultures. *Streptococcus pyogenes,* the streptococcus of group A, is the etiologic agent for many human diseases which are differentiated clinically according to portal of entry, tissue of localization, and presence or absence of a skin rash.

If the primary invasion is in the uterus following childbirth, the disease is known as **puerperal fever.** If entrance is gained through breaks in the skin, the condition may be **impetigo** or **erysipelas.** These diseases will be discussed later with the contact group.

If entrance is gained through the respiratory tract, **streptococcal sore throat, scarlet fever,** or **bronchial pneumonia** may develop. If the alpha-hemolytic strain *Streptococcus salivarius* enters the bloodstream from traumatized areas of the mouth or intestinal tract and becomes lodged on the endocardium of the valves of the left side of the heart, the dangerous condition subacute **bacterial endocarditis** may develop. Once *Streptococcus pyogenes* has gained entrance to the body, secondary complications such as **rheumatic fever** or **nephritis** (kidney infection) may develop. We will now deal with the two primary respiratory diseases, and with rheumatic fever, which often follows these conditions.

Scarlet fever is streptococcal sore throat in which the infectious agent produces an erythrogenic toxin in a patient having little antitoxic immunity. Symptoms include fever, sore throat, exudative tonsillitis or pharyngitis, and rash caused by the toxin. The rash usually appears on the neck, chest, folds of the axilla, elbow, and inner thighs. Diagnosis may be confirmed by the **Schultz-Charlton** test, in which a small amount of potent antitoxin is injected into the skin of the patient. Fading of the rash at the site of injection is a positive sign of scarlet fever. Long lasting immunity against the erythrogenic toxin usually develops within a week of the onset. Both active and passive immunizations are possible, but of little apparent value. Chemoprophylaxis with oral sulfonamide drugs or penicillin is advocated for persons who have had rheumatic fever.

Streptococcal sore throat is sometimes designated scarlet fever without a rash. Absence of the rash suggests that the organism is not a good toxin producer, or that the patient has a high degree of antitoxin immunity.

Rheumatic fever is an occasional sequel of upper-respiratory-tract infection by *Streptococcus pyogenes.* Symptoms usually occur two to three weeks after the streptococcal infection has been recognized. A chronic disease of the heart valves results and tends to recur with each subsequent hemolytic streptococcal infection. A primary cause of death among children aged six to ten years, rheumatic fever may be a hypersensitivity response following recovery from streptococcal infection. No practical preventive measures are known except prophylaxis against Group A streptococcal infections.

Meningococcal meningitis caused by *Neisseria meningitidis* is an acute bacterial infection characterized by sudden onset of fever, intense headache, nausea, signs of inflammation of the meninges (membrane covering the brain and spinal cord), and often a rash. Delirium and coma often appear early and occasionally acute overwhelming blood invasions develop so rapidly that the patient dies within five to six hours after the onset of symptoms.

The infectious agents can usually be cultivated from the blood, spinal fluid, and nasopharynx. They grow best on media enriched with serum or heated blood (chocolate agar) and incubated in an atmosphere of about 10% carbon dioxide. The cells are small coffee-bean-shaped, gram-negative diplococci. Virulent strains from infected spinal fluid and young cultures are usually encapsulated.

Although epidemics of meningococcal meningitis occur infrequently, isolated cases may develop. During nonepidemic periods the carrier rate for the organism may be as high as 25%, and during epidemics it may rise as high as 70 to 80%. Before the advent of modern chemotherapy, the fatality rate was from 40 to 50%. The use of sulfadiazine, penicillin, and the tetracyclines has reduced the fatality rate to below 5%.

As suggested by the low ratio of cases to carriers, natural susceptibility is slight. The disease may occur at any age, but statistics suggest that younger persons are most susceptible. The duration of immunity following recovery is not known, and no generally accepted methods for inducing artificial immunity have been established.

Tuberculosis is a chronic disabling disease which has long been a cause of fatal illness. Any tissue of the body is susceptible to infection with *Mycobacterium tuberculosis*, but pulmonary infection is most common. Characteristic symptoms include pleurisy, chest pain, coughing, fever, weakness, and weight loss. Characteristic nodules (tubercles) form in the lungs. The tubercle results from a proliferation and aggregation of certain body cells which respond to stimulation by the tubercle bacillus, and its products and tend to surround and wall off the forces of infection. The bacilli continue to multiply within the nodule, and, in some cases, the tubercles break open into the bronchi, thus liberating virulent bacilli. In other cases, the walling off may be successful, and the infection may persist for years without further development.

The isolation of the tubercle bacilli from such body discharges as sputum, spinal fluid, or urine constitutes diagnosis. In some cases the organisms can be demonstrated in stained smears of body discharges. The bacteria grow slowly on selective culture media. They are difficult to stain with the usual dyes, but, once stained, the high-fat content of the organisms renders them resistant to destaining with acid and alcohol. This acid-fast characteristic is the most important staining feature of the tubercle bacillus.

The three principal species are *Mycobacterium tuberculosis, M. bovis,* and *M. avium* designating their host as man, cattle, and birds (Fig. 17.3). Both the bovine and human species are virulent for man, but over 90% of all human cases are caused by *M. tuberculosis.* The bovine strain usually causes tuberculosis of bones or the lymphatic system and gains entrance to man through ingestion of infected milk or beef. The tubercle bacilli belong to the order Actinomycetales, which are moldlike, filamentous, higher bacteria.

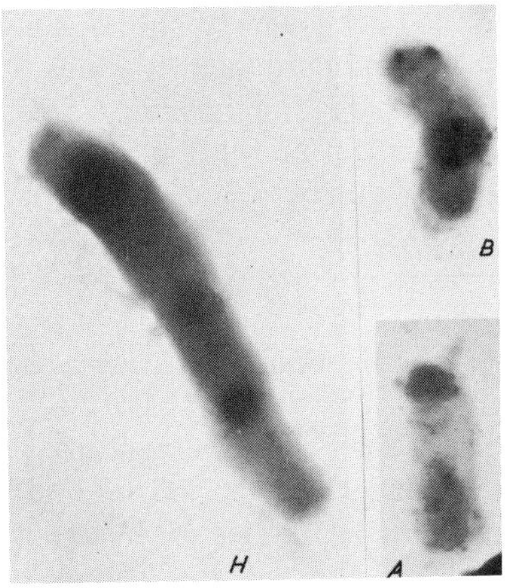

Fig. 17.3. The tubercle bacilli. Electron micrographs of (*H*) *Mycobacterium tuberculosis,* the cause of tuberculosis in humans, (*B*) *Mycobacterium bovis,* the cattle tuberculosis species, and (*A*) *Mycobacterium avium,* the bird tuberculosis species. *Photos by Rosenblatt, Fullam, and Gessler: Amer. R. Tuberculosis, XLVI, 587–599, Dec. 1942, courtesy* S.A.B. *LS-21.*

In response to tuberculosis infection the body develops a hypersensitivity to bacillary cell substance making possible the *tuberculin test,* which is of additional diagnostic value, especially in children and cattle. The test involves the intracutaneous injection of small amounts of tuberculin, a protein derivative from cultured tubercle bacilli. An inflammatory allergic reaction at the site of injection is a positive sign of existing or past infection of adults. A positive test in a child strongly suggests active infection. X-ray examination reveals lung lesions and is used in conjunction with the tuberculin test for diagnosis.

No completely satisfactory immunizing method has yet been developed, although some success has been reported in Europe with vaccination programs using an attenuated avirulent strain of *M. tuberculosis.* The organism BCG (the bacillus of Calmette and Guerin) is used on tuberculin-negative members of special groups in which high rates of infection and serious disease may be expected.

Treatment for tuberculosis involves complete rest, occasional surgery to remove or collapse an infected lung, and therapeutics. Since the bacterial cells localize inside the impermeable tubercles, they are difficult to reach with chemotherapeutic agents. Streptomycin, in conjunction with isonicotinic acid hydrazide, is effective when the disease organisms are accessible to drug action. Early diagnosis and treatment has dramatically reduced the number of deaths resulting from tuberculosis; however, thousands of cases still occur each year, and the death rate among younger people is still high.

Actinomycosis is a chronic suppurative process which may be localized in the jaw, thorax, or abdomen. Infection characteristically begins in the back lower jaw or the tonsils and involves tissues of the face and neck. Subcutaneous nodules form over the infected area, which becomes hard and swollen. Later, the infected areas soften, and pus drains from multiple openings in the skin. The disease usually progresses slowly with severe injury to the affected parts. Bones as well as soft tissues may be destroyed. Death may result from secondary invasion by streptococci or other pathogens which invade injured tissues.

The infectious agent, *Actinomyces bovis,* is a gram-positive bacillary and branching anaerobic form which belongs to the order *Actinomycetales.* The organisms tend to grow as a tangled mass of branched filaments which are organized into yellowish granular bodies called sulfur granules. Presence of the yellow granules in discharges from draining sinuses is the primary diagnostic characteristic. Confirmation of diagnosis is made by anaerobic culture on enriched medium.

Though primarily a disease of cattle, human actinomycosis continues to occur sporadically all over the world. Frequency is highest in males fifteen to thirty-five years of age, but both sexes and all age groups are susceptible. Treatment involves prolonged administration of sulfonamides and antibiotics.

FUNGAL AGENTS

A relatively small group of fungus diseases are referred to as **deep mycoses** or **systemic mycoses.** The causative fungi characteristically enter the body through the respiratory tract and invade the lungs or other internal parts of the body. Relatively rare, these diseases are quite serious and frequently fatal. Since they often produce symptoms similar to other respiratory infections, accurate diagnosis is necessary for suitable treatment. We will now briefly discuss a few of the more common systemic mycoses.

Cryptococcosis may involve only the lungs or skin, but is often fatal when infection spreads through the bloodstream to the brain and meninges. The disease is slowly progessive. The patient may die of respiratory failure after weeks or months of illness.

The causative agent is *Cryptococcus neoformans.* It reproduces by budding but does not form a mycelium. Small masses of the organisms enclosed in gelatinous capsules develop in the infected meninges. They are often large enough to be seen with the naked eye and are similar to the nodules of tuberculosis.

Coccidioidomycosis is caused by *Coccidioides immitis.* Although mild cases ending in full recovery are more frequent than fatal ones, this disease is one of the most dangerous of the fungus infections. Mild cases may involve skin lesions only, but the lung infection with symptoms similar to those in tuberculosis is more characteristic. In fatal cases, the organisms are spread by the bloodstream, causing a generalized infection of the internal organs.

A large portion of the cases reported in this country have originated in the San Joaquin Valley of California. The condition is common among vineyard workers. Probably dried spores of the fungus are inhaled or introduced through skin abrasions.

The organisms may be readily identified in the pus of lesions as cyst-like, spherical bodies, which have a thick doubly-contoured capsule. They are characterized by the presence of endospores and the absence of budding.

Histoplasmosis is primarily an infection of the reticuloendothelial system. Lesions in the lungs similar to tubercular lesions are common. Ulcerations of the tongue, pharynx, larynx, and the mucosa of the nose may occur. The spleen, liver, and lymph nodes are generally enlarged.

In the United States, the majority of cases occur in the Mississippi Valley region. Infants and children as well as adults may be infected. The mortality rate from histoplasmosis is the highest of all the fungus infections.

The organisms can be recognized in phagocytic cells of blood smears. The infectious agent, *Histoplasma capsulatum,* is a small, oval, yeast-like fungus as observed intracellularly. In culture, at room temperature, it is a typical mold-like filamentous fungus. Old cultures contain large, round to pyriform, thick-walled spores, which are characteristic and of diagnostic importance.

VIRAL AGENTS

Smallpox or **variola major** is a severe infectious disease characterized by a sudden onset of fever, chills, headache, backache, and prostration of three to four days duration. These constitutional symptoms are followed by a rash of small papules, which develops first along the hairline and later on the face, forearms, wrists, and hands. Usually within a week the pustules become enlarged and filled with fluid. Scales or crusts from the pustules disappear after two to three weeks, leaving the characteristic crater-like scars of smallpox. A fatality rate of 30% is characteristic. *Variola minor* (alastrim) is a milder form of the disease with a fatality rate of less than 1%.

Smallpox is transmitted directly from person to person by droplet infection or by fomites contaminated with nasal and buccal secretions.

It may be transferred from the pustules by the hands. Immune persons may harbor the virus and serve for short periods as carriers.

Since mild cases are often difficult to diagnose, laboratory confirmation is sometimes required. The elementary bodies of the virus can be demonstrated in stained smears of skin scrapings; the virus can be cultivated from pustular fluid on the chorioallantoic membranes of embryonated chicken eggs, or human cutaneous lesions may be used for antigens in a complement-fixation test with rabbit antiviral serum.

Recovery from an attack of smallpox usually renders lifelong immunity. Artificial immunization with vaccine of virus from cowpox lesions has been particularly successful since its introduction by Jenner in 1796. Smallpox vaccination, as performed today, involves infection of the susceptible person on the arm or leg with purified material obtained from skin lesions of calves or sheep infected with vaccinia virus. More recently, tissue cultures or the chorioallantoic membrane of the chick embryo have been used for growing the vaccinia virus. Infants should be vaccinated between the third and twelfth months and again when they enter school. Revaccination is recommended for all persons facing unusual exposure such as travel to parts of Asia, Africa, and South America where the disease is still largely uncontrolled.

Chicken pox, or **varicella**, is a viral infection of childhood characterized by typical skin eruption. Cutaneous lesions usually appear first on the back and then extend to the face and other parts of the body. Susceptibility is universal among those not previously attacked, but in most metropolitan communities 70% of the inhabitants have had the disease by the time they reach 15 years of age. Recovery from one attack confers immunity of long duration. Ordinarily the disease is more severe in adults than in children.

Measles, or **rubeola**, an acute disease, is characterized by fever, inflammation of the respiratory passages, coughing, skin eruption, and small white patches (Koplik's spots) on the mucous membrane of the mouth and throat. Death from uncomplicated measles is rare, but the disease often leads to such serious complications as pneumonia, otitis media, and mastoiditis.

Since it is a common childhood disease, few persons pass the age of 23 without an attack. Permanent immunity is usual after recovery. Offspring of mothers who have had the disease are usually immune for the first few months. The administration of gamma globulin within three days of exposure can prevent measles. Complications should be treated with appropriate antibiotics or sulfadiazine.

German measles, or **rubella**, a mild febrile disease of viral etiology, is characterized by a rash of variable character and a swelling of the lymph glands below the ear and at the nape of the neck. As the patient usually recovers within a week or less, the disease is sometimes called "three-day measles."

One attack of this disease results in permanent immunity. Approximately 10% of living infants born to women who develop rubella during the first three months of pregnancy have serious congenital defects, such as cataracts, heart disease, and deaf mutism. Passive immunization with immune serum globulin is advocated for adult female contacts who are within the first four months of pregnancy and have no history of rubella. Deliberate exposure of healthy female children to the disease before puberty is recommended by some authorities.

Mumps, or **epidemic parotitis,** is an acute viral infection of sudden onset which is characterized by swelling and tenderness of the parotid glands or, less frequently, the sublingual or submaxillary glands. Involvement of ovaries and testicles is frequent in persons past puberty. Bloodstream transfer of the virus can result in pancreatitis and meningoencephalitis.

An attack of mumps is usually followed by permanent immunity. Effective vaccines are available but have limited value since the artificially-induced immunity is of relatively short duration. Convalescent serum given from 7 to 10 days following exposure usually affords protection from infection to children. Death from mumps is exceedingly rare. The clinical disease appears less frequently than the other common communicable diseases of childhood.

Influenza is an acute highly infectious disease which is characterized by an abrupt onset with fever, chills, coryza (an acute inflammation of nasal mucous membrane), headache, muscle pains, sore throat, malaise, and prostration. Pneumonia is a frequent secondary complication. Deaths are most frequent among the debilitated, aged, women in late pregnancy and infants in which the acute illness is neglected.

The disease is ordinarily recognized by its symptoms and confirmed by laboratory examination of the virus from throat washings or by demonstration of significant rise in antibody content of the blood serum of the patient. Three types of influenza virus (A, B, and C) are recognized. The disease epidemics show a cyclic tendency in which influenza A appears at shorter intervals than influenza B. Influenza C has appeared only in localized outbreaks. The 1957–1958 pandemic of "Asian Flu" was caused by a strain of influenza A. This pandemic was clinically mild but extremely widespread. Highly fatal pandemics developed in 1889 and in 1918.

The production of active immunity with influenza virus vaccine has the disadvantage of comparatively short duration. Attempts to passively immunize man against all influenzal virus types have not been successful.

The **common cold** is an acute catarrhal infection of the upper respiratory tract characterized by coryza, eye watering, irritated nasopharynx, and malaise which lasts for 2 to 7 days. Although probably never fatal, it temporarily disables more people than any other infectious disease and is potentially serious because it lowers body resistance and is frequently complicated by sinusitis, otitis media, laryngitis, tracheitis, and bronchitis. Most persons have from 1 to 6 colds a year.

Recovery from the disease is followed by limited and transient immunity. No satisfactory cold vaccine is available since none includes all the strains of viruses causing the disease. Except in the advent of secondary complications, use of antibiotics is not recommended.

Virus pneumonia, or **primary atypical pneumonia,** is an acute respiratory infection characterized by a gradual onset of symptoms including fever, chills, headache, malaise, and fatigue. X ray examination of the chest reveals early patchy infiltration of the lungs. The illness usually lasts for about one week, and complications are rare. Although virus pneumonia was one of the most common of the respiratory infections of World War II, the fatality was about 0.1% of reported cases.

Poliomyelitis, or **infantile paralysis,** is an acute illness characterized by fever, malaise, headache, and stiffness of the neck and back. In severe cases damage to motor nerves results in paralysis of voluntary muscles. Death from respiratory failure may ensue if the respiratory muscles are involved (Fig. 17.4). Many infections of the nonparalytic type are mild with vague nervous symptoms. Most common are abortive cases in which no nervous-system symptoms appear.

The virus of polyomyelitis can be isolated by tissue culture from feces or throat secretions. An increase in complement-fixing or neutralizing antibodies denotes recent infection and is of diagnostic value. Three different immunological types of the virus have been identified.

Children from 1 to 16 years of age are more frequently infected than adults. In many areas of the United States, however, the proportion of cases among older children and young adults is greater than it used to be. In areas where artificial immunization has been widely employed, the occurrence of paralytic cases has progressively decreased. Overall death rates vary from 5 to 20%. In bulbar polio, which involves damage to the respiratory center of the brain, the fatality rate is higher.

Abortive infection gives lasting protection against subsequent infection with the same type of virus. Vaccination with formalin-killed cells prepared from virus grown on monkey kidney tissue (Salk vaccine) has been successful. An oral vaccine of living attenuated virus is being developed.

Psittacosis is a virus disease of birds which may be transmitted to

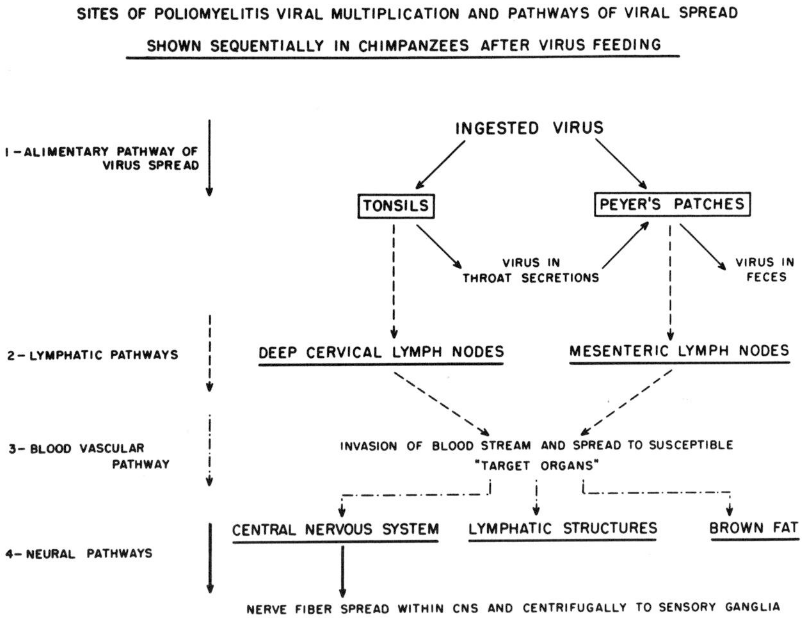

Fig. 17.4. This diagram illustrates the primary sites of viral implantation and multiplication after the ingestion of poliomyelitis virus by chimpanzees and the pathways of subsequent viral spread in the body. This schematic diagram of the pathogenesis of poliomyelitis is based on the studies of poliomyelitis in man as well as in chimpanzees. *Diagram by David Bodian: Science, CXXII, 105–8, July 15, 1955, courtesy S.A.B. LS-328.*

man. It is an acute generalized infection characterized by chills, fever, loss of appetite, sore throat, and spotty pneumonic consolidation. Laboratory diagnosis is made by demonstrating an increase in complement-fixing antibodies during convalescence.

The causative agent is a virus of the psittacosis-ornithosis group—one of the large viruses which responds to chemotherapeutic agents. Treatment with the tetracycline antibiotics has brought about a drastic decline in fatalities to the extent that the death rate is less than 1% for reported cases.

DISEASES SPREAD BY FOOD AND WATER

A number of diseases are spread as a result of fecal contamination of water and food. If the contaminated water is not subjected to sanitary control, the pathogens are **water-borne** to the susceptible host. Out-

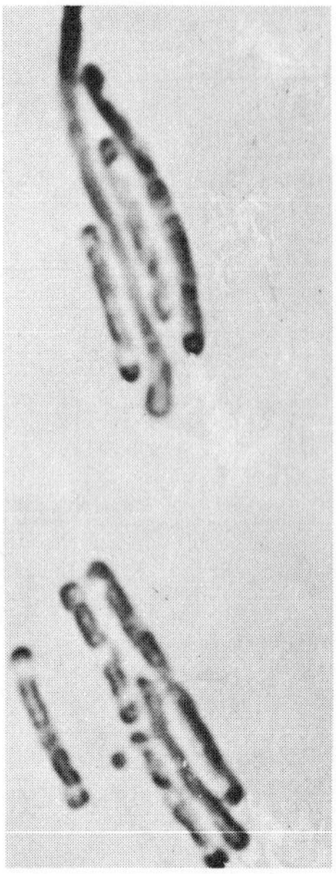

Fig. 17.5. *Salmonella typhosa* stained to show cell wall and nuclear material. *Photo by Davis, Winterscheid, Hartman, and Mudd: J. Histochem. and Cytochem., I, 123–137, 1953, courtesy S.A.B. LS-305.*

breaks of **food-borne** infection may be initiated by careless food-handlers who are carriers of the causative organisms.

Food may serve simply as a vehicle to transfer the pathogen, or the pathogen may multiply in the food before it is ingested. The term "food-poisoning" is commonly applied to noninfectious diseases which result from ingestion of food containing such toxins as those produced by *Clostridium botulinum* or *Staphylococcus aureus.*

Bacterial Agents. **Typhoid fever** is an acute infectious disease caused by *Salmonella typhosa.* It is characterized by a gradual rise in fever and by systemic invasion through the lymphatic system and bloodstream. Diagnosis can be made by laboratory isolation of the causative organism from blood and stool specimens and by specific agglutination of *S. typhosa* with blood serum from the patient (Fig. 17.5). Prophylactic immunization and improved sanitation have dramatically reduced incidence and death rate.

Paratyphoid fever is very similar to typhoid fever, but usually less severe. *S. paratyphi, S. schottmuelleri,* and *S. hirschfeldii* are commonly associated with the infection in man.

Gastroenteritis is a food infection characterized by an acute onset with diarrhea and caused by *Salmonella* species, many of which thrive in the intestinal tracts of animals other than man. The most common species are *S. enteritidis, S. oranienburg,* and *S. typhimurium.* Symptoms usually occur a few hours after infection and probably result from the liberation of endotoxin when large numbers of these microbes are ingested with contaminated food.

Shigellosis is bacillary dysentery caused by one or several species of *Shigella.* Symptoms of the disease are intestinal inflammatory diarrhea and water stools which contain blood, mucus, and pus. The incubation period is usually about four days. *Shigella* and *Salmonella* are both gram-negative rods which cannot be readily differentiated by morphology. They are identified by serologic tests, fermentation reactions, and endotoxin production.

Asiatic cholera remains endemic in India and southwestern Asia, yet no cases have appeared in the United States for nearly fifty years. Mild cases resemble the gastroenteritis of paratyphoid, but the symptoms of severe cases include vomiting and profuse diarrheal "rice-water" stools. Extreme dehydration and loss of minerals may lead to death. The infectious agent, *Vibrio comma,* is a motile, slightly curved, gram-negative rod (Fig. 17.6). Active immunity of short duration can be produced with a vaccine of killed cholera cells. Sanitation is the best preventive of cholera.

Staphylococcal food poisoning is produced by a potent exotoxin which is designated the "enterotoxin." Virulent staphylococcal cells may be inoculated from the skin or mucous membrane of food-handlers infected with toxin-producing strains. Such foods as salads, custards, cream-filled pastries, milk products, and meats, if allowed to incubate in a warm place for several hours, will become toxic. If the infected food is ingested, symptoms begin to develop in about two hours. The enterotoxin causes nausea, cramps, diarrhea, and vomiting. Symptoms persist for several hours, but the illness is rarely fatal.

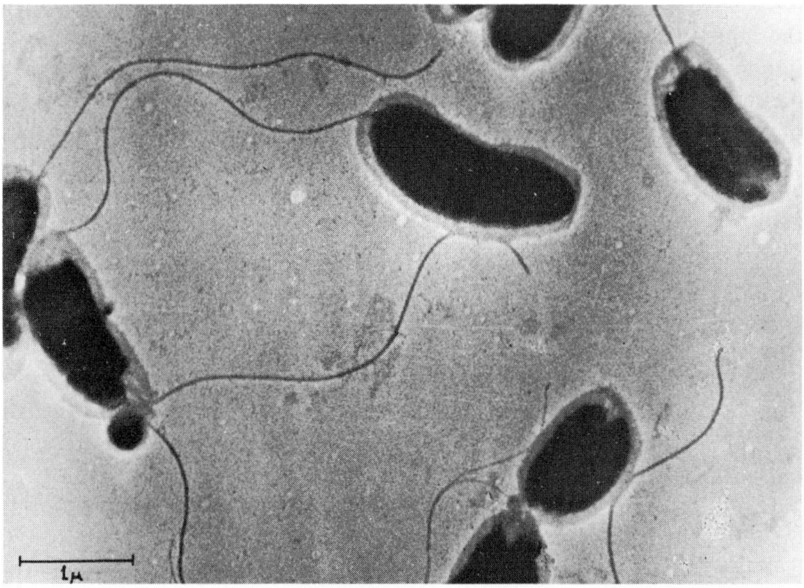

Fig. 17.6. Electron micrograph of intact cells of *Vibrio comma,* the causative organisms of cholera. The cytoplasm is shrunk away from the less dense cell wall of these monotrichous cells each showing a single polar flagellum. *Photo by Anderson and Polevitzky, courtesy S.A.B. LS-100.*

The anaerobic sporeformer, *Clostridium botulinum,* produces a true food poisoning as the result of its liberation of one of the most potent toxins known to man. Most **botulism** results from the consumption of improperly sterilized home-canned foods. Spores of *Cl. botulinum* are extremely resistant to heat. If not destroyed by the food processing methods, these anaerobic bacilli may germinate, grow, and liberate exotoxin in canned vegetables or meats.

Ingestion of the preformed toxin results in the appearance of symptoms after 12 to 36 hours. Fatigue, headache, and dizziness are followed by paralysis of muscles of eyes, pharynx, respiratory system, and heart. Death by cardiac or respiratory failure occurs in about two-thirds of all cases within 3 to 7 days. The intramuscular administration of botulinum antitoxin is advisable but not often effective in therapy, since the toxin has usually damaged the nervous tissues by the time toxic symptoms appear.

Because of its high mortality rate, botulism is very serious, but fortunately the incidence is low. Compared to staphylococcus poisoning, it is infrequently encountered.

Viral Agents. **Infectious hepatitis** is probably conveyed by ingestion of food or water contaminated with infected feces or urine. Symptoms of the illness include fever and gastrointestinal distress. Liver function is impaired, and, in more severe cases, a yellow discoloration of the skin (jaundice) appears, which accounts for the synonyms **epidemic jaundice** or **catarrhal jaundice** of this disease. The illness is usually benign and the fatality rate is low.

Protozoal Agents. The onset of **amebic dysentery** is usually less abrupt and the symptoms less severe than those of bacillary dysentery. Infection is caused by the pathogenic ameba *Endamoeba histolytica,* which is swallowed in the encysted form with contaminated food or drink. Upon reaching the small intestine the cyst walls of the organism break down and eight active ameba are formed from each cyst. They pass into the large intestine and penetrate the intestinal epithelium. Occasionally the ameba penetrate small mesenteric blood or lymph vessels and are spread to the liver, lung, and brain.

Infection with *E. histolytica* is widespread in backward areas; but even in cities with good sanitary facilities up to 5% of the people are carriers. If an infected individual is not properly treated, he may remain a carrier of the ameba for an indefinite period. Diagnosis is made by identification of the ameba or its cysts in the feces or by the ameba in smears from lesions.

CONTACT DISEASES

Perhaps the most certain method by which a pathogen can be transferred from one infected person to another is through contiguous personal association. A number of highly virulent bacteria and viruses are transferred in this way.

Bacterial Agents. Gonococcal urethritis, or gonorrhea, the most common of the venereal diseases, is caused by *Neisseria gonorrhoeae,* a gram-negative diplococcus which is similar to the meningococcus. The disease is specific for man and usually involves invasion of the mucous tissues of the genital tract. Young girls occasionally become infected from fomites which contain pus from active cases.

Diagnosis may be made by demonstrating the organisms within polymorphonuclear leucocytes in smears from exudates. Cultures of the organisms are grown on media enriched with serum or heated blood. Optimum growth occurs at 36°C in an atmosphere of 5 to 10% carbon dioxide. No apparent immunity develops from an active case nor can immunity be induced by artificial means. Treatment with penicillin and other antibiotics is effective.

An inflammation of the eyelid of newborn infants, ophthalmia neonatorum, is contracted during birth by gonorrheal infection from the mother and may lead to blindness. Many states require that dilute silver nitrate, argyrol, or penicillin be applied to the eyes of the newborn child as a prophylactic treatment for this condition.

Syphilis is a venereal disease of man which is caused by the spirochete, *Treponema pallidum.* The normal course of the disease involves three stages, the first of which is characterized by the development of an ulcer with a hard margin called a chancre. During the second stage, the chancre disappears but the spirochetes spread throughout the body, and lesions appear on the skin and in the mouth. Involvement of the heart and central nervous system often characterizes the third stage. Congenital syphilis may result by placental transfer from an infected mother during the early months of pregnancy.

Diagnosis of the primary and secondary stages are made by dark-field examination of material from lesions. Complement-fixation and precipitin tests are used for serologic diagnosis. False-positive serologic tests are common and may be excluded by special tests which involve immobilization of the spirochetes by the serum of diseased patients. Syphilis can be effectively treated with penicillin, erythromycin, or the tetracycline antibiotics.

Chancroid is a venereal disease which is less common and less serious than gonorrhea or syphilis. It is caused by *Haemophilus ducreyi*, which is a gram-negative, non-spore-forming, nonmotile, small rod. Diagnosis is made by microscopic examination of stained exudates or from bacteriologic cultures of pus. The sulfonamides, tetracycline antibiotics, or chloramphenicol may be used for treatment.

Yaws is a nonvenereal, direct-contact disease caused by the spirochete, *Treponema pertenue*, which is similar to the syphilis spirochete. Ulcerative lesions of the skin and bone destruction are characteristic of the infection, but the disease is rarely fatal. Diagnosis is usually made by dark-field examination of lesion exudates; penicillin is the common treatment.

The same hemolytic **streptococci** which can cause disease as they enter the respiratory route can also cause different disease symptoms if they enter the susceptible host through abrasions on the skin or mucous membranes. A few of the more common of these conditions which result from direct contact are discussed in the following.

Puerperal fever, or **puerperal septicemia,** is an acute infection which causes a large proportion of the maternal deaths at childbirth. Most often it is caused by hemolytic streptococci which reach the uterus via contaminated hands or instruments. A number of other bacterial agents including nonhemolytic streptococci, anaerobic streptococci, *Staphylococcus aureus, Escherichia coli,* and *Clostridium perfringens* may cause clinically similar symptoms. With the advent of antibiotic therapy, the fatality rate has dropped more than 80% in the United States during the last 20 years.

Impetigo contagiosum is a nonfatal but often disfiguring disease caused by streptococci in conjunction with staphylococci. Characterized by vesicular lesions occurring on the face or hands, it is transmitted by direct contact with an infected person or fomites.

Erysipelas is an acute inflammation of the skin which is caused by hemolytic streptococci entering a wound, fissure, or abrasion. The lesion extends peripherally from the site of infection as a red thickening of the skin. The face and legs are most often involved. One attack seems to predispose to subsequent attacks, but recurrence can be prevented by the use of sulfonamide drugs or penicillin.

The **staphylococci,** normal inhabitants of the skin and mucous membranes, are particularly likely to pass through these barriers if they are broken. Under normal conditions, the invasive characteristics of the staphylococci are balanced by the body defense mechanisms, so that invasion is not initiated (Fig. 17.7). If the balance is upset by lowered body resistance or a particularly virulent bacterial form, any one of a number of disease conditions of varying severity may develop. Most common are the boils, abcesses, carbuncles, and infections which

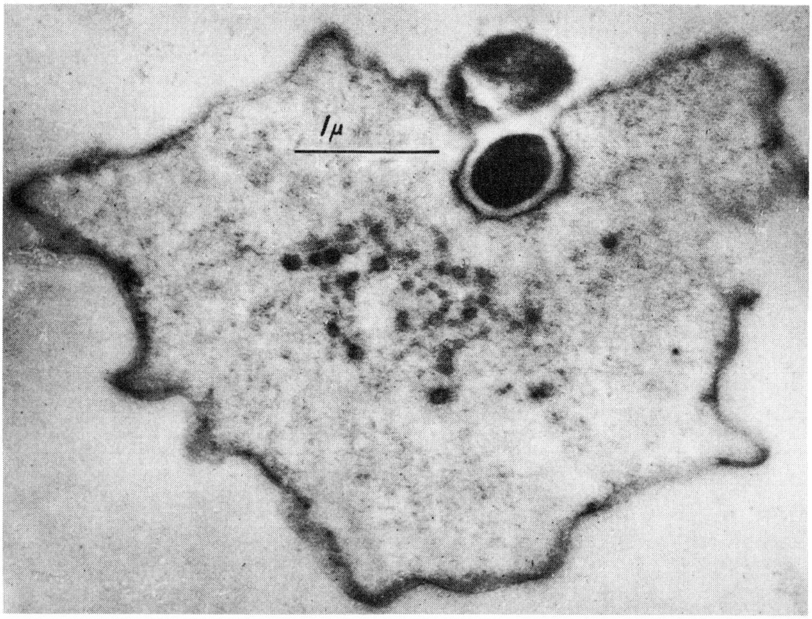

Fig. 17.7. An electron micrograph of a thin section of a portion of a neutrophil which is in contact with two staphylococcal cells. The pseudopod of the neutrophil has started to engulf the nearest staphylococcal cell. *Photo by J. R. Goodman, courtesy S.A.B. LS-354.*

accompany accidental or surgical wounds. The staphylococci are the most common cause of osteomyelitis and are frequently associated with cases of impetigo contagiosum. Staphylococcal septicemia may be particularly dangerous. A fulminating form is characterized by profound toxemia and death within a few hours.

Staphylococcal infection is usually diagnosed by examination of stained smears and bacteriologic culture. The coagulase test is of some value in differentiating pathogenic from nonpathogenic forms. Shortly after its introduction, penicillin was an effective antibiotic against most staphylococcal strains. A number of problems have developed in recent years, however, as a result of the development of highly virulent penicillin-resistant strains for which the antibiotic has no therapeutic value.

Leptospirosis is a systemic infection which may be caused by a number of spirochetes of the genus *Leptospira* including *L. icterohemorrhagiae*, *L. canicola*, *L. autumnalis*, and *L. pomona*. Transmission to man is usually accomplished by direct contact with water that has been contaminated with urine from infected animals or by direct contact with the infected animals. Cattle, hogs, pigs, rats, skunks, raccoons, and oppossums may serve as reservoirs and sources of infection. Symptoms of the disease include fever, headache, chills, and malaise. Kidney damage and jaundice may develop in severe cases. Diagnosis is usually confirmed by serologic means. Although a number of antibiotics effectively inhibit the leptospirochetes in laboratory tests, they seem to be of little value for treatment of human infections.

Viral Agents. **Lymphogranuloma venereum** is a venereal disease caused by a virus immunologically similar to the virus of psittacosis. It is characterized by the development of suppurating lesions, multiple lesions, and enlargement of the genitalia. Although no conclusive diagnostic tests are available, diagnosis may be aided by the demonstration of complement-fixing antibodies against the lymphogranuloma venereum-psittacosis viruses or by a skin test. The disease is worldwide in distribution but occurs most frequently among Negroes in tropical and subtropical climates. Sulfadiazine and the tetracycline antibiotics are effective here as they are against the other large viruses.

DISEASES SPREAD BY WOUND INOCULATION

A number of potentially harmful bacteria exist as highly resistant forms in the soil and may gain entrance into the body as contaminated soil is injected through the skin barrier during wounding. Still others, including some virus pathogens, gain entrance into the body through wounds resulting from the bite of an infected animal. A few representative bacterial and viral diseases which are initiated by the wound-inoculation form of contact are considered here.

Bacterial Agents. **Tetanus** or **lockjaw** is an acute disease with a high fatality rate which is caused by an obligately anaerobic sporeformer, *Clostridium tetani.* The disease is characterized by painful contractions of muscles of the jaw, neck, and trunk. The anaerobic conditions existing in deep wounds are optimum for the development of the organism, which elaborates a highly potent neurotropic exotoxin. Active immunization with tetanus toxoid produces good protection, and a single reinforcing booster injection on the day of an injury essentially insures that no ill effects will result from tetanus infection. Passive immunization with tetanus antitoxin is sometimes used for those who have not been immunized with toxoid.

A number of clostridial forms including *Clostridium perfringens* may cause **gas gangrene** in man. The disease is characterized by a spreading destruction of muscular tissue together with the development of hydrogen gas in the affected tissues. One component of the exotoxin of these pathogens is thought to be a lecithinase, which breaks down lecithin, an important constituent of cell membranes, thus permitting invasion and destruction of these tissues. Death may result from general toxemia as exotoxin spreads over the body from the site of infection. Treatment is best effected by surgical removal of infected tissues. Prompt use of gas-gangrene antitoxin helps to prevent the development of symptoms.

Viral Agents. **Rabies** is a particularly severe, acute encephalitis caused by a virus. The disease in man is characterized by headache, fever, malaise, and numerous psychological changes including alternating periods of stimulation and depression. Spasms of throat muscles may occur as the victim attempts to drink. Death may result from paralysis of respiratory muscles. The disease is usually transmitted to man from the bite of a rabid animal or by the entrance of saliva from an infected animal into a scratch or break in the skin. Although dogs are the usual carriers, a large group of wild and domestic animals including the fox, coyote, wolf, cat, skunk, raccoon, and bat also serve as reservoirs and sources of infection.

The incubation period for man varies from several days to several months but is usually from two to six weeks. Prevention of the disease is accomplished by means of the Pasteur treatment which involves the administration of a series of injections of attenuated virus daily for 14 to 21 days, depending on the number and severity of the original bites. Diagnosis of the disease in the suspected animal carrier is confirmed by demonstration of **Negri bodies** in the nerve cells of the brain.

ARTHROPOD TRANSMITTED DISEASES

Characteristically, a number of the infectious diseases of man are transmitted from host to host by means of certain members of the animal phylum, Arthropoda. The arthropod agent of transmission is designated the **vector,** and the natural host for the pathogen is designated the **reservoir.** In the Arthropoda, two classes are involved: the Insecta; which includes the fleas, lice, flies, and mosquitoes, and the Arachnida, which contains the ticks and mites. Typically, these diseases occur seasonally in correspondence with the life cycle of the vector.

Bacterial Agents. **Tularemia** is a disease of wild and domesticated mammals which is occasionally transmitted to man by the bite of infected ticks or fleas. Symptoms of the disease include chills, fever, and swollen lymph nodes in the area of the original infection. The etiologic agent is *Pasteurella tularensis,* a small, gram-negative, nonmotile bacillus. In diagnosing the disease, specific antibodies are detected in the patient's serum, or the causative agent is isolated. The fatality rate for untreated cases is about 5%. Streptomycin, the tetracyclines, and chloramphenicol provide effective treatment.

Bubonic plague is an especially severe infectious disease in man which is transmitted from the natural reservoir (wild rodents) by the bite of an infective rat flea. Characteristic of the disease is the development of painfully swollen lymph nodes called **buboes.** These acutely inflamed nodes develop in the area which drains the site of the primary infection.

The etiologic agent, *Pasturella pestis,* is a small gram-negative, coccobacillus which is nonmotile. Diagnosis is made by demonstration of the bacteria in fluid from buboes. The disease is of great potential danger as it continues to exist among wild rodents in the western part of the United States. Fortunately for man, however, the disease is rarely transmitted by infective fleas. Although a high fatality rate of 25 to 50% is characteristic of untreated cases, treatment with streptomycin, the tetracyclines, chloramphenicol, or the sulfonamides has sharply reduced fatalities.

Pneumonic plague occurs less frequently than bubonic plague but is more frequently fatal. During epidemics of bubonic plague, the bacilli are characteristically borne by air from one infected human to another by aerosols from respiratory-tract discharges or by materials from infected buboes. In the pneumonic form, buboes do not develop, but large numbers of *Pasteurella pestis* appear in the alveoli and sputum.

Viral Agents. **Yellow Fever** is an acute infectious disease of short duration which is transmitted from one infected human to another by the bite of one species of the **Aedes** genus of mosquitoes. Symptoms of the disease include fever, backache, nausea, and vomiting. The major reservoir of the virus is man; however, monkeys and certain marsupials may harbor the infective agent.

Laboratory diagnosis is carried out by demonstration of the virus in blood by animal inoculation or by the demonstration of a rise in neutralizing antibody titer during the course of the disease.

Although no specific treatment is advocated for yellow fever, prevention of the disease by control of the mosquitoes or by active immunization with attenuated virus have essentially eliminated it from many areas. The fatality rate is about 30% in infected humans, but outbreaks rarely occur now in the Americas.

Rickettsial Agents. **Epidemic typhus fever** is a rickettsial disease transmitted by lice which become infected by feeding on the blood of infected humans. Man is the reservoir for the pathogen, and he usually becomes infected by rubbing feces from the lice into the wound caused by the vector's bite. Symptoms of the disease include generalized pains, fever, chills, and headache. Fatality may be as high as 40% in untreated cases.

The causative agent is the *Rickettsia prowazekii* var. *prowazekii*. Confirmation of diagnosis may be made by the Weil-Felix serologic reaction in which heterologous antigen, Proteus OX-19, gives a positive test for antibodies against the rickettsial pathogen. Treatment involves the oral administration of the tetracyclines or chloramphenicol.

Endemic typhus, or **murine typhus,** is a milder disease similar in symptoms to louse-borne typhus. It differs from epidemic typhus in that rats are the reservoir, and the rat flea is the vector. The mechanism of transmission is similar in that feces from the infected flea contaminate the bite wound after the flea takes a blood meal. The etiologic agent is the *Rickettsia prowazekii* var. *typhi.* The Weil-Felix reaction can be used for preliminary diagnosis, but serologic tests which involve the use of rickettsial suspensions for antigens are required to differentiate the two types of typhus. The fatality rate from murine typhus rarely exceeds 2%. The specific treatments for endemic and murine typhus are the same.

Rickettsialpox is a relatively mild disease caused by the *Rickettsia akari.* The house mouse serves as the reservoir, and the rodent mite transmits the infection to man. Symptoms of the disease include chills and fever, muscular pain, and a generalized rash with no characteristic distribution. Diagnosis is confirmed by a complement-fixation test. Cases appear annually among inhabitants of older apartment houses in New York City, and infrequent cases appear in other crowded cities of the eastern part of the United States. Fatality is less than 1% in untreated cases. Chloramphenicol and the tetracyclines are effective for treatment.

One of the more severe rickettsial diseases now occurs throughout most of the United States during the spring and summer months. **Rocky Mountain spotted fever** is most prevalent in the western states as a disease of adult males and in the Middle Atlantic states as a disease of children. The infectious pathogen, *Rickettsia rickettsii,* finds reservoir not only in mammals, such as rabbits, field mice, and dogs, but also in ticks which serve as the vectors of the disease. Once a tick has become infected, it continues to harbor the pathogen for life, and, more important, it may pass the rickettsiae from one generation of the tick to another.

Transmission to man may be accomplished by the bite of an infected tick or by contamination of the skin with infected tick feces or crushed tissues. Symptoms of the disease include sudden fever, headache, and a generalized rash which spreads to most of the body parts including the palms and soles. Diagnosis may be confirmed by the Weil-Felix reaction with Proteus OX-19 and OX-2 and by complement-fixation tests. Untreated-case fatalities are about 20%. Specific therapy involves daily oral administration of the tetracycline antibiotics or chloramphenicol.

Protozoal Agents. Although **malaria** causes thousands of deaths annually, it has, for all practical purposes, been eliminated as a scourge to man in the United States through control of the insect vector, the *Anopheles* mosquito. The disease is characterized by the development of cycles of chills followed by fever and sweating which occur every 48 hours for the pathogen *Plasmodium vivax*, and every 72 hours for the protozoal parasite *Plasmodium malariae*. A third form of the disease caused by *Plasmodium falciparum* is characterized by more frequent paroxysms occurring over a period of less than two days. The time interval between cycles corresponds to the developmental period of the malarial parasite in the erthrocytes of man, since there is a synchronous release of parasites every 24 or 48 hours with the breakdown of the blood cells.

Although higher apes have been suggested as possible reservoirs for *P. malariae*, man is the major sustaining host for all forms. The female *Anopheles* mosquito becomes the vector as she ingests a blood meal from an infected human. The parasites undergo a complex series of changes within the arthropod vector and finally settle in her salivary glands from which they are effectively transmitted to another human host with the next blood meal.

Laboratory diagnosis depends on demonstration of the protozoal pathogens by microscopic examination of blood films. Fatality rates in untreated cases may be as high as 10%. A number of specific antimalarial drugs, including chloroquin diphosphate, amodiaquin dihydrochloride, and primaquin diphosphate provide effective treatment. Fatality rates among treated cases rarely exceed 0.5%.

African sleeping sickness is caused by the flagellated protozoan pathogens, *Trypanosoma gambiense* and *Trypanosoma rhodensiense*. A number of local wild African game animals, unaffected by the disease, serve as natural reservoirs for the flagellates. The tsetse fly is the vector for transmission of the infective agent to man. Metabolic products of the parasites have a paralyzing effect on the central nervous system resulting in symptoms varying from tremors and delusions to deep "sleep." Laboratory diagnosis involves the demonstration of the parasites in blood or spinal fluid smears. An organic arsenic-containing drug, tryparsamide, may be used as a specific for treatment.

Kala-azar, a chronic disease caused by the flagellated protozoan, *Leishmania donovani,* is characterized by irregular fever, dysentery, a dusky skin hue, and enlargement of the liver and spleen. Dogs are frequently infected and may serve as natural reservoirs. Sandflies of the genus *Phlebotomus* serve as vectors of transmission. Diagnosis is dependent on demonstration of the parasites in biopsies of skin, spleen, or liver, by blood culture and by a group of serologic reactions including a highly specific complement-fixation test. Untreated cases usually result in death from secondary infections. A number of antimony compounds have been used as specifics for treatment.

SUMMARY. Microbiology developed from the impetus that followed the success of Koch and Pasteur with infectious diseases. Modifications of their methodology were effective in surmounting the problems encountered with diverse microbes. Epidemics have been brought under control and functional methods for prophylaxis and therapy of most infectious diseases are available. Continued success in these endeavors rests on understanding the nature of the pathogen.

18

The Microbiology of Water

Potential sources of water for human consumption are **atmospheric water**, as rain and snow, **surface water**, in lakes, rivers, and streams, and **ground waters**, from wells and springs.

Atmospheric Water. The bacteria, viruses, molds, yeasts, algae, and protozoa present in rain or snow reflect the microbial population in the air at the time the meteoric water formed. They are, therefore, chiefly of soil origin. Near the oceans, marine organisms are dispersed into the air by the action of wind and waves. Numerous bacteria and viruses from man and animals are released into the air in saliva or mucous droplets. The microbial population is greatest at the beginning of a rain or snowfall since the precipitation washes most of the dust to which the bacteria are attached from the atmosphere. The number present is determined to some extent by the nature of the area. More dust, and consequently more bacteria, are present in the air over a city than over open country. Thus rain or snow from an urban area ordinarily renders a higher count than that from a suburban area.

Surface Water. The rivulets of run-off water from cultivated land contain large numbers of bacteria as well as extracted organic and mineral matter. Run-off from rocky areas naturally contains fewer bacteria. Seasonal variations in rivers occurring as a result of rainfall or melting snow introduce fresh washings from the ground. A stream heavily loaded with sewage often shows the largest bacterial count when the stream is lowest and the sewage, therefore, least diluted. The flora of such a stream contains a mixture of soil and sewage forms, while a stream without sewage pollution shows a predominance of soil and water forms.

In a slow-moving stream receiving little polluted matter, a considerable reduction in bacterial population often takes place, since the suspended matter to which the bacteria are attached has settled out. A similar situation prevails in lakes and impounding reservoirs. Further natural reduction takes place as a result of ultraviolet light, antagonisms with other forms, and starvation.

Underground or Ground Water. In some areas ground water contains few bacteria because of the filtering action of the soil, but this condition is not universal. Where the subsurface is predominantly limestone, for example, the surface water may reach the underground level through caves and channels with little or no change in bacterial population, and pollution from surface sewage may move directly to the subsurface water. In general, water from shallow wells (less than 100 feet deep) contains more bacteria than water from deep wells.

Water from springs is comparable to water from deep wells in the number of existing bacteria. However, surface contamination is difficult to exclude, and spring water may show a flora more characteristic of shallow than of deep wells. The bacteria in special types of water, such as oilfield brines, are of considerable interest. When these waters contain sulfates and the organism *Desulfovibrio,* which reduces sulfates to sulfide, a special microbiological problem results. The water may become corrosive or may precipitate insoluble sulfides, whereas the industry involved needs a water free of precipitate. Also, this water is unsuited for human consumption.

KINDS OF BACTERIA IN WATER

The normal flora consists of representatives of the *Chlamydobacteriales* (including the iron and sulfur bacteria), certain little-known stalked forms, the *Caulobacteria* (which grow attached to some object), spiral forms (some of which may be quite large and some of which have not been cultivated on artificial media), organisms concerned in the cycle of nitrogen (both nitrogen-fixing bacteria and the ammonia and nitrite oxidizing forms), and a variety of chromogenic rods and cocci. Soil sporeformers and other soil types, such as *Pseudomonas fluorescens,* are commonly found, but they probably are not true-water bacteria even though they do find suitable growth conditions in water. They are probably adventitious invaders, temporarily present, thriving only where the water is high in impurities. The most widely studied adventitious water bacteria are those of sewage origin: the coliforms, the sewage streptococci, certain types of obligate anaerobes, and other intestinal forms.

Certainly no one set of cultural conditions will detect all the types of bacteria present in a water sample. The type of medium, the temperature of incubation, the oxygen tension, and other cultural environmental conditions must be adjusted to the requirements of the particular organisms or group to be detected.

SANITARY EXAMINATION OF WATER

The normal water bacteria are not of sanitary significance. However, most sources of water for municipal use are subject to undesirable contamination and consequently may contain pathogenic types of human intestinal origin. Therefore, water for domestic use must be subjected to regular bacteriological examination. Epidemiological evidence has established beyond doubt the relationship between water-borne disease and the presence of organisms of intestinal origin (Table 18.1), and thus the value of sanitary bacteriological examinations for the evaluation of the safety of the supply. Probably no single bacteriological test is more frequently performed than the examination of water. Certainly none is more productive of significant data.

Table 18.1. The Water-borne Diseases at which Water Treatment is Primarily Aimed

Disease	*Organism*	*Description*
Typhoid fever	*Salmonella typhosa*	Gram negative Non-spore-forming rod
Paratyphoid fevers	*Salmonella paratyphi*	Gram negative Non-spore-forming rod
Bacterial dysentery	*Shigella dysenteriae*	Gram negative Non-spore-forming rod
Cholera	*Vibrio comma*	Gram negative Non-spore-forming curved rod
Amebic dysentery	*Entamoeba histolytica*	Protozoan of the genus *Amoeba*

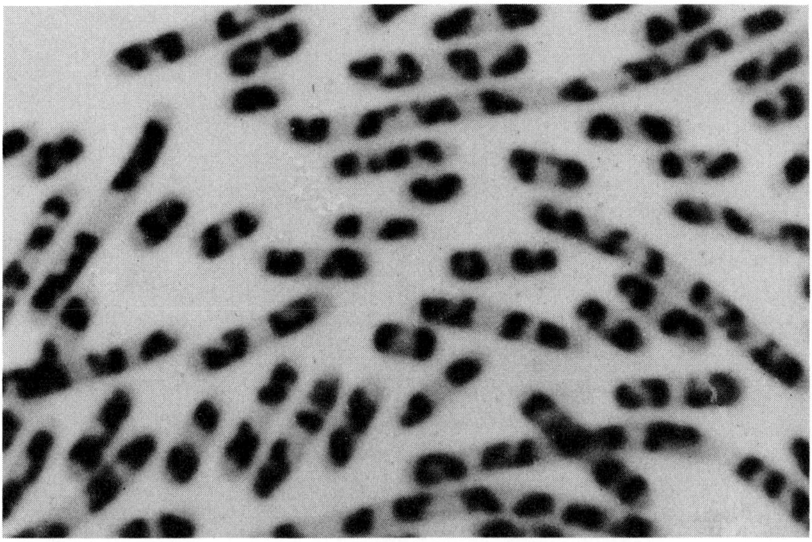

Fig. 18.1. *Escherichia coli* stained to show nuclear structure was widely studied as an organism of sanitary significance long before it became the favorite tool of the microbial geneticist and biochemist. *Photo by Mudd and Smith: J. Bact., LIX, 561–573, April 1950, courtesy S.A.B. LS-274.*

Pathogenic bacteria in water supplies are present in such small numbers compared with other types having the same source in nature and the same general requirements for growth that the other bacteria are likely to overgrow and obscure the pathogen sought. If intestinal discharges have soiled the water, large numbers of coliforms (*Escherichia coli* and related forms) are certain to be present (Fig. 18.1). These types are more easily recovered and identified than the pathogenic forms. For these reasons no effort is made to detect pathogens in the routine examination of water. The routine test checks for an organism which, by its presence, indicates the possible presence of a pathogenic organism. Such an organism is termed an **indicator organism.** More important, its absence indicates that intestinal pathogens probably are not present. Several groups of bacteria serve as indicator organisms: the hydrogen sulfide-producing anaerobes and the intestinal streptococci; but none has proven more reliable than the coliforms (Fig. 18.2).

A water supply may contain coliforms without containing, at the same time, pathogenic bacteria of the same source in nature. However, the accumulated epidemiological evidence indicates that water free of coliform bacteria is safe to drink. Many wells and springs con-

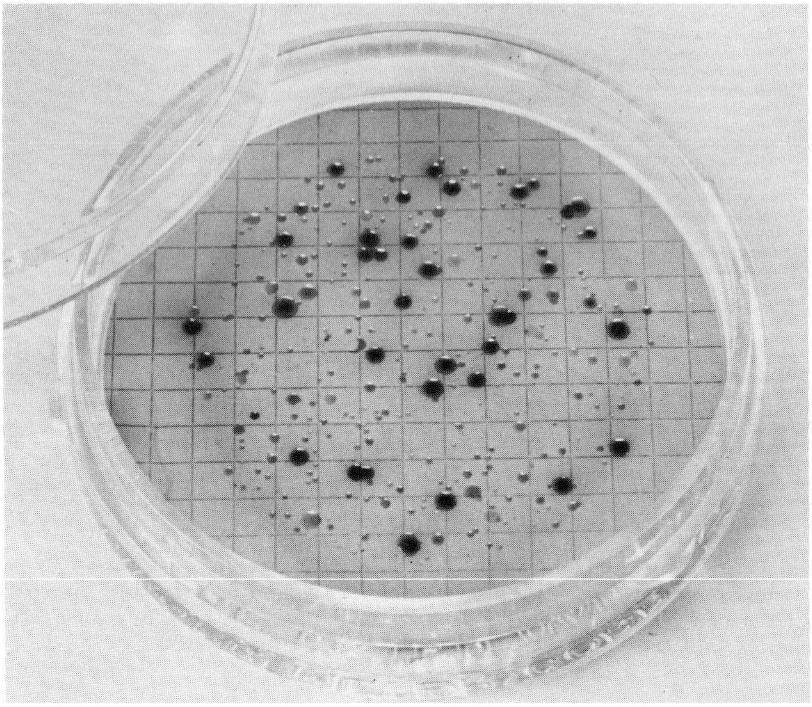

Fig. 18.2. The dark colonies with metallic sheen on this plate are typical coliforms indicating pollution in the water tested here. *Photo courtesy Millipore Filter Corp.*

taining coliforms have been used by small groups for years without ill effects. However, the contamination from the combined sewage of numbers of persons will eventually contain the excrement of one infected with intestinal disease. In sewage from large cities one pathogen usually exists for every ten million coliforms. Pollution of water almost certainly results in infection with pathogenic bacteria when a susceptible individual consumes the water.

A sanitary chemical examination of water reveals the state of the nitrogen present in the water. If contamination with organic matter has been recent, the nitrogen present is chiefly in the form of albuminoid and ammonia nitrogen. If the contamination was remote, nitrites and nitrates account for most of the nitrogen present. A higher-than-normal level of sodium chloride suggests contamination with domestic waste. However, chemical examination does not yield information from which the sanitary quality of a water supply can be evaluated with certainty. Nitrogenous material of plant origin cannot be chemically differentiated from that of animal origin. A sanitary survey of the watershed together with a sanitary chemical examination will supply suggestive data, but only a bacteriological examination can determine with certainty the sanitary quality of the water.

The Sanitary Bacteriological Examination of Water. Methods for the bacteriological examination of water are recommended by a committee of the American Public Health Association and are given in the *Standard Methods for the Examination of Water and Waste Water* of the Association. The complete examination consists of three carefully specified tests, and the recommendations are periodically revised to incorporate the latest developments (Table 18.2).

Table 18.2. Synopsis of the Qualitative Microbiological Examination of Water

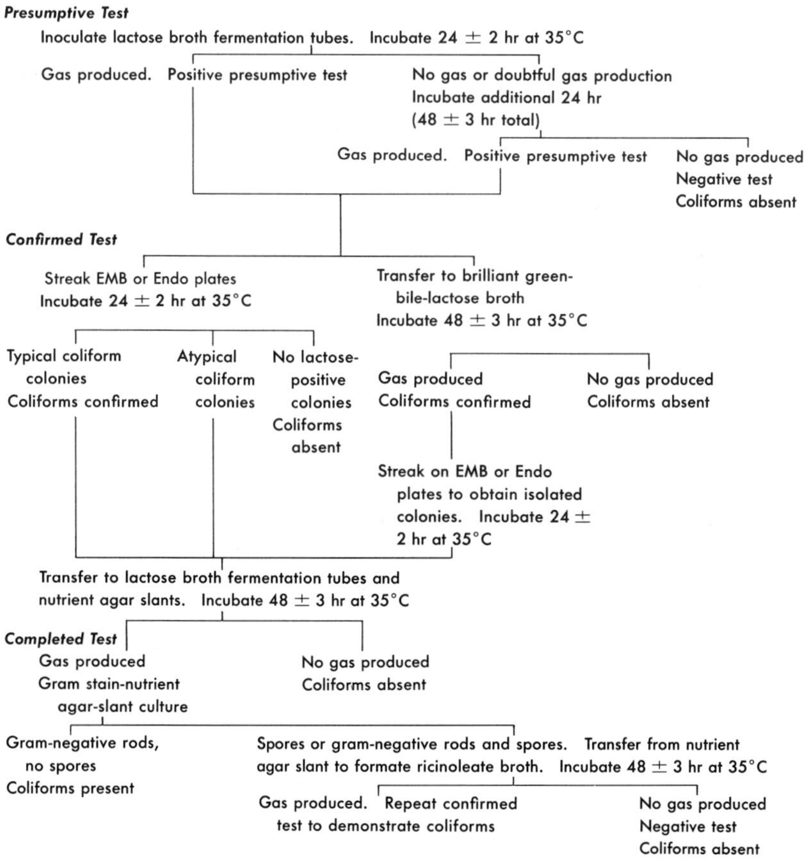
Presumptive Test
Inoculate lactose broth fermentation tubes. Incubate 24 ± 2 hr at 35°C
Gas produced. Positive presumptive test
No gas or doubtful gas production
Incubate additional 24 hr
(48 ± 3 hr total)
Gas produced. Positive presumptive test
No gas produced
Negative test
Coliforms absent
Confirmed Test
Streak EMB or Endo plates
Incubate 24 ± 2 hr at 35°C
Transfer to brilliant green-bile-lactose broth
Incubate 48 ± 3 hr at 35°C
Typical coliform colonies
Coliforms confirmed
Atypical coliform colonies
No lactose-positive colonies
Coliforms absent
Gas produced
Coliforms confirmed
No gas produced
Coliforms absent
Streak on EMB or Endo plates to obtain isolated colonies. Incubate 24 ± 2 hr at 35°C
Transfer to lactose broth fermentation tubes and nutrient agar slants. Incubate 48 ± 3 hr at 35°C
Completed Test
Gas produced
Gram stain-nutrient agar-slant culture
No gas produced
Coliforms absent
Gram-negative rods, no spores
Coliforms present
Spores or gram-negative rods and spores. Transfer from nutrient agar slant to formate ricinoleate broth. Incubate 48 ± 3 hr at 35°C
Gas produced. Repeat confirmed test to demonstrate coliforms
No gas produced
Negative test
Coliforms absent

Presumptive Test. Not many bacteria other than the coliforms ferment lactose with the production of gas. Graduated amounts of water are placed in fermentation tubes of lactose broth, each containing at least twice as much medium as the portion of sample being tested. Each of five tubes is inoculated with 10 ml portions of water, or five tubes with a 100 ml portions. Incubation is at 35° C for 48 hours. The absence of gas after 48 hours terminates the examination with a report as negative. However, if gas is produced within 48 hours, the presence of coliforms is indicated, and the examination is recorded as a positive presumptive test. This test determines the most probable number (MPN) of coliforms per 100 ml of sample according to computations tabulated in the *Public Health Reports* and reprinted in *Standard Methods*.

If only coliform bacteria gave positive results under the conditions described, additional tests would be unnecessary. Unfortunately, other organisms cause gas formation in lactose broth. The anaerobic *Clostridium* types and the aerobic *Aerobacillus* species are sporeforming rods that ferment lactose with the formation of gas. Gas formation may also result from that type of bacterial association known as synergism. Synergism results in the production of acid and gas from lactose by an association of organisms, neither of which effects this result when grown separately. One member of the pair attacks lactose with the production of intermediate split products from which the second, lactose negative, member of the pair produces gas.

The Confirmed Test. Samples from tubes of positive presumptive tests are transferred to either a differential lactose-agar medium or to a selective liquid medium. The most commonly used solid medium is probably eosin-methylene-blue (EMB) agar. Plates are streaked so as to obtain isolated colonies. After incubation at 35° C for 24 hours, the plates are examined; if typical coliform colonies are observed, the test is recorded as positive. If the positive presumptive tests had resulted from a *Clostridium,* no suspicious colonies on the aerobically incubated plate will appear. If positives resulted from an *Aerobacillus,* the colonies will be atypical but sufficiently similar to coliforms to justify further examination. The lactose-splitting member of a synergistic pair likewise may give an atypical, but nevertheless lactose-positive, colony. Transfers from typical or atypical colonies should be made for final identification.

Several liquid confirmatory media have been developed, the most satisfactory of which is brilliant green-bile-lactose broth. When inoculum from a positive presumptive test produces acid and gas in this medium, the presumptive test is confirmed. The organisms responsible for false presumptive tests are inhibited by the brilliant green dye and by the bile so that gas formation is a positive indication of the presence of coliforms. EMB agar is employed to secure isolated colonies from positive liquid-confirmatory tests for use in the completed test.

Completed Test. The completed test establishes that typical or suspicious colonies appearing on the plates of the confirmed test are actually of the coliform group. Inoculations from isolated colonies are made to a lactose fermentation tube and to an agar slant. A coliform begins prompt fermentation, and a stain from the slant will reveal a gram-negative, non-spore-forming rod.

Probable Origin of Coliforms. Additional tests on pure cultures of coliforms can determine their species and their probable origin. Since all coliforms have sanitary significance, the isolation and identification of strains has little significance in sanitation studies. However, determination of possible fecal origin is accomplished by the IMViC tests. Indol (I), methyl red (M), Voges-Proskauer (V), and citrate (C) utilization constitute the IMViC tests. All possible IMViC types have been encountered, but coliforms of known fecal origin are predominately IMViC + + − −; nonfecal types are usually IMViC − − + + (Table 18.3).

Standard of a Potable Water. The Public Health Service decrees that water used on interstate carriers (buses, airlines, and trains) shall have less than one coliform per 100 ml. This is determined by planting multiple presumptive tests, and if less than 10% of the tubes planted with 10 ml of water are positive, probability tables indicate that the water meets the Public Health standard. Since the ratio of coliforms to pathogens is about ten million to one, the probability is negligible that a consumer would imbibe a pathogen in such water. Proven incidents of water-borne disease have not been demonstrated in cities where the water met the coliform test, since a single intestinal pathogen seldom leads to disease.

Quantitative Examination. The total number of bacteria in water may be important. In the food industry the use of a high-count water for

Table 18.3. The IMViC Reactions

	Indol	*Methyl Red*	*Voges-Proskauer*	*Citrate*
E. coli (fecal)	+	+	−	−
A. aerogenes (nonfecal)	−	−	+	+

cooling processed cans results in increased spoilage. The cans leaving the retort are under pressure, and vacuum develops with cooling. If a minute amount of cooling water is sucked in through an imperfect spot in the seal as the vacuum develops, spoilage will probably appear in a few days.

THE MEMBRANE-FILTER PROCEDURE

This technique, a relatively new application which recently has been accepted as a standard method, has several advantages over the multiple-tube fermentation test: (a) a greater degree of reproducibility is possible; (b) larger volumes of water may be tested thus improving sensitivity of coliform detection; (c) results may be obtained more rapidly. Analysis by filtration requires less equipment and is generally less cumbersome than the tube test; for example, a sample may be filtered in the field and then shipped to the laboratory on a preservative medium (Fig. 18.3).

However, the membrane method does have limitations. Water containing algae or other suspended matter filtered in volumes large enough for dependable determination may clog the membrane; furthermore, deposition of material on the filter will interfere with development of bacterial colonies. In water samples containing large numbers of noncoliforms, estimates of numbers of coliforms will be low in comparison to expected values.

The filter membrane is a thin layer of complex cellulose structure which has practically no absorptive capacity and functions as a physical screen. Pore size is determined primarily by the chemical composition of the membrane and the temperature of drying and humidity during the manufacturing process.

The procedure is quite simple and rapid. A test sample, the volume of which depends on suspected quality of the water, is passed through the filter. The filter membrane is placed aseptically, bacteria side up, in a sterile petri dish over an absorbent-paper pad saturated with modified Endo medium. Nutrient diffuses up through the filter pores to the cells trapped on the membrane. After incubation coliform colonies may be observed growing on the membrane.

WATER PURIFICATION

Since most waters for municipal use are subject to contamination with coliform bacteria and consequently may contain pathogenic forms

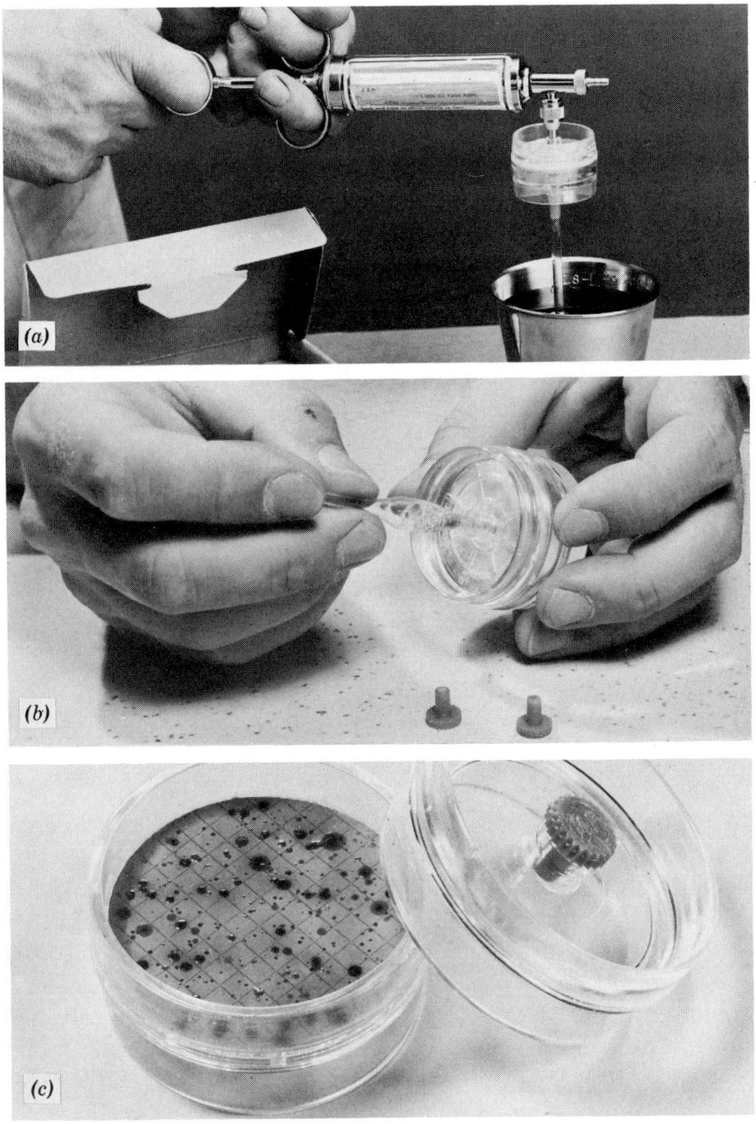

Fig. 18.3. Field test of water with membrane filters. (*a*) A measured amount of water is drawn through the filter. (*b*) A sterile ampoule of broth is applied to the back of the filter. (*c*) After 18 hours incubation, colonies showing typical sheen indicate polluted water. *Photos courtesy Millipore Filter Corp.*

as well, the water must be treated for domestic use. Since water is not the natural habitat of pathogenic bacteria, their numbers tend to decrease naturally. However, purification by sedimentation, the antagonistic effect of plankton, or the action of ultraviolet rays of sunlight cannot be depended on to yield a safe water in any reasonable time.

The objective of water purification is to render a water of unsafe or uncertain quality suitable for domestic use. The nature of the supply and the cost of purification under the particular circumstances determine which method should be employed. A clear water may be rendered satisfactory by disinfecting treatment alone, but a turbid water must be clarified as well as disinfected.

The earliest method of artificial water purification was by slow sand filtration. Introduced into the United States about 1870, this method had been successful for some time in England. A slow sand filter consists of a bed of coarse stones layered successively with pebbles, gravel, and sand. Water, flooded on the surface to a depth of two to three feet, slowly trickles through to be collected at the bottom of the filter. The bacterial load is reduced 95 to 99%; odor and organic matter are also reduced and turbidity is lessened. Though efficient, this method has several limitations. Water which is not fairly clear will clog the filter with silt within a short time; a large area of filter bed is required since the capacity of a slow sand filter is only from 2½ to 5 million gallons per acre per day. The bed must be protected against freezing. At intervals the sand must be washed or replaced. This relatively slow operation requires an alternate filter bed to maintain purification service while the major filter is being cleaned.

The filtering action is a combination of physical, chemical, and biological actions. The suspended particles are physically strained out, and suspended matter is biologically removed and biochemically oxidized through the action of the **Schmutzdecke** (the zoogleal mass that develops on the sand grains after a short period of use and consists of various living organisms). Rapid sand filtration avoids most of the limitations of slow sand filtration and has almost completely superseded the older procedure. Developed in the United States to purify turbid water, the procedure essentially consists of adding flocculating chemicals, such as iron or aluminum sulfates, to the water. After holding the water for a few hours while the particles settle out (thereby removing most of the suspended matter and bacteria) it is passed through filter beds similar in construction to slow sand-filter beds, but of greater capacity. Residual suspended matter is trapped by the filter, and a clear effluent results. When the filter becomes badly clogged the flow of water is reversed, thereby washing the filter which can then be returned to service.

Filtration is not adequate to remove all bacteria. Samples of filtered but otherwise untreated water frequently show coliforms. Water is chemically treated with chlorine gas or with hypochlorite to kill pathogenic bacteria. Activated charcoal may be added to adsorb objectional tastes and odors. The sanitized water should contain a residue of 0.1 to 0.2 part per million of available chlorine.

The value of water purification is emphasized by comparing the incidence rates of water-borne disease before and for a year or two after purification in a number of cities. A city with a high water-borne disease rate almost certainly has a water supply of inferior quality or has experienced a break in water treatment resulting in an epidemic. In past years typhoid fever was a common urban disease, but today water-borne typhoid is essentially a disease of country areas where people depend on water of uncertain sanitary quality.

SEWAGE DISPOSAL AND SEWAGE PURIFICATION

Sewage is the water supply of a city after it has been used. It contains various industrial and domestic wastes and is rich in highly putrescible organic matter. Consequently, sewage requires a great deal of oxygen (a high biochemical oxygen demand, BOD) for the oxidation of this organic content.

In some cases purification before disposal is not required, but most cities demand some degree of purification. Untreated sewage may be dumped into the sea in coastal cities not located near oyster beds or bathing beaches, but few cities are so fortunately located. Similarly, raw sewage may be allowed to flow into a river. However, the volume must not be great enough in relation to the volume of the stream to create anaerobic conditions with resulting damage to fish and wild life. Also, the operation must not affect a city using the river as a water source.

Under special climatic and soil conditions where toxic industrial wastes are not present, sewage may be used as irrigation water. A sandy soil, a relatively dry, warm climate, and a suitable crop are necessary for the successful disposal of sewage as irrigation water. Truck crops, especially vegetables to be eaten raw, should not be irrigated with sewage.

In all sewage purification procedures the bacteria naturally present in the soil or water transform the sewage organic matter from an unstable to a stable form. Nitrogen, for example, goes through the cycle from protein to nitrate. Much of the carbon ends as carbon dioxide, and other substances likewise approach or attain the stable end form

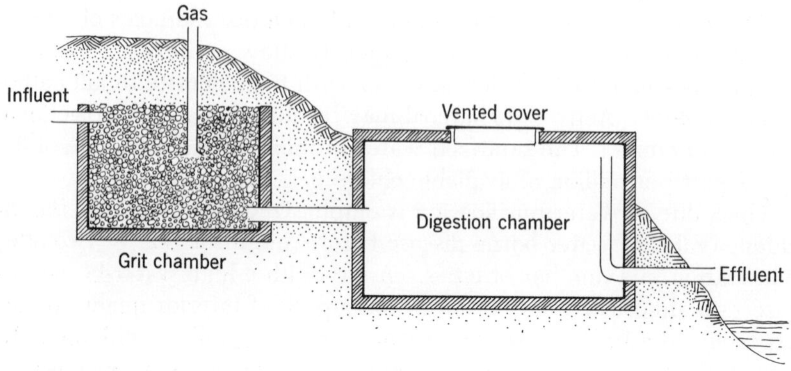

Fig. 18.4. The Cameron tank. A modified septic tank for disposing of the domestic sewage of a single family in a rural area. Effluents are of poor quality but do not become too objectionable in thinly populated regions.

typical of each. In the artificial purification of sewage the bacterial action occurring naturally in the cycles of the elements is harnessed in an engineering device designed to favor the development of a particular physiological type.

The simplest procedure employing the activity of anaerobic bacteria is found in the septic tank with subsurface porous tiles to distribute the effluent. These tanks are necessarily small installations used generally for single dwellings. The Cameron tank is a somewhat more elaborate installation operating on the same principle (Fig. 18.4). The sewage is only partially purified, the effluent still being highly putrescible and requiring further (aerobic) bacterial activity for stabilization. Preliminary anaerobic digestion facilitates final aerobic oxidation. Such a tank may be combined with an aerobic device, such as a contact bed, or the effluent may be distributed through a subsurface tile system providing low-cost purification for small installations.

The Cameron tank was improved by combining a sedimentation chamber and a digestion chamber. The resulting structure, the **Imhoff tank,** may be either circular or rectangular (Fig. 18.5). Sewage solids settle into the lower chamber where they are digested by anaerobic bacteria. The effluent, considerably reduced in suspended solids, is still putrescible and requires further treatment. The slowly digesting solids accumulate in the lower chamber, and at intervals this **sludge** is removed and dried for fertilizer.

The **contact bed** is the simplest of the several devices for employing aerobic bacteria in the purification of sewage effluent. A bed of crushed-coarse stone or similar material is treated with sewage so as to encourage a heavy growth of aerobic bacteria. The bed is filled, allowed to stand a short time, drained, and rested; then the cycle is repeated. If the sewage is distributed over a similar bed through sprinkler heads, the installation is known as a sprinkling filter. The heavy growth of aerobic organisms with accumulates on the stones traps particles, including sewage bacteria. The sewage material is then decomposed by aerobic action.

The activated-sludge method is a widely used purification procedure using the action of aerobic bacteria (Fig. 18.6). This method is frequently combined with a preliminary sedimentation tank to remove the large suspended particles and expose them to anaerobic digestion. Effluent from the preliminary sedimentation tank is passed to an aeration tank where it is vigorously agitated with air. In the course of six to nine hours in the aeration tank essentially all of the organic matter is

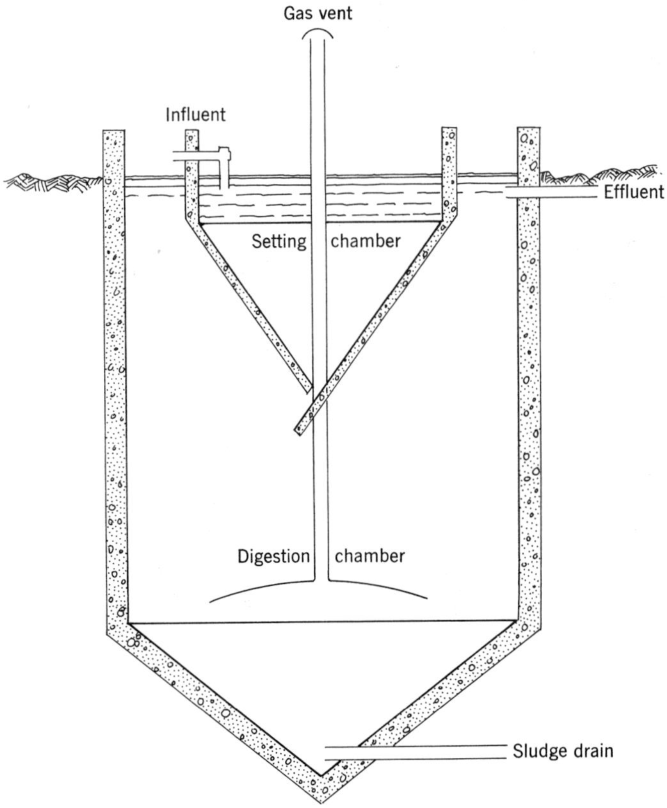

Fig. 18.5. The Imhoff tank provides for settling and sludge digestion in a single tank.

changed to a stable form, the effluent having a very low BOD. The slowly digestible, flocculent sludge is settled out in a settling basin and pumped back to the aeration tank. The stable effluent is drawn off and may or may not be chlorinated before final disposal. Sludge accumulates slowly, and periodically a part must be drawn off to prevent overloading of the system. This excess sludge is added to the solids collected in the primary settling tank in an anaerobic digestion tank. The large volume of inflammable gas produced by anaerobic digestion contains corrosive gases and is customarily burned off. After several months in the anaerobic digestion tank where microbial action compacts the sludge and modifies it to a brown humus, it is drawn off, dried, and used as fertilizer. The thermophilic conditions in the digestion tanks destroy the pathogens.

Such a plant operating properly and efficiently is practically odorless except in the vicinity of the influent. The effluent is usually chlorinated to eliminate or reduce pathogens that may have survived the treatment. Essentially free of oxidizable matter, the effluent is very likely of better quality than the stream into which it is discharged.

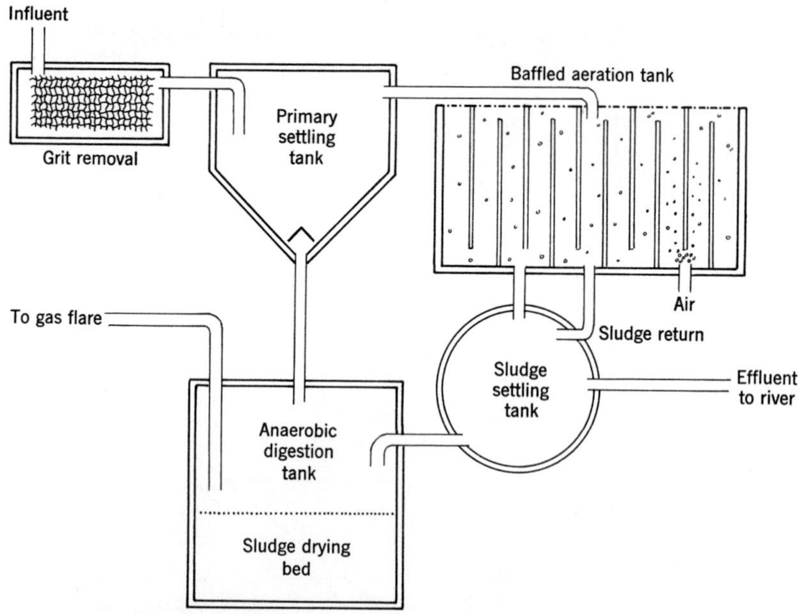

Fig. 18.6. The activated sludge system depends on pumping air through the settled sewage and returning much of the settleable solids to the tank to maintain a high inoculum of aerobic bacteria.

Fig. 18.7. A sewage lagoon requires an area of low rainfall and high sunlight. Anaerobic decomposition of the settleable solids occurs at the bottom, and the algae growing near the surface produce oxygen to satisfy the BOD.

Recent engineering advances have resulted in processes of sedimentation, filtration, clarification, aerobic oxidation, and sludge treatment combined into more complex, but more or less self-contained, units.

Large volumes of industrial waste, such as those produced by a food factory processing seasonal products, frequently exceed the capacity of a purification plant. Under this condition purification of the excess waste is carried out by the combined action of anaerobic bacteria and algae in a lagoon (Fig. 18.7). The organic materials in the waste are stabilized by bacterial action. Photosynthetic oxygenation at the surface by algae keeps the pond from becoming putrid and restores dissolved oxygen to the liquid. In locations with a mild winter climate, lagooning may provide satisfactory year-round purification.

SUMMARY. Because many healthy persons and animals carry intestinal diseases, sewage must always be suspected of pathogens, even in areas where no clinical illness has been reported. Where intestinal organisms cannot be excluded, they must be removed or killed. The coliform organisms are easily detected and are removed at the same rate and with the same procedures that remove or kill intestinal pathogens. Since they are ten million times as numerous in sewage as are the pathogens, the absence of coliforms is accepted as a fairly safe indication of the absence of pathogens.

Sewage disposal requires that microbiological action mineralize the dissolved solids or incorporate them into microbial cell bodies, so that they may be removed with the colloidal and sedimentible solids; the elements of organic matter must be converted to their stable, odorless forms, that is, sulfur compounds to sulfates, nitrogen compounds to nitrates, phosphorus to phosphates and carbon to CO_2. The solid materials are compacted by microbial action to produce a usable fertilizer. The liquid is oxygenated so that it will not interfere with aerobic life in the water into which it is discharged.

19

Bacteriology of Milk and Milk Products

The natural use of milk in the nourishment of a young mammal depends on direct transfer from the lactating animal to the offspring. As the milk is not exposed to the environment, little or no possibility of contamination exists. Under artificial methods of collecting and handling, milk receives bacteria from practically everything with which it comes in contact. Hence, if the milk remains at incubation temperature for any length of time after collection, a great increase in bacterial population may attack the quality of milk. If pathogenic bacteria are among those which gain entrance, the consumer's health is jeopardized. The problem of securing good milk and good dairy products through dairy sanitation involves constant vigilance and close attention to all details of operation.

Although the family with one cow faces the same bacteriological problems which assail the large dairy, the commercial dairy's problems and responsibilities result from its large-scale methods of production and processing. This chapter discusses the bacteriology of milk and milk products as a unit rather than considering the problems of large and small-scale operations separately.

SIGNIFICANCE OF BACTERIA FOR DAIRY PRODUCTS

Control of the numbers and kinds of bacteria in dairy products has four major applications. The first is in determining the market standards of fluid milk. The letter grade of milk is based on a number of factors, one of which is the number of bacteria present in the milk at the time of delivery. Obviously, a knowledge of the important sources of bacteria, of the methods for preventing their entrance in large numbers, and of procedures for interfering with their growth has much economic importance to a milk producer.

Dairy bacteriology is also concerned with prevention of spoilage of milk and milk products. Uncontrolled bacterial growth in milk and its derivatives causes deterioration ranging from slight flavor or texture losses to extensive spoilage. Here, also, a knowledge of sources of bacteria, modes of entrance, and control of activity has great value in lengthening the shelf life of the product.

Bacteria and related microorganisms are employed in the manufacture of such dairy products as fermented milks, butter, and cheese. Desirable flavor of each of these commodities is associated with the controlled activity of special microorganisms. Improvements in procedures and in the quality of the product become possible only as knowledge of the organisms concerned is developed.

Finally, dairy products, chiefly fluid milk, are instrumental in the transmission of certain infectious diseases. Investigations of many epidemics have proven the infectious agent to be milk-borne. The health of the consumer can be adequately protected only by a knowledge of the sources and controls of infectious organisms.

SOURCE OF BACTERIA IN MILK

In dairy manufacturing operations, milk cannot be produced that is totally free of bacteria. Consequently, the dairy bacteriologist has to establish the relative importance of the various sources of milk-dwelling bacteria as a first step toward the inauguration of adequate control procedures. The bacteria of raw milk are of both endogenous and exogenous origin.

Endogenous Origin. A few bacteria can be found in freshly drawn milk, even when milk herds have been thoroughly examined and found sound and healthy, and when the milk has been drawn under as nearly aseptic conditions as possible. Numerous such observations have led to the conclusion that milk as it occurs in the udder is not sterile. The normal udder contains a few bacteria which presumably have entered through the teat canal and become established in the milk-duct system. Such bacteria are of a few types and are present in relatively small numbers, commonly only a few hundred per milliliter at most.

Exogenous Origin. Bacteria of exogenous origin come from a variety of sources including the barn air, the coat of the animal, the hands and clothing of the milker and milk handlers, and the utensils and equipment used in processing the milk for delivery to the consumer. During hand milking bacteria may enter the milk more readily than with machine milking since the milk is more exposed to the dust carried in the barn air, to material from the coat of the animal, to the hands and clothing of the milker, and to flies.

Contamination from exogenous sources during hand milking can be kept at a low level by the use of a small-top milk pail, thereby decreasing surface exposure. Other important precautions include not sweeping or feeding hay shortly before milking, cleaning the coat of the animal with a damp cloth, and washing the udder. The milker should wear clean apparel and wash his hands before milking. Since bacteria are carried in droplets from the respiratory tract, the milker should avoid sneezing, coughing, even talking, over an open pail.

In all milk collection the most important sources of bacterial invasion are the items of dairy equipment. Milk on the farm is commonly strained or filtered to remove any solids which may be present in it. Of little or no value in reducing the bacteria, this operation actually may add bacteria if the strainer is not clean.

All dairy equipment should be so constructed that it can be cleaned readily and thoroughly. Irregular surfaces, seams, and joints make removal of milk residue difficult. Properly maintained milking machines, pipe lines, covered storage tanks, and similar equipment serve to reduce exposure to the environment. Such equipment should be dismantled and promptly washed with cold or tepid water, not hot water, to remove the milk, and then scrubbed in hot water containing a cleansing agent. Just before use the equipment should be rinsed with a fast-acting chemical germicide such as a chlorine or quaternary-ammonium compound. Pipe lines should be constructed and installed in such a way that cleaning can be done satisfactorily without dismantling.

Milk and other dairy products are now widely packaged in single-service paper containers. The accumulated evidence indicates that such containers do not pose any bacteriological problems.

TYPES OF BACTERIA FOUND IN RAW MILK

The types of bacteria which may be present in raw milk are most conveniently considered from the standpoint of physiological groups. Though all types do not appear in every raw-milk sample, each occurs widely.

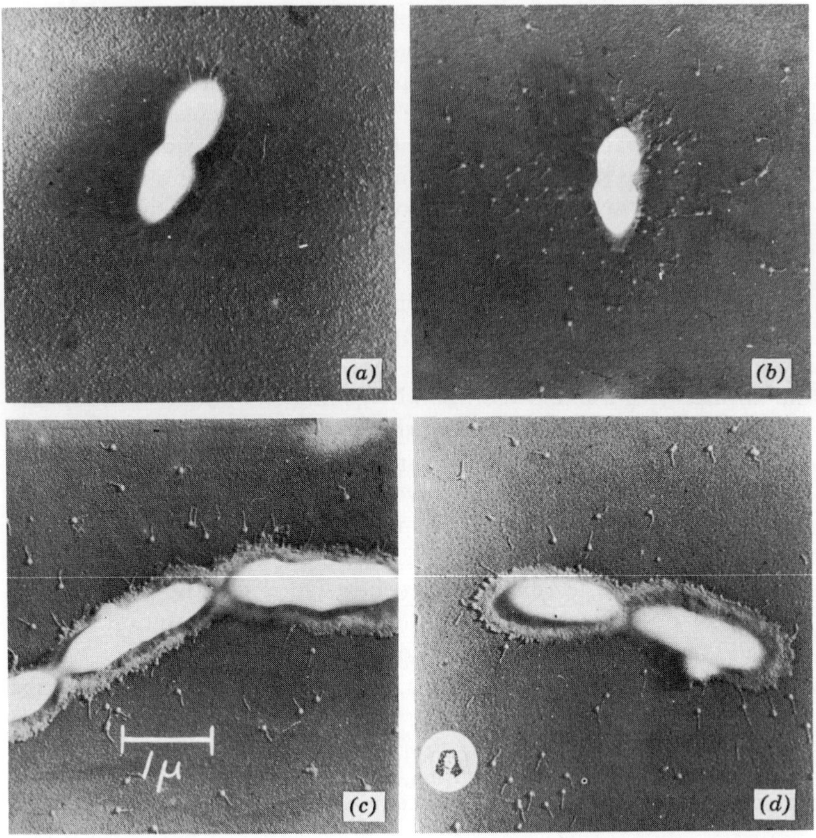

Fig. 19.1. Starter cultures must be protected from attack by bacteriophage. The electron micrographs show (*a*) normal *Streptococcus cremoris*, (*b*) 15 minutes after exposure to phage, (*c*) 45 minutes after phage attack, and (*d*) cells with abnormal morphology bursting. *Photos by Parmelee, Carr, and Nelson: J. Bact., LVII, 391–397, April 1949, courtesy* S.A.B. *LS-283.*

Udder Flora. Relatively few bacterial types are able to exist under the conditions which prevail in a healthy udder. Although rod-shaped forms have been noted, micrococci are most common. This udder flora is sometimes described as inert since it produces only minor changes in milk.

Desirable Fermenters. The most common change occurring in raw milk is nongaseous souring resulting from the production of lactic acid which coagulates the casein. This common change, termed normal fermentation, is caused by organisms of exogenous origin, probably coming chiefly from dust from grain and other feeds. They include

Streptococcus lactis, and related streptococci, and certain *Lactobacillus* types, chiefly *Lactobacillus casei* (Fig. 19.1). Natural souring may serve to check the action of other organisms thus acting as a preservative.

Undesirable Fermenters. Souring by certain yeasts, members of the genus *Clostridium,* or members of the coliform group is accompanied by gas formation and in some instances by disagreeable flavors and odors. The gas may be trapped in the curd and cause extensive foaming. Coliforms, coming chiefly from animal manure or barn dust, are present in most milk by the time it leaves the milking shed. They do not have the same significance as when present in water, but their presence in appreciable numbers does indicate improper attention to dairy sanitation.

Proteolytic Bacteria. The proteins of milk can be broken down by any proteolytic organism which finds its way into milk. Most commonly, the causal organisms are aerobic sporeformers of dust origin. *Streptococcus faecalis* var. *liquefaciens* grows over the range of 10°C to 45°C, best at about 37°C. By a rennin-like enzyme it causes a rapid coagulation of milk of low acidity. Proteolysis begins shortly after coagulation and progresses with the growth of the organism (Fig. 19.2).

In raw milk the aerobic sporeformers are of little significance because they are overgrown by the lactic acid bacteria which survive pasteurization; however, they can germinate and grow without restraint if the milk is held for any length of time within the range of about 20°C to as much as 55°C. A slight amount of protein breakdown imparts a bitter flavor to milk. Even the very slow growth of psychrophilic bacteria occurring in refrigerator storage gives an off-flavor in four to seven days.

Bacteria Producing Unusual Changes. In rare instances the growth of certain bacteria may impart a color to milk. *Pseudomonas synxantha* produces an intense yellow to orange color in cream; *Pseudomonas syncyanea,* growing in sour milk produces a blue color, and various species of *Serratia* produce a red color. Ropy or slimy milk may be caused by several organisms, a common one being *Alcaligenes viscolactis.*

Pathogenic Bacteria. Studies of dairy products as vehicles for the transmission of pathogenic bacteria have so developed and improved dairy production that large outbreaks of milk-borne infectious disease are now uncommon. Diseases which are spread through dairy products fall into two groups: (1) those of animal origin affecting animals only, or both man and animal; and (2) those of human origin.

The bovine disease organisms transmissible to man through milk are

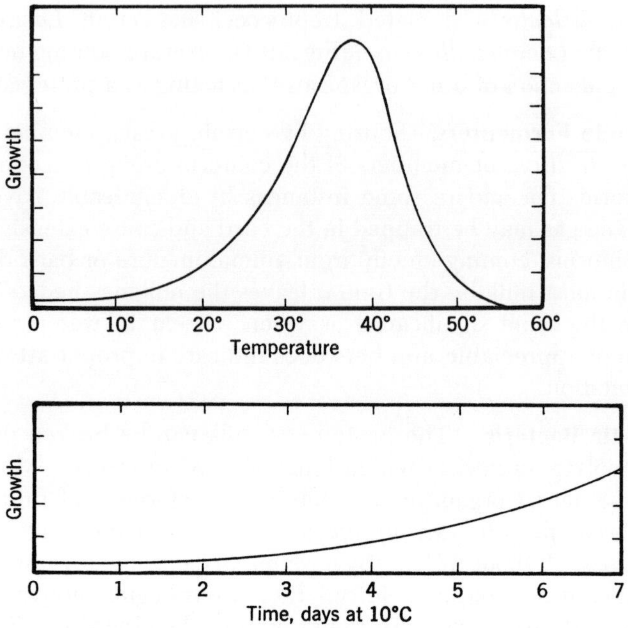

Fig. 19.2. Growth of proteolytic bacteria. Although the optimum temperature of this fecal streptococcus is 37° C, it will make significant growth in a week at 10° C.

those involved in cattle mastitis, tuberculosis, brucellosis, and Q fever. Mastitis, or inflammation of the udder, may be caused by any one of several organisms, the most common being *Streptococcus agalactiae,* which is not pathogenic for man. The closely related human pathogen, *Streptococcus pyogenes,* can also cause mastitis. Septic sore throat or scarlet fever may develop in persons who drink raw milk containing this organism. *Staphylococcus aureus* may also cause mastitis. Some strains of the organism produce an exotoxin which causes severe human gastroenteritis.

At one time bovine tuberculosis was the most significant animal disease transmitted to humans by milk, but this is no longer true in the United States. The detection and elimination from the herd of tubercular cows and the pasteurization of milk have greatly lessened the incidence of milk-borne tuberculosis in areas of the world where these control measures are practiced.

Clearly the most important animal disease transmitted by dairy products at present is brucellosis. Three species of *Brucella* cause brucellosis, or undulant fever, in man: *Brucella abortus,* the cause of contagious abortion, or Bang's disease, in cattle; *Brucella suis,* the cause of a similar condition in swine; and *Brucella melitensis*, the cause of diseased condition in goats. *Brucella abortus* is less virulent for man than either of the others but is of greatest importance in the United States because of its prevalence.

Q fever is a milk-borne febrile disease of man caused by a rickettsial organism *Coxiella burnetii*. This organism is sufficiently resistant to heat to occasionally survive pasteurization.

The intestinal pathogens, easily transmitted human-disease organisms, are introduced into the milk by handlers and can infect the consumer. Diphtheria has been milk-borne in a number of instances; the causal organism usually gains entrance directly from a carrier who is a milk handler or occasionally from a diphtheritic lesion on the udder or teat of the cow. Septic sore throat, scarlet fever, and gastroenteritis may follow direct infection of the milk by a milk handler.

CONTROL OF BACTERIA IN MILK

The contamination of milk can be greatly reduced by guarding against the recognized sources of contamination. As quickly as possible, after collection, the milk should be chilled and held at a low temperature to restrain the growth of organisms unavoidably present in it.

Pasteurization. Though low initial bacterial content can be produced by attention to production sanitation, it remains uncertain that any raw milk, or milk product prepared from raw milk, is completely safe for human consumption. The occurrence of undetected disease in the animal, the possibility of infection from human sources, and the fact that milk is an excellent medium for the survival and growth of bacteria combine to make raw milk a potential hazard to the health of the consumer. Sanitary care in production must be supplemented to insure a raw milk safe for domestic use. Pasteurization effectively treats the milk, ridding it of all harmful microbes.

Pasteurization is a modification of the process developed by Pasteur for the treatment of beer and wine to prevent bacterial deterioration. In the dairy industry pasteurization consists of heating at the minimum time-temperature combination adequate to destroy the most heat-resistant pathogenic organism which might be present—the tubercle bacillus. In practice, a slight increase above the minimum is added as a safety margin to compensate for unavoidable variations in operation which might affect the results. Pasteurization does not sterilize the milk, but it does destroy most of the non-spore-forming bacteria present.

Pasteurization is carried out in two ways: In the low temperature-long time, or holding method, milk is heated in a vat for 30 minutes at 143°F (62°C); by the high temperature-short time, or flash method, the milk is heated at 161°F (72°C) for at least 15 seconds. The holding method is best for small lots of milk; the flash method, which permits continuous operation, is preferable for large lots. After either process the pasteurized milk should be cooled promptly to below 50°F (10°C) and protected against recontamination in all subsequent operations.

The effectiveness of the pasteurization process can be determined by the phosphatase test. Raw milk always contains the enzyme, phosphatase, which is slightly more heat resistant than the tubercle bacillus. If pasteurization has been properly done the enzyme will be destroyed. In the test, a small quantity of milk is added to a solution of disodium phenylphosphate. If active phosphatase is present the compound splits, and the liberated phenol reacts with an indicator giving a blue color.

The public-health value of pasteurization has become so well established that most market milk today is pasteurized. When properly done the nutritive value of the milk is not significantly affected.

BACTERIOLOGICAL EXAMINATION OF DAIRY PRODUCTS

Milk may be examined bacteriologically for the total number of bacteria and for special groups of bacteria. Recommended procedures are described in *Standard Methods for the Examination of Dairy Products* of the American Public Health Association.

Quantitative Determinations—Plate Count. The most widely used procedure for taking the bacterial count of milk is to culture an aliquot in liquefiable solid medium, count the colonies which develop, and calculate the number on the assumption that each colony comes from a single cell (Fig. 19.3). The results of the test are greatly influenced by slight variations in laboratory technique. In any case, the procedure detects only those bacteria which can grow under the conditions of the test. Thus, at best, the recorded count is only an approximation of the true number of bacteria in the sample. Despite the limitations of the plate-count method, the data it yields are adequate to evaluate the bacterial condition of a milk supply.

Direct-Microscopic Count. The most rapid method of determining the total bacterial content of milk is by direct microscopic counting. A measured quantity of milk is spread uniformly over a marked glass slide and stained. The bacteria in a number of fields of known diameter are

Fig. 19.3. A membrane filter through which was passed 10 ml of milk diluted 1:1000. The filter was transferred to a peptone-glucose medium and incubated for 24 hours. The grid marked on the filter facilitates counting the colonies. This filter method is now widely used as a refinement of the plate count. *Photo courtesy Millipore Filter Corp.*

counted. Calculation of the total count requires only simple arithmetic.

Direct microscopic counts allow a rapid determination of the bacterial quality of milk as received at a collecting station; thus satisfactory and unsatisfactory lots are not mixed. Counts of clumps of cells rather than of individual cells give results which most nearly approximate plate counts.

Dye Reduction Tests. Certain dyes which show a difference in color between the oxidized and reduced forms have been used in a rapid test of milk quality. During growth, bacteria exhaust the dissolved oxygen in a medium thereby causing a lowered oxidation-reduction potential at a rate directly related to the number of active cells present. Thus a short reduction time indicates many bacteria, a long time, few. The test does not give an accurate quantitative measure of the bacterial content but does permit the grading of raw milk.

The dyes used may be either methylene blue, which is blue in the oxidized form and colorless when reduced, or resazurin, which changes from blue through pink to colorless with reduction.

Examination for Special Organisms or Groups. Coliforms in milk can be enumerated by plating an aliquot in a differential medium which yields characteristic colonies, such as violet-red-bile agar, or by inoculation of dilutions of the sample into a sufficient number of fermentation tubes of lactose broth to permit statistical calculation of the most probable number. Coliforms are almost always present in raw milk and are not objectionable in very low numbers. Large numbers suggest negligence in production. Their presence in pasteurized milk indicates recontamination after pasteurization.

Wisconsin Curd Test. A test for gas-forming bacteria which interfere with cheese making can be done by coagulating an aliquot of the milk with rennet, pressing out the whey, incubating the curd, and observing for evidence of the growth of undesirable types. Heat resistant or **thermoduric** bacteria, which survive pasteurization, indicate a lack of cleanliness of equipment if present in appreciable numbers. These can be detected by a comparison of results from cultures made before and after pasteurization. True thermophiles can be detected by incubating cultures at an elevated temperature.

GRADING OF MILK

The standards of quality for milk and cream are established by local ordinance and consequently may vary from city to city. In an effort to establish uniformity in production and processing practices, the Public Health Service of the Federal Government recommends the adoption of a standard milk ordinance which specifies in detail the requirements for both farm and dairy plant. The suggested bacteriological procedures are those of the *Standard Methods.*

Bacterial quality is important in determining the grade of market milk. Grades A, B, and C for both raw and pasteurized milk are recognized in the standard ordinance, but most milk today is grade A pasteurized. The maximum numbers of bacteria permitted per milliliter at the time of delivery to the consumer for grades A, raw and pasteurized are:

	Before Pasteurization	After Pasteurization
Grade A raw	50,000	......
Grade A pasteurized	200,000	30,000

The numbers of bacteria permitted are doubled in the case of cream and are disregarded for buttermilk and sour cream.

Certified Milk. Certified milk is produced under the supervision of a medical milk commission only by dairies operated under the rigid specifications of the American Association of Medical Milk Commissions. Developed when much of the market milk was raw milk of indifferent quality, certified milk production was designed to provide safe milk for infant and invalid feeding. It was originally raw milk but today may be either raw or pasteurized. The total count may not exceed 10,000 per milliliter for raw, or 500 for pasteurized, and the coliform count must be less than 10 per milliliter.

Ungraded Milk is a milk which, for some reason, usually a lack of sanitary inspection at the source of production, cannot be assigned a grade. The term indicates a lack of full information and nothing else.

DAIRY PRODUCTS

Fermented milks are produced by growing lactic acid bacteria, either in pure or mixed culture, in raw or whole milk. The acid produced curdles the milk and gives it an agreeable sourness. The characteristic flavors of different types of soured milk result from the types of organisms responsible for the souring, the composition of the milk, or the temperature at which it was incubated.

The use of soured milk goes back beyond recorded history and has been common to all peoples in all countries in which milk was available. Since variations in flavor among batches may sometimes occur with natural souring, dairy plants have adopted standardized production methods with starter cultures. Usually skim milk is heated for about 30 minutes at 180 to 190°F (82 to 88°C), cooled to 70°F (21°C), and inoculated with a starter culture which has been selected on the basis of flavor, production, and activity. The milk is incubated at about 70°F (21°C) until properly acid; the curd is broken to a smooth consistency and then held at about 40°F (5°C) for several hours and bottled. The flavor of the product can be improved by adding 0.1 to 1.2% citric acid or sodium citrate to the milk to serve as a source for diacetyl formation during fermentation. The organisms most commonly used to produce commercial buttermilk are a mixture of *Streptococcus lactis* and *Streptococcus citrovorus.*

Of the many fermented (soured) milks, each is characteristic of specific peoples or areas. Bulgarian buttermilk, which is prepared with *Lactobacillus bulgaricus,* once had considerable vogue as a remedy for autointoxication. Acidophilus milk, a popular fermented milk, is prepared by souring sterilized skim milk with *Lactobacillus acidophilus.* Yoghurt, extensively recommended for special diets, is prepared by fermenting a concentrated milk with a mixture of *Lactobacillus* (probably *L. bulgaricus*) and *Streptococcus thermophilus* at a temperature of from 104 to 115°F (40 to 46°C), followed by fermentation by a film-forming yeast.

Butter. Butter has a very delicate and easily affected flavor. It presents many interesting bacteriological problems in production and in preservation. Commercially produced butter is of two types, sweet cream and sour cream butter. Formerly, most butter was produced from cream which had been soured by lactic acid bacteria, either naturally or following inoculation with a starter culture; however, now sweet cream butter is more popular.

The flavor of sour cream butter is greatly influenced by the culture used in ripening the cream. Earlier, special cultures selected for their ability to produce desirable flavor compounds were strains of *Streptococcus lactis* or related types. Later, mixed cultures of *Strep. lactis, Leuconostoc citrovorum* (*Streptococcus citrovorus*), *Leuconostoc dextranicum,* and *Streptococcus diacetilactis* were introduced. Mixed cultures are used almost exclusively at present. The cream is ripened at 70°F (21°C). The most important desirable flavor component of butter is diacetyl. Sweet cream butter can be given a desirable flavor by incorporating a distillate of starter cultures containing volatile flavor compounds, or by working the culture into the butter.

Organisms which can tolerate the conditions of salt and low moisture found in butter may produce undesirable flavors attributable to the end products of growth or may actually lead to decomposition. Bacterial deterioration is best controlled by the use of only high-quality raw product, pure water, and careful attention to sanitation of plant and equipment.

Butter is not a sterile product. Restraining of bacterial activity by low temperature storage is essential to preserve butter which must be held for extended periods between manufacture and consumption.

Cheese. The essential ingredients for the manufacture of cheese are milk, microorganisms, salt, and, in most cases, rennet. There are about 400 varieties of cheese, representing some 20 general types, prepared by varying the conditions of manufacture and curing.

Cheeses can be divided into three main groups—soft, semihard, and hard cheese—on the basis of the moisture content of the finished product. Cottage cheese and cream cheese are unripened soft cheeses. Other varieties of cheese are ripened by bacteria, molds, or a combination of bacteria and molds.

Good quality cheese is a product of good quality milk. Cheese was once made from raw milk, but, since numerous undesirable types of bacteria may interfere with the ripening process, pasteurized milk is now used for most cheese manufacturing.

In cheese manufacture, milk is warmed to growth temperature, inoculated with lactic acid bacteria, *Streptococcus lactis*, or *Streptococcus cremoris* (Fig. 19.4). These bacteria are allowed to grow for a short time; the milk is then coagulated with rennet, and a firm curd is allowed to form. The curd is cut, the whey allowed to separate, and the remainder is salted, shredded, and pressed into forms for ripening. The appearance and flavor of the ripened cheese are determined by the kind and manner of action of the organisms present, and the technology of manufacture (such things as the way the curd is prepared for ripening and the temperature and time of storage). Most of the semihard and hard cheeses are virtually the same in appearance and flavor before ripening.

Fig. 19.4. Starter culture, one of the agents that causes milk to coagulate, is added to the vat as paddles rotate to stir it thoroughly into the milk. Stainless steel vats of this type hold 18,000 pounds of milk—enough to make 1800 pounds of cheese. *Photo courtesy Kraft Foods.*

Table 19.1. Microbiology of Cheese

Type of Cheese	Name	Organisms Involved in Production and Main Function
Hard	Cheddar	*Streptococcus lactis*—acid production *Lactobacillus casei*—curing
	Swiss	*Propionibacterium freundenreichii* *P. shermanii*—flavor and holes
Semihard	Roquefort	*Penicillium roquefortii*—flavor and color
Soft	Limburger	*Brevibacterium linens*—primarily (actively proteolytic) thought to be responsible for flavor
	Camembert	*Penicillium camembertii*—primarily responsible for flavor *Geotrichum sp.* and *Brevibacterium linens* may be present during ripening Curd inoculated with *P. camemberti*

Practically all the hard cheeses, such as Cheddar or American cheese, are ripened under conditions which favor growth throughout the mass and not on the surface. The soft cheeses such as Limburger and Camembert are ripened by a growth of organisms on the surface, the enzymes concerned in the changes diffusing into the cheese. Semihard cheeses, such as Roquefort, are ripened by a combination of surface and interior growth. The latter is obtained by piercing the cheese with needles inoculated with mold spores to provide access of the oxygen needed for the obligately aerobic mold. The molds used are carefully selected strains of *Penicillium roquefortii*. This organism produces the distinctive flavor as well as the color of the "blue" cheese (Table 19.1).

Microbial deterioration of cheese results largely from molds. Paraffin coating or other wrapping which excludes oxygen prevents mold growth. Wrappings dipped in calcium propionate solution also have been used.

SUMMARY. The microbiologist is interested in milk from the point of view of (1) grading, (2) spoilage, (3) disease, and (4) products. Pasteurization aimed primarily at the tubercle bacillus has eliminated the hazards involved in milk consumption. In the current production of foods that require microbes, such as cheese, modern microbiology imitates the conditions permitting the natural fermentation encountered in the historical development of the product.

20

Food Bacteriology

Whatever is food for man or animal is also food for microorganisms. Following the slaughter of a food animal or the harvesting of a fruit or vegetable, decomposition begins. Natural enzymes of the food cause part of the decay, but most results from the growth of microorganisms which were naturally present or were added in the handling of the food. If the activity of the food enzymes and microorganisms is not inhibited or controlled, decomposition proceeds until the foodstuff is no longer acceptable to a discriminating consumer. The extent to which decomposition may proceed before food is inedible varies with the foodstuff and the consumer. Some products, beef especially, may be improved by a limited amount of enzymatic and microbial activity. Both nationally and individually, certain items of food are preferred which evidence a deteriorative change. However, any foodstuff may finally reach a stage at which it is unacceptable. Prevention of deteriorative changes is the primary objective of food preservation.

The activity of microorganisms often produces desirable changes in the flavor or texture of a foodstuff. Thus decomposition may be controlled and directed to yield a product of distinctive character.

Occasionally a food may become contaminated with a pathogenic organism. Though most pathogenic bacteria can sometimes be food-borne, a few which are frequently transmitted by food are considered of greatest importance in food-borne illness. These organisms are especially likely to soil food because of their origin in nature, the way the food preparation is conducted, and their ability to survive and grow in the food.

FOOD SPOILAGE

No food, whether in its natural environment or in its preparation for use, is free of microorganisms. Yeast, molds, and bacteria are always present, and any one or all of these microbes may take part in food deterioration. The type of organism concerned in food spoilage is determined by the nature of the specific product. Likewise, the rapidity of spoilage is affected by the characteristics of the food. Yeast, molds, and bacteria do not grow at the same rate under similar natural conditions of exposure, and an environment which favors one will rarely, if ever, equally favor the others.

All natural foodstuffs are acid in reaction. If the food is high in acid—pH 4.5 or less—virtually all bacteria will be inhibited since few can tolerate acid (Fig. 20.1). Yeasts and molds are most often encountered in spoilage of such foods. In some instances molds are more common and in others, yeasts; in a few cases yeasts, molds, and acid-tolerant bacteria may all occur. Microbial spoilage under acid conditions is chiefly a breakdown of nonproteinaceous constituents of the food; the food gives off the rather distinctive odors of fermentation and its texture is softened.

Foods low in moisture are subject to mold attack, since molds gener-

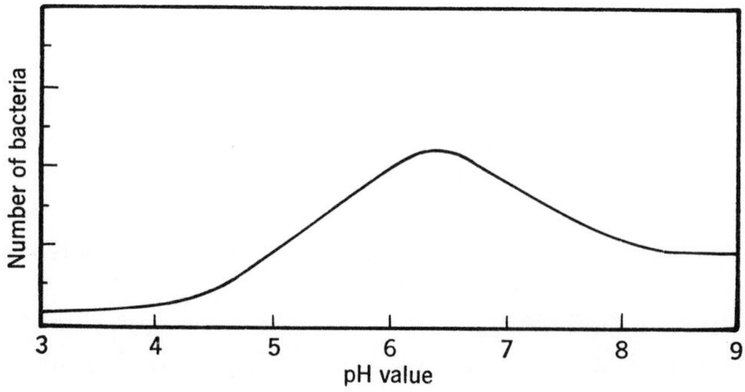

Fig. 20.1. A pH curve for a bacterial culture isolated from spoiled food. Food spoilage bacteria grow slowly at pH values below 5, and under such conditions they usually yield to yeasts and molds.

ally grow at lower levels of moisture than do yeasts or bacteria. Thus fats and fatty foods may support only mold growth. Bacteria sometimes grow in microscopic droplets of water within a fatty foodstuff, but growth is rarely if ever as luxuriant as in food with more abundant moisture. Short-chain organic acids, such as butyric, may occur among the breakdown products and impart rancid odors and flavors.

Bacteria are most active in foods with a reaction nearer the neutral point—pH 5.5 to 6.5—and with a moisture content of 45% or more. They act chiefly on the protein component of the food. Protein-breakdown products may serve as flavor contributors when present in low concentrations, as in the flavorful cheeses. However, when deterioration is well advanced, the nitrogenous and sulfur-containing volatile end products render the food too disagreeable in odor for consumption. Changes in texture and a darkening in color characterize advanced decomposition.

FOOD PRESERVATION

Fresh, succulent foods contain enzymes and carry microorganisms which cause spoilage unless their activity is restrained. Food preservation inhibits or delays the deteriorative changes attributable to these agencies without impairing the nutritive value of the food. The palatability of a foodstuff is important in preservation. Little is gained if preservation processes yield a product which is unsavory to the consumer. Food preservation, then, is designed to preserve the physical structure of the food in such a way that its nutritive value and overall quality are maintained.

Theoretically, any procedure, chemical, physical, or biological, which will interfere with microbial activity is adaptable to food preservation. In actual practice, not all are. A substance such as formaldehyde, for example, interferes with microbial activity but does not meet the minimum requirements for an acceptable food preservative.

Under any method of preservation, food must be handled carefully to keep the load of contaminating microorganisms at as low a level as possible. Practical food-preservation operations are geared, at best, to moderate contamination and may fail if the contamination is excessive or includes unusually resistant types. The useful life of many foodstuffs would be measured in days if it were not for the intervention of man. The procedures which man has found suitable for extending storage life include: (1) Salting and sugar preserving; (2) Pickling and fermenting; (3) Dehydration; (4) Refrigeration; (5) Chemical preserving; (6) Canning; and (7) Radiation sterilization.

SALTING AND SUGAR PRESERVING

Salting. The use of sodium chloride to prevent spoilage of meats antedates recorded history. The demand for heavily salted meat and fish has decreased in the past century because new preservation methods yield a more palatable product. Food may be salted by immersion in brine or by dry salting. Distribution of the salt throughout the tissue is most rapid from brine, but penetration during dry salting is sufficiently rapid to be effective.

Not all microorganisms are equally affected by salt. In general gram-negative bacteria are more sensitive than gram-positive; anaerobes are more sensitive than aerobes or faculative forms, and rods are more easily inhibited than cocci. Most bacteria are restrained by about 5 to 15% salt concentration, some being inhibited by as low as 3% salt. A few forms, however, grow up to saturation. Yeasts and molds may grow at relatively high salt levels—greater than 15%—if conditions are otherwise suitable. As a food preservative, salt is generally a bacteriostatic agent, not a bactericide. Though the action of sodium chloride is not fully understood, it results in part from osmosis or dehydration. A specific toxic effect and some interference with enzyme action, especially proteolytic enzymes, are also involved.

Chiefly meats and fish are preserved by salting. Salt-tolerant microorganisms, some of which are pigmented and some luminescent, may cause deterioration of properly salted foods. Frank spoilage of heavily salted foods is uncommon.

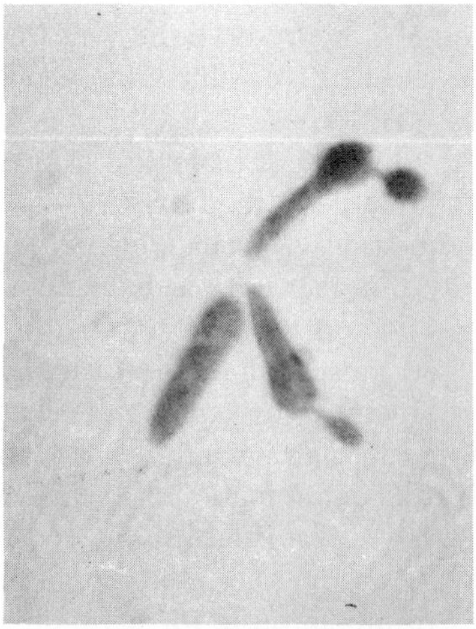

Fig. 20.2. A yeast isolated from fruit preserves where it caused spoilage of the highly sugared product.

Sugar Preserving. The most important use of sugar in the food industry is to improve flavor and maintain good appearance in fruits. In high concentration, it acts as a preservative in such products as fruit jams and jellies and sweetened condensed milk. The storage life of the heavily sweetened product is greatly extended over that of the same material without added sugar, but slow growth of yeasts (Fig. 20.2) and molds at sugar concentrations up to as much as 70% can eventually

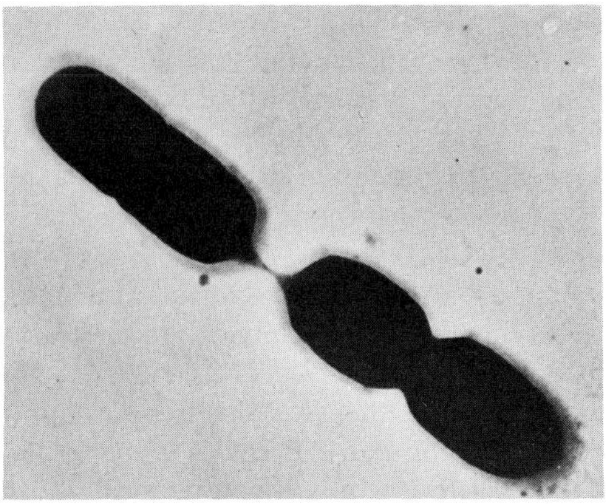

Fig. 20.3. Electron micrograph of the gram-positive, non-spore-forming, acid-producing rod, *Lactobacillus acidophilus.* Like all lactic acid bacteria, the lactobacilli are weakly or not at all proteolytic and are relatively tolerant of acid. *Photo by Mudd, Polevitzky, and Anderson: J. Arch. Pathol., XXXIV, 199–207, 1942, courtesy S.A.B. LS-78.*

cause spoilage. Therefore, heat treatment is usually employed to destroy low-resistant forms in sugar preserving. The finished product, of course, must be protected against contact with the air to prevent reinfection. The action of sugar seems to be a purely osmotic effect.

FERMENTATION AND PICKLING

The storage life of some foodstuffs is considerably extended by creating a pH in the food which is unfavorable for the growth of most spoilage-causing bacteria. In pickling, a preformed edible acid, such as acetic acid in the form of vinegar, is added to the food; in fermentation the food carbohydrates are acted on by microorganisms yielding lactic acid, which gives the final product a desirable flavor and texture. Minor changes in the fat and protein components of the food during fermentation also may contribute to the flavor.

The organisms which ferment most foods are members of the family *Lactobacilliaceae* (Fig. 20.3). These bacteria are somewhat tolerant of both salt and acid. Thus, salt added to a food material to be fermented inhibits most of the contaminating organisms, especially the proteolytic ones, and selectively favors the growth of the *Lactobacilli.* Acid production renders the food unfavorable for the growth of all except acid-tolerant microorganisms, chiefly yeasts and molds. Through its osmotic action, salt extracts, from the food, the cell fluids containing sugar and other soluble cell constituents. The sugar is acted on by the microorganisms and broken down to various products of metabolism. The brine solution is diluted by the fluid drawn from the tissue cells. Consequently, close control of the salt level during the early days of a fermentation is essential to maintain its selective action.

Vegetables which are preserved by lactic fermentation in salt brine include cabbage, as sauerkraut; cucumbers, as salt stock for pickles; and okra, corn, green beans, and olives (Table 20.1). Fermented dairy products include butter and cheese. Silage is an important fermented animal food, especially for dairy herds. Silage is produced from a variety of such agricultural plants as young corn, maize, or pea vines. The fermentable carbohydrate content of the plant material being made into silage is often fortified by the addition of agricultural molasses.

In some products, such as catsup in which acidity has an important role, a preformed acid, usually acetic acid in the form of vinegar, is added instead of producing acid in the food by fermentation. Citric acid is also extensively used in the food industry.

Table 20.1. Some Natural Food Fermentations

	Sauerkraut	*Pickles*	*Olives*
Raw Material	Cabbage	Cucumbers	Green Olives
Preparation	Cabbage is shredded and packed in salt, and weights are applied. The action of the weight and salt withdraws juice from the cabbage.	Fresh cucumbers are packed in tanks and covered with brine.	Green olives are washed first in dilute lye to remove some bitterness and then in water. Washed olives are packed in oak barrels, and brine is added at once.
Salt Concentration	2.5%	10–20%	12%
Organisms involved in fermentation	*Leuconostoc mesenteroides* *Lactobacillus brevis* *L. plantarum* *L. pentosus*	*Lactobacillus plantarum*	*Lactobacillus pentosus* or *L. plantarum* or *L. brevis*

Undesirable contaminants may interfere with the fermentation and cause serious damage in instances where the proper salt concentration has not been maintained. Spoilage of the finished product by acid-tolerant organisms will occur if the food is not protected against contamination. If such organisms use much of the acid of the food in their growth, the pH becomes favorable for the growth of a variety of bacteria, and decomposition results.

DEHYDRATION

Microorganisms require a certain level of moisture for growth, about 40% for bacteria, probably about the same for yeast, and substantially less for molds. The keeping quality of a foodstuff, obviously, is closely associated with its water content. Dehydration as a means of food preservation is based on reducing the water content of the food below the level necessary for the growth of microorganisms.

Dehydration is, perhaps, the oldest form of food preservation. Such foods as peas, beans, rice, and cereal grains are preserved naturally by water loss with maturity. At some prehistoric time, man began consciously to preserve fruits, vegetables, and meats by drying. In warm dry climates foods were dried by exposure to the sun's rays. In humid regions fire and smoke were used. Each method is still used today, both commercially and privately.

Theoretically, dehydration has much to offer as a method of food preservation. Reduction of bulk by water removal at the place of production, and restoration at the place of consumption, permits tremendous savings in transportation and warehousing. Dehydration has been successfully and extensively used for many years for such foods as fruits and fish. Considerable manufacturing use has been made of dried onion flakes, garlic, and chili peppers in preference to the fresh product. Modern procedures of **lyophilizing** (drying from the frozen state) are yielding more acceptable products.

PRESERVATION AT LOW TEMPERATURE

Storage at low temperature is an old and effective method of food preservation, either frozen storage well below freezing or refrigeration at a temperature near, but still above, freezing. A low temperature prevents, or retards, the growth of many spoilage microorganisms. Since enzyme action continues slowly at low temperature, those foods which are subject to enzymic deterioration must be blanched before freezing to inactivate the enzymes.

Development of the frozen food industry has been encouraged by the introduction of mechanical refrigeration into the market and home. Frozen foods are not sterile but do have a long storage life if held in the frozen condition. Once food is thawed, the cellular juices leak from the frost damaged cells and the contaminating bacteria resume activity and quickly cause spoilage unless arrested by cooking.

There are two methods for preparing frozen foods. Quick freezing is accomplished in 30 minutes or less by blowing air at $-34°C$ over the food. In slow freezing greater deterioration of vitamins takes place; autolysis is not immediately stopped, and the formation of larger ice crystals results in tissue damage.

PRESERVATION BY CHEMICALS

In preservation by a chemical additive, an antimicrobial substance not toxic for the consumer is incorporated in the food. There are few such substances. Antioxidants, which do not have antimicrobial properties, are not ordinarily regarded as chemical preservatives. Salt, sugar, vinegar, spices, alcohol, or wood smoke have preservative action but are usually added for their flavor, sometimes to mask deteriorative flavors.

Prior to the development of the Pure Food and Drug Act, a number of substances were used as food preservatives which are no longer permitted. Some of these, particularly boric acid, or borax, and salicylic acid, persisted in home use long after elimination at the commercial level. Chemical preservatives are never a substitute for care in selection and cleanliness in preparation of the foodstuff for processing. Use of chemical food preservatives is controlled by rigid specifications and supervision by federal and state agencies.

Sodium and calcium propionates are widely used as mold inhibitors. The shelf-life of bakery products can be extended by incorporation of propionate in the mix. Surface molding of moist packaged commodities can be restrained by wrappings which have been dipped in propionate solution. Sodium benzoate is permitted only in products which constitute a minor part of the diet. Sorbic acid is an effective inhibitor of yeasts and molds (Table 20.2).

Some broad-spectrum antibiotics have been approved as a dip for poultry, and their use may in time extend to other foodstuffs which require cooking before use. The shelf-life of poultry under refrigeration can be extended several days by antibiotic dipping. The small amount of antibiotic remaining on the fowl is destroyed in cooking. Close control of the operation is essential. If drug-fast variants of

Table 20.2. Chemical Preservatives Currently in Use in the United States

Chemical	Examples of Foods where Used
1. Sulfur dioxide	Dried fruits, fruit juice
2. Ethylene oxide	Fruits, spices
3. Smoke	Meat and fish
4. Propionic acid and propionate salts	Bread, cake, pie crust, figs, berries, food wrappers
5. Benzoic acid and benzoate salts	Beverages, relishes, jams, ice for fish storage
6. Sorbic acid	Syrups, cheeses, margarine, salads, candy
7. Sodium hypochlorite	Washing fruits and vegetables
8. Broad spectrum antibiotics (Chlorotetracycline, etc.)	Poultry, vegetables, ice for fish storage

spoilage significance develop in the dipping vat, the procedure will, of course, cease to be effective.

Gaseous ethylene oxide is very effective in the sterilization of foods, such as spices, which cannot be treated satisfactorily by other methods. The food material is sealed in a chamber; a vacuum is created and released either with pure ethylene oxide or with ethylene oxide mixed with carbon dioxide to reduce the explosion hazard. Sulfur dioxide treatment of dried fruits eliminates insect infestation as well as mold growth.

CANNING

In the canning process, food is preserved by heat sterilization in a hermetically sealed container. Heating destroys the organisms present in the container; hermetic sealing prevents the entrance of others. The combination of time and temperature required to destroy the most heat-resistant spoilage microorganism for a particular food is termed the **process** for that food. Processes vary, depending on the chemical and physical natures of the foodstuff and the size of the container. Acid foods, such as fruits and tomatoes, require only mild heating to destroy yeasts, molds, and acid-tolerant bacteria. Low-acid foods, such as corn and peas, require a process severe enough to destroy heat-resistant spores. The sterilization process requires more heat and/or time than is necessary to cook the food to edibility. The nutritive value of a food is not affected by processing, although the flavor and texture may be.

Spoilage of canned foods may result from under-processing or from container leakage. In most cases of under-processing the contaminating organisms have spores of unusually high resistance, although infrequently heavy contamination with large numbers of spores of moderate resistance will result in such spoilage.

Of the three main types of spoilage due to under-processing, the most frequently observed is the **flat sour,** in which acid without accompanying gas is produced by *Bacillus stearothermophilus.* Since gas is not formed, the container is flat, hence the descriptive name. This spoilage is most commonly encountered in low acid foods, such as peas and corn (Table 20.3).

The second most common cause of spoilage is *Clostridium thermosaccharolyticum.* Since this organism produces large amounts of gas as well as acid from the food sugar, the container becomes swollen (**hard swell**) and frequently bursts. This spoilage occurs in semi-acid foods, such as greens and asparagus, as well as in low acid foods.

Both types of spoilage are caused by a thermophilic organism, and neither presents any hazard to health. The large amount of lactic acid which is formed as the major metabolic end product renders the food too sour to eat. Microscopic examination of the spoiled food shows large numbers of bacteria, but cultures will not yield growth unless made early. This condition of high acidity which quickly kills out the bacteria is known as **autosterilization.** Occasionally contamination with heat-resistant spores of mesophilic soil anaerobes may cause the spoilage characterized by a swollen container and putrefactive decomposition of the food.

In all cases of under-processing the causal organism is present in pure culture, and the food is uniform in appearance and odor. However,

Table 20.3. Microbial Spoilage of Canned Foods

Organism	*pH Range*	*Type of Change*
Bacillus stearothermophilus	5.3 and above	Flat sour
Bacillus thermoacidurans	4.2 and above	Flat sour
Clostridium thermosaccharolyticum	4.8 and above	Acid and gas (hard swell)
Clostridium nigrificans	5.3 and above	Putrefaction, blackening
Clostridium sporogenes	Above 4.5	Putrefaction, blackening
Yeasts	3.7 and below	Yeasty odor

when spoilage is caused by container leakage the food is quite varied in appearance and odor and a variety of organisms are present, including non-spore-forming types such as cocci.

RADIATION STERILIZATION

Ultraviolet radiation is used to control surface contamination of some foods and to sterilize sugar under special conditions. In recent years other types of radiation have been used experimentally. Perfected methods of radiation sterilization would avoid the difficulties of handling food at low temperature and might have some advantages over thermal processing.

Sterilization can be effected by exposure to a beam of electrons, beta radiation, or by exposure to electromagnetic radiation in the form of gamma rays. Beta rays do not penetrate deeply and hence have little importance for food treatment. Gamma rays, which are more penetrating, have a limited practical use. Unfortunately, some foods develop disagreeable flavors when treated sufficiently to inactivate the food enzymes and kill contaminating microorganisms. Effective radiation doses are now known, that is, those ranges necessary for enzyme denaturation, sterilization, pasteurization, and reduction of total bacterial population. However, much more research is necessary before radiation sterilization can be widely used.

ILLNESS RESULTING FROM FOOD

Bacteriologists use the term **food poisoning** to describe illness arising from the consumption of (1) food infected with certain types of living bacteria, or of (2) food in which certain bacteria have grown and produced toxic substances (Table 20.4). Illness following the consumption of poisonous plants, fungi, fish and shellfish, or food accidentally or maliciously contaminated with toxic chemicals are not included.

Although food may serve as a vehicle for the transfer of almost any pathogenic microorganism, food poisoning is limited to illnesses caused by a few microorganisms. The chief offenders, in decreasing order of frequency of occurrence, are: *Staphylococcus, Salmonella,* alpha type *Streptococcus,* and *Clostridium botulinum* (see Chapter 17). Before the true relationship of bacteria to food poisoning was recognized, illness resulting from unwholesome food was attributed to basic nitrogenous products of protein breakdown known as ptomaines. It is now accepted that food illness is not due to ptomaines and that the term

Table 20.4. General Outline for Laboratory Diagnosis of Food Poisoning

Food Sample

A	B	C. (Special procedures for identification of botulinum toxin)	
Direct microscopic examination: estimation of contamination load, types of organisms	Enrichment broth ↓ Plating on differential and/or selective media ↓ Incubation 20–24 hr at 37°C ↓ Isolated organisms: Biochemical tests phage typing (*Staph.*) Serotaxonomy (Salmonella) ↓ Animal injection or feeding (used primarily in diagnosis of botulism), e.g., Dolman Kitten Test for *Staph.* enterotoxin	Animal feeding or injection 1. Test animal unprotected 2. a. Control animal heated food sample b. Control animal protected with specific antitoxin ↓ Note condition of animals: Development of flaccid paralysis Death	Enrichment cultures for *Clostridium botulinum* ↓ Proceed with animal tests

"ptomaine poisoning" is a misnomer. Ptomaines are not toxic when taken by mouth, even in high concentrations. In low concentrations, they serve as flavor contributors in such foods as ripened cheeses.

Bacteriological examination of foods suspected of having caused food poisoning sometimes shows large numbers of one or another organism of uncertain etiological relationship to the illness, such as *Pseudomonas, Proteus,* molds, coliforms, or sporeforming rods. Probably the ingestion of large amounts of bacterial protein cause a minor digestive upset in some persons, but no one of these is significant as a cause of food poisoning.

Excluding botulism, which was discussed in Chapter 17, the two groups of major significance are the staphylococci and the salmonellae. Food is contaminated with staphylococci by food handlers with boils, cuts, or sores on the hands or fingers, or by handlers who sneeze or cough frequently. Protection against *Salmonella* infection of food is not so simple. *Salmonella* carriers can be found among healthy food animals, chiefly swine and poultry, and *Salmonella* infection of eggs is common. Thus, naturally infected food, which cannot be differentiated from noninfected food, may be encountered. *Salmonellae* may be introduced into food through poor personal sanitary habits of a carrier who is a food handler, and by rodents and vermin. Complete reliance cannot be placed on cooking as a sterilizing measure, but thorough cooking will serve to reduce the contamination even if it does not eliminate it.

Foods, which are "fingered and fussed over," such as croquettes, filler for cream-filled pastries, and salads, prepared well in advance of the meal and not stored properly either before or after cooking are responsible for most cases and outbreaks of food illness. Leftover foods are potential sources of food poisoning even when handled with great care and should not be used, especially for mass feeding, if they have remained unrefrigerated for even a few hours.

SUMMARY. Microbiology in the food industry is involved in food spoilage by bacteria, molds, and yeasts. It is also concerned with food and utensils as vehicles for carrying pathogens from the sick to the well. The illnesses which result from eating foods made toxic by microbial growth are referred to as food poisoning. In food processing where microbes modify flavor and textures, the microbiologist must inhibit the undesirable organisms and promote those useful to his purpose. In most of these processes the organisms or sequences of organisms are well-known and many are carried out by selected strains cultured in the microbiology laboratory.

21

Industrial Application of Microbiology

The development of microbiology into an important scientific discipline is a consequence of investigations initially concerned with infectious diseases. The studies of pathogenic bacteria led to a better understanding of the activities of microorganisms in general, and specifically of those concerned in such historic processes as the leavening of bread, the retting of flax, and the manufacture of wine and beer. Modern microbiology has improved these processes and developed many others in which the activity of microorganisms is economically significant. Today many microbiologists are employed by industry to study microbes and to learn how to put them to profitable use.

Several factors determine whether a microbiological industrial process is practicable and profitable. Organisms may be required which will produce a desired end product by their metabolic activity. Sometimes this is a fairly easy task, but again the search may be long and tedious. Even if an organism is found, the yield of end product may be too low to permit its profitable use. In such cases, "training" the organism, or mutating by exposure to some such mutagen as ultraviolet light, may succeed in developing a high-yielding strain. The medium must be studied to determine optimum conditions of aeration, concentration of medium components, pH, and temperature.

Industrial microbiology can be divided into several categories.

1. The production of microbial cells or cell material.
2. The production of fermentation products.
3. The modification of materials to make more valuable products.
4. The use of microorganisms to eliminate undesirable materials.
5. The deteriorative effects of microorganisms as they affect industry.

The Production of Microorganisms. Yeast is produced in large quantities for use in leavening bread. A pure culture of the selected yeast strain is transferred from a test tube to a flask, and, after good growth is obtained, this inoculum is "built up" by transfer to larger volumes of broth until sufficient inoculum is obtained for a large fermentation tank. Great care must be taken to exclude contamination at any stage in the process. The yield of cells is favored by cultivation under aerobic conditions. The crop of cells is harvested by centrifuging and filtering and marketed as a moist cake, dried and marketed as dry yeast cake, or processed to yield an effective complex of enzymes.

Yeast may also be cultivated for consumption as food. Yeast cells are rich in most of the nutrients required for animal nutrition. Enormous quantities of yeast are produced in the brewing of beer and are reclaimed and processed into animal food. Wood chips used in the manufacture of paper must first be cooked in sulfite liquor to extract the soluble constituents of the wood. *Torula utilis*, a yeast with a satisfactory flavor, has been grown in such waste sulfite liquor and harvested for food use. The culture of algae for food has received extensive study and is employed commercially in Japan.

The strain of *Rhizobium*, which fixes nitrogen with any legume, is specific for that particular plant and is usually present in the soil in low numbers. Furthermore, these organisms in their natural environment are often inefficient fixers of nitrogen. Hence, the inoculation of seed of various legumes with selected, highly efficient strains of *Rhizobium* increases yields and is commonly used wherever a legume is grown as a main crop. Industrial laboratories devoted to the production of cultures of *Rhizobium* are an important adjunct to agriculture.

Laboratories for the production of starter cultures for the manufacture of dairy products are of great industrial importance. Such cultures are used in the manufacture of buttermilk and the special types of soured milk, such as acidophilus, in the ripening of cheese and in the ripening of cream for processing into sour cream butter. The organisms are strains of *Lactobacillus* and *Streptococcus* selected to contribute the desired characteristics of flavor, odor, and texture to the final product.

One important phase of the biological industry is the mass cultivation of organisms to be used in vaccines. The bacteria may be grown in the usual way, as in the preparation of vaccine for prophylaxis against pertussis, or the vaccine against typhoid and paratyphoid fevers. Viruses and rickettsiae for processing into antiviral vaccines can be grown in fertile eggs (Fig. 21.1), in tissue culture, or in animals. Toxins and

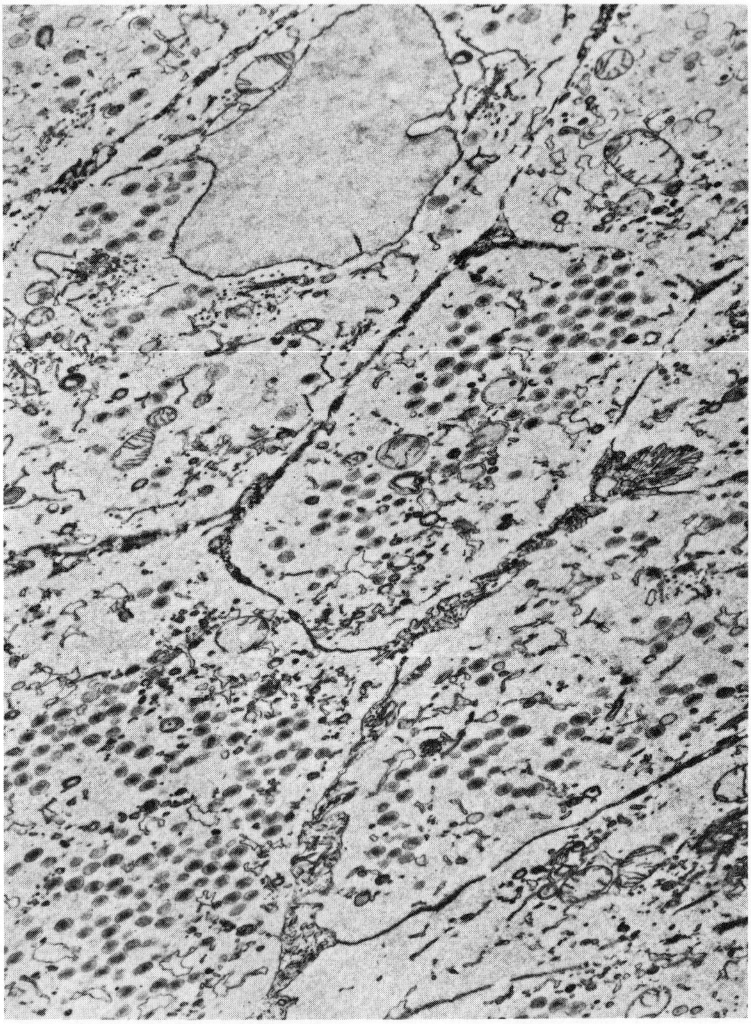

Fig. 21.1. The cells from the chick embryo shown in this electron micrograph are heavily infected with the virus employed for making smallpox vaccine. *Photo by Norton McDuffie, Univ. of Texas.*

toxoids are prepared for prophylaxis and for diagnostic reagents. All such products must be tested for effectiveness and for safety. Conditions for manufacture are carefully controlled. The expanded use of biologicals in veterinary medicine has opened a huge market in that field. Recently biological insecticides have been produced by mass cultivation of microorganisms. Sprays of *Bacillus thuringiensis* are very effective against the alfalfa caterpiller, the tobacco hornworm, and the worm variously known as the corn earworm, the cotton bollworm, and the tomato worm. The bacterial spray is harmless to the plant and to other animals, including humans.

The Production of Fermentation Products. The fermentations industry is that branch of industrial microbiology which produces useful products through the action of microorganisms. These processes may involve carbohydrate breakdown to produce the solvents, alcohol, acetone, and butanol; or the acids, lactic, citric, gluconic, and acetic; or the sugar, sorbose. Fermentation processes yielding the vitamins, riboflavin and cyanocobalamin (B_{12}); the amino acids, lysine and glutamic acid, as well as those yielding the antibiotics, require specialized media for the formation of these nitrogen-containing substances. Many other products can be produced by fermentation, and this list is likely to be expanded to include new products as new processes are developed. Some products will be removed from the list as the chemists work out methods for synthesis that are cheaper than production with microbes.

The alcohol fermentation, wherein the yeast *Saccharomyces cerevisiae* converts sugar almost quantitatively to ethyl alcohol and carbon dioxide, is still the largest volume process, although in the United States about 75% of the industrial alcohol (this excludes beverage alcohol) is produced from petroleum by chemical synthesis. Fermentation alcohol production may utilize a cheap sugar source, such as molasses, or it may employ grain in which the starch is first converted to sugar by amylase from sprouted barley (malt). Some alcohol is produced through fermentation of the paper mill wastes (the sulfite liquors), which contain sugars extracted from wood pulp. In northern Europe cellulose waste, such as sawdust, is utilized following conversion to sugar by boiling with mineral acids.

In all these processes, a mash is made by adding such yeast nutrients as ammonia and phosphate. The pH is adjusted to a value of about 4.0 to inhibit most bacteria, and since the fermentation is an anaerobic process, molds fail to develop. Furthermore, the large inoculum of a yeast strain, selected for rapid development in the mash, outgrows any contamination, and a successful fermentation is complete in two days without costly sterilization of the mash. Cooling coils in the tanks remove the heat produced by the fermentation and maintain the temperature at about 25° C. The alcohol is recovered by distillation and the residual "slops" may be concentrated for feed or fertilizer.

The butanol-acetone fermentation was developed during World War I, based on research done by Chaim Weismann, a scientist-politician who became the first president of Israel. The sporeforming, anaerobic *Clostridium acetobutylicum* is inoculated into a mash prepared by cooking 10% ground corn in water. No malt is necessary since *Clostridium acetobutylicum* produces its own starch-digesting enzyme. The pH at the beginning of the fermentation is about 6 and at the end it is about 4. Calcium carbonate is added if necessary to neutralize excess acid. The temperature is maintained at 37° C, and after 48 hours the solvents are separated by fractional distillation. From 100 lb of corn the yield will be about 16 lb of butyl alcohol, 7 lb of acetone and 2 lb of ethyl alcohol. When molasses is used as a substitute for corn, other strains of clostridia are employed.

Although many lactic acid bacteria (streptococci and lactobacilli) as well as molds of the genus *Rhizopus* yield lactic acid almost quantitatively from sugar, most fermentation lactic acid is produced anaerobically using strains of *Lactobacillus delbrueckii.* The sugar mashes are adjusted to a pH of 5 and the temperature is maintained at 45° C. The organism requires a rich medium containing vitamins and amino acids. The acid is neutralized with calcium carbonate and when the fermentation is complete, the liquor is concentrated by evaporation to precipitate the crude calcium lactate. Edible and pharmaceutical grades of lactic acid are purified from this crude product.

Aerobic fermentations usually involve incomplete oxidations. A number of these processes involve *Acetobacter suboxydans* which carries out restricted oxidations to give useful products. Among the industrial processes now in use, this acetobacter converts glycerol to dihydroxyacetone, a substance widely used in suntan lotions. It will also convert sorbitol to sorbose, a sugar subjected to further chemical manipulations to produce vitamin C (ascorbic acid). *L. delbrueckii* has been used to ferment glucose to gluconic acid and to 5-ketogluconic acid, although the former compound is produced more efficiently by molds of the genera *Penicillium* and *Aspergillus.*

The partial oxidation of ethyl alcohol to acetic acid by the highly aerobic gram-negative rod, *Acetobacter aceti,* is the basis of vinegar production. The commercial vinegar fermentation is usually carried out in a generator where a 10% alcohol solution is sprayed over and percolates through a 10 foot layer of wood shavings. A counter current of air is pumped up through this container to supply the oxygen to the acetobacter, which grows as a gelatinous zoogleal mass attached to the wood.

The raw material is usually hard cider or wine, but diluted alcohol may be used if it is enriched with peptone or other organic material to stimulate the growth of the organism.

Citric acid was once obtained from cull citrus fruits. Now most of it is produced by *Aspergillus niger* growing in shallow uncovered pans on a 15% sugar solution, adjusted to about pH 2, and enriched with ammonium and mineral salts. Because of the simple medium, the high sugar content, the low pH, and the large inoculum, contamination is not a problem. The mold forms a pad on the surface; after almost quantitative conversion of the sugar to citric acid, the medium may be replaced and the mold pad may ferment a new batch of sugar. The citrate is recovered from the broth by precipitating it as a calcium salt. The fermentation product is believed to result from a defective respiration involving a failure to convert citrate efficiently to the next compound in the citric acid cycle. Therefore, citrate accumulates in the cells and is excreted into the medium. The mold used is a strain selected for this defect, or the medium may be made deficient so as to cause the failure in further metabolism of the respiratory intermediate.

The production of vitamins, amino acids, and antibiotics involves moderate pH and rich nitrogenous media wherein contamination cannot be tolerated. The problems of maintaining sterility in this industry have taxed the ingenuity of fermentation engineers (Fig. 21.2). These products are usually produced in small amounts in the broth, and methods of recovery may involve countercurrent extraction with solvents, adsorption on colloidal substances such as charcoal, as well as precipitation as insoluble salts.

Vitamin B_{12} is produced in a cobalt enriched organic medium by a wide variety of microbes. The processes actually employed by the industries are often secret, but it is known that strains of *Propionbacterium freudenreichii, Bacillus megaterium,* and *Streptomyces olivaceous* produce high yields of B_{12} under industrial procedures. Riboflavin for the pharmaceutical industry is produced mainly by chemical synthesis, but that used for animal feed is produced by fermentation. The mold *Ashbya gossypii* or the yeast-like *Eremothecium ashbyii* is inoculated into a sterile medium containing approximately 1% of a crude sugar, 1% corn steep liquor, 0.5% of some peptone derived from an animal source, together with an antifoaming agent. After aeration for 4 days the broth, together with the cells and products, are dried for incorporation into animal feed; such concentrates may contain up to 2.5% riboflavin.

Lysine is an amino acid which is often deficient in the foods of people living on a restricted diet. A mutant of *Escherichia coli* grown under suitable conditions will release into the medium large quantities of the distinctive bacterial cell wall constituent, diaminopimelic acid.

Fig. 21.2. Filtration. When the yield of fermentation products is at its peak in the huge fermentor, the contents of the fermentor are drawn off and passed through rotary vacuum filters, where the mycelium is filtered off. This is the first step in the recovery of the fermentation product from the culture liquor. *Photo courtesy Chas. Pfizer & Co.*

Removal of a carboxyl group from diaminopimelic acid yields lysine; this can be done by an enzyme produced by *Aerobacter aerogenes*. Glutamic acid is produced by many organisms in a glucose-ammonia medium, rich in solubilized protein, but a successful commercial process employs the gram-positive non-sporeforming short rod, *Brevibacterium luteum*.

Currently, the antibiotic, chloromycetin, is produced by chemical synthesis; all others are produced by fermentation. Successful commercial production of antibiotics (Chapter 12) depends on the selection of high-yielding strains, the utilization of optimum conditions of growth (including nutrition, temperature, pH, and degree of aeration), the utilization of efficient methods of extraction, and careful testing for efficacy and safety. Since the dollar value of the antibiotics marketed in 1960 exceeded that of all other pharmaceutical products combined, it is evident that no stone is left unturned in the search for strains producing new products or higher yields of accepted products. The medium usually employs corn steep liquor plus carbohydrate, peptone, buffer, antifoam, and mineral enrichment. Many of the details are trade secrets.

Microbiological Modification of Materials to Make More Valuable Products. Microorganisms were used empirically to modify or transform material for centuries before the existence of microorganisms was recognized. Bread dough has been leavened since before recorded history. Bits of dough from one fermenting mixture were preserved and used to inoculate the next lot of dough. Today the manufacture of bread is no longer an art but an industry in which are various steps are controlled on the basis of experimentally derived information.

Fibers of flax and hemp are separated for weaving into linen in the process known as **retting**. The fibers are held together in bundles in the plant stem by pectin, a cementing material. When the stems are submerged in water, the bundles are broken down by the enzyme pectinase, which is released by *Clostridium* species growing in the soaking vats. The individual fibers can then be recovered and processed.

Hides for tanning are prepared by removal of hair, blood, and as much other extraneous material as possible. They are next soaked in tanks where bacteria digest out materials which would interfere with leather manufacturing.

The manufacture of alcoholic beverages comprises one of the largest industrial applications of microbiological activity. The nondistilled alcoholic beverages produced in largest volume are wine and beer. Wine can be made from many fruit and berry juices, but most of it is made from grape juice. Fermented apple juice gives hard cider, and fermentation of a solution of honey yields the historic beverage, mead.

The organism responsible for the wine fermentation is *Saccharomyces ellipsoides* (Fig. 21.3). The juice is treated with enough sulfur dioxide to inhibit undesirable organisms but not interfere with the growth of the yeast. Starter cultures can be added to the vat, or fermentation can be carried out by the yeasts naturally present. If all the fruit sugar is used up, a dry wine is formed. If fermentation is stopped while some unfermented sugar remains, the product is a sweet wine.

Beer is prepared by the fermentation of grain carbohydrates with selected strains of *Saccharomyces cerevisiae*. The starch of grain to be fermented by yeast is first hydrolyzed enzymatically. In the germination of barley, an abundance of amylase is formed. The barley is dried and ground to give malt. Malt is steeped with ground corn and rice to give wort, which is then fermented to give beer. Sake is a beer made from rice. The starch of rice is hydrolyzed to a fermentable form by fungal enzymes.

In recent years steroid hormones such as cortisone, hydrocortisone,

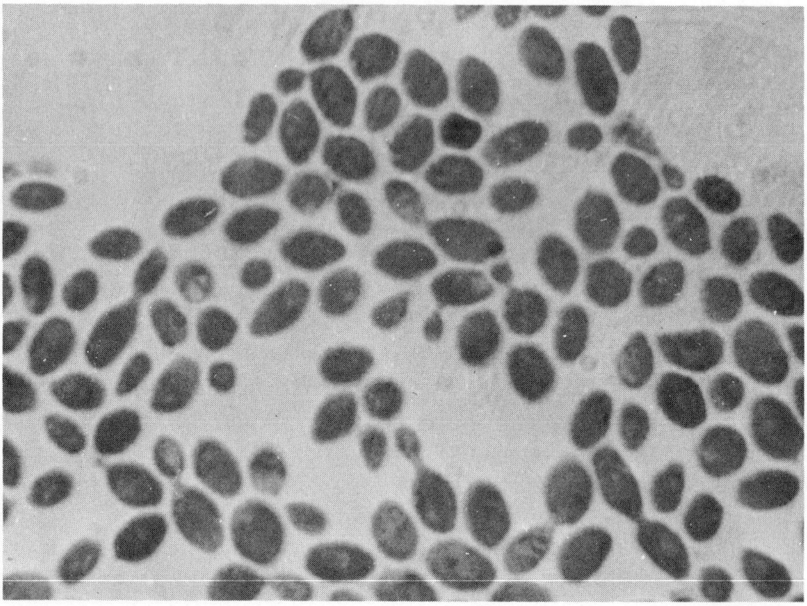

Fig. 21.3. A wine yeast. While French wines are fermented by the yeasts, naturally occurring on the grapes, American wines are often fermented by carefully selected strains cultured in the laboratories of the wineries.

and several other related hormones from the adrenal gland have occupied a prominent place in the therapy of a number of organic diseases. The naturally occurring hormones are difficult to recover from animal tissues and thus are too expensive for large-scale production. Synthesis likewise is difficult and expensive. A number of abundant, naturally occurring steroids can be converted to the hormone structure in part by microbial action. The industrial development of this transformation of the steroid molecule has made cortisone and related hormones available at a price the average patient can afford.

Use of Microorganisms to Eliminate Undesirable Materials. Industrial wastes containing substances toxic to the bacteria concerned in sewage purification cannot be disposed of in the same system as the domestic wastes. Such wastes may, however, be purified under conditions favoring the growth of types of organisms which destroy the toxic waste material. Phenolic wastes are disposed of successfully by an activated sludge type of treatment. The organisms concerned are probably species of *Pseudomonas.* Dilute formaldehyde can be rendered harmless by bacterial action. Detergent wastes, introduced into sewage systems both by housewives and industry, pose a threat when present in any appreciable amount. These compounds are also susceptible to bacterial decomposition. Patents have been issued on the disposal of garbage by fermentation. The compost which results is a valuable fertilizer.

Deteriorative Effects of Microorganisms. Microorganisms are responsible for much economic loss from the deterioration of textiles, leather, paper, painted surfaces, rubber, concrete, and metals. One of the most important organisms concerned in deteriorative processes is *Desulfovibrio desulfuricans.* This obligately anaerobic organism reduces sulfate to sulfide. The reduction process is extremely corrosive to concrete and to all buried or submerged metal.

SUMMARY. The problems of industrial microbiology are extremely varied. Some industrial microbiologists deal entirely with medical problems, as in the production of vaccines and other biologicals. Others are occupied in the production of useful chemical substances, and the microbes are used as an adjunct to the chemical industry. Their work is being extended to improving techniques for carrying out such historic processes as the retting of flax, tanning of hides, and brewing of beer. The development of new approaches in microbiology has revealed new methods for controlling deterioration. As mankind becomes more crowded on this planet, scientific modifications of the microbiological conversion of industrial wastes help relieve some of the problems of congestion.

22

Microbiology and Soil

The soil is the mother of all life, microbes, plants, animals, and men. The hypothesis on the origin of life with the greatest scientific support suggests that life originated in a "soup" of organic matter which collected on the surface of the earth during the early stages of the formation of this planet. Formed as a result of chemical reactions catalysed by the mineral elements, the organic matter was acted upon by the high temperatures, radiations, electrical discharges, and lack of oxygen in the atmosphere. Laboratory experiments imitating those conditions show very clearly that such synthesis does occur. As the earth cooled, complex aggregates were formed that maintained themselves and "grew," using the chemically synthesized organic matter as building material. Gradually these forms became more distinct from the organic soup and can be regarded as the primitive forms of life. At this level they lacked the ability to synthesize their own substance; they could only assimilate it from the environment, and, in this respect, they were autocatalytic nucleoproteins similar in some respects to the modern viruses (Fig. 22.1).

As certain necessary substances in the organic soup were depleted by being tied up in the bodies of these primitive microorganisms, growth ceased until in some organism, an enzyme, developed which could catalyze the formation of the necessary substance from smaller organic mole-

Fig. 22.1. The influenza virus is simple in structure and in a suitable environment (the mucous membranes of man) behaves as an autocatalytic nucleoprotein. *Photo courtesy Virus Lab, Univ. of Calif., Berkeley.*

cules in the soup. The acquisition of additional biosynthetic reactions and the necessary accompanying source of energy eventually yielded forms related to our heterotrophic anaerobes. Further evolution led to microbial photosynthesis by the photoorganotrophs; this was followed by the advent of photolithotrophic bacteria, and finally by green-plant photosynthesis. Green-plant photosynthesis produced oxygen, and, with the appearance of oxygen in the atmosphere, aerobic life was possible (Table 22.1).

The aerobes rapidly decomposed the nonliving organic matter in the organic soup, thus creating conditions favorable for autotrophic bacteria. In the other direction, with the development of higher animals and plants, strains of parasitic microbes developed. Further organic evolution is of direct concern to the microbiologist only insofar as higher plant and animal cells provided environments in which completely dependent viruses could again exist.

SOIL ECOLOGY

Myriads of microorganisms persist and thrive in the soil and the ocean sediments. The soil is composed of a mineral structure covered with a smear of organic matter. The spaces between the particles contain water and air. If the soil is very wet, the air is restricted and it is

Table 22.1. A Recent Theory on the Origin of Life

Probable Sequence of Events

1. The earth condenses and cools to the liquid and solid state.
2. Organic matter is synthesized by physicochemical reactions.
3. Organic soup condenses to aggregates which accumulate more of the organic material to themselves.
4. These aggregates develop membranes and acquire a chemical environment inside of the "cell" different from that outside. Catalytic reactions proceed to form complex molecules not present in the soup.
5. Anaerobic heterotrophic metabolism develops.
6. Photosynthetic pigments permit use of light for energy by photoorganotrophs.
7. When organic matter is used up, photolithotrophic bacteria (purple and green sulfur bacteria) develop.
8. The algae acquire additional enzymes and as a result gain independence of both organic matter and reduced sulfur. They give off oxygen (green-plant photosynthesis).
9. Aerobic life appears.
10. A few microbial types (autotrophs) acquire all enzymes necessary for chemolithotrophy (energy from oxidizing inorganic substances; carbon from CO_2).
11. Higher plants and animals provide an environment of organic compounds. Microbes invade these and lose synthetic abilities which are superfluous in parasitism. Some obligate parasites and viruses lose all or almost all synthetic ability, thus approximating the first forms.

anaerobic; if it is dry it is aerobic. Every soil particle presents a special environment for the growth of microorganisms. One side of a particle may be aerobic, the other anaerobic. One particle may have high sugar content; another may be suited only for autotrophic growth. Where organic matter is decomposing, heat is produced and a thermophilic environment is available. Not far away the temperature may be suitable for mesophiles. One soil particle may be acid, another alkaline. Thus the soil is not analogous to a large test tube of broth but rather to millions of tiny test tubes each with distinctive growth conditions. Thus thousands of diverse types of microbes can and do persist and flourish in the soil (Fig. 22.2).

Such conditions are not static. When the dead body of a worm begins to decay, aerobic species rapidly use up the oxygen in the soil, and other organisms which are anaerobic continue the putrefaction process. If the area is well insulated and enough heat is produced, the anaerobic mesophiles may yield to thermophilic species. As the products of decomposition diffuse, they are in turn attacked by still other organisms. When the thermophiles complete their life cycle, their dead cell structures and the residue of food unavailable to them are

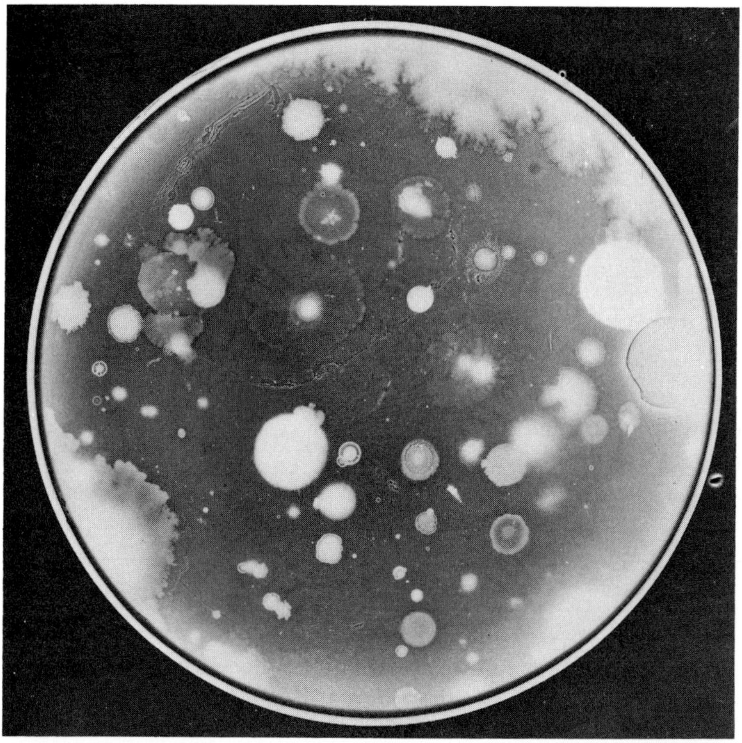

Fig. 22.2. A plate count of soil shows numerous and diverse organisms. On this plate are only the aerobic organisms that will grow on nutrient agar at 37°C. For every organism that gave rise to a colony on this plate there are in the soil at least 10 that failed to grow under these conditions.

attacked by other organisms. As the processes slow down, oxygen diffuses into the area faster than it is consumed, and aerobic microorganisms finally convert all the carbon to CO_2. In the absence of organic matter, autotrophic bacteria oxidize the ammonia or sulfur for energy, and use CO_2 to build their structure. So cycles of growth and death continue, each type or organism growing explosively when conditions are favorable and yielding to a better-adapted growth type as the environment is changed.

THE SOIL ORGANISMS

The outer layers of the earth contain the soil microbes. An acre furrow slice (the upper 6 inches) of a rich upland soil contains about

400 pounds of bacteria, 4000 pounds of fungi, and an equal amount of protozoa and actinomycetes. The bacteria exist as microcolonies attached to the soil particles. In plate counts of soil the colonies are broken up in the dilution bottle, and the number of living organisms can be counted. Up to 100 million bacteria may be found per gram of rich soil, but even on the best medium these make up only one-tenth the number that can be seen microscopically. Counts of molds and actinomycetes are less significant because the numbers depend on fragmentation of the mycelium. Direct microscopic examination of the soil reveals that the bacteria exist attached to solid particles as small colonies of from 10 to 1000 individual cells. Wet swampy soil contains mostly anaerobes; under such conditions organic matter accumulates. Organic accumulations in such wet areas are called peat; the slowly decomposing residual organic matter of upland soils is called humus. If the soil is well aerated, aerobic bacteria are more abundant, and filaments of molds and actinomycetes bridge the gaps between the soil particles. Especially high bacterial counts are found on particles of animal and plant material in the soil; plant roots excrete food material for microbes, and higher numbers of organisms are found near roots of living plants.

Enrichment Cultures. Although the soil contains a vast array of organisms, certain individual processes can be studied, and the organisms can be isolated by the enrichment-culture procedure. For example, adding relatively high concentrations of ammonia to the soil favors the growth of the ammonia-oxidizing bacteria; the soil will teem with them, and they can be observed and isolated. Such studies can be carried out with any other material on which microbes are active. The soil may be enriched with organisms that destroy plastics, bacterial capsules, mold mycelium, vitamins, or any other material by the same procedure. Or an enrichment culture may be developed by inoculating some soil into a medium containing the material on which microbes are active. After several days a transfer is made into a new flask of the same medium. Repetition will yield a subculture predominantly of one type of microorganism, which can be isolated into pure culture by plating or dilution techniques.

Soil microorganisms may be controlled by (1) limitation of desirable growth conditions, (2) bacteriophages that invade the cells, and (3) protozoa and slime molds that eat the cells. In addition to decreased food supply, the same factors which affect growth and death in the test tube are operative in the soil. Soils that become acid as a result of deposits of pine needles contain many less microbes than neutral soils. Very dry or very wet, very cold or very hot soils have lowered counts. Although data on the virus population of the soil is scanty, we do know that soil bacteria and actinomycetes are susceptible to bacteriophage attack and phage can be isolated from soil (Fig. 22.3). The total weight of the soil protozoa probably exceeds the total weight of the soil bacteria.

Our Interest in Soil Organisms. We are interested in soil microbes for the following reasons:

1. A few soil microorganisms are pathogenic to man. These include the bacteria causing botulism, tetanus, and gas gangrene. In addition certain molds cause skin diseases and deep mycoses. *Histoplasma* and *Actinomyces* also have their habitat in the soil. Many plant pathogens reside in the soil.

2. The production of microbial capsules improves the soil tilth. The physical condition of the soil, especially the formation of a desirable crumbly soil for a seed bed, is promoted by microbial growth.

3. The production of acids by soil organisms dissolves minerals necessary for plant nutrition. The mineral particles which contain in-

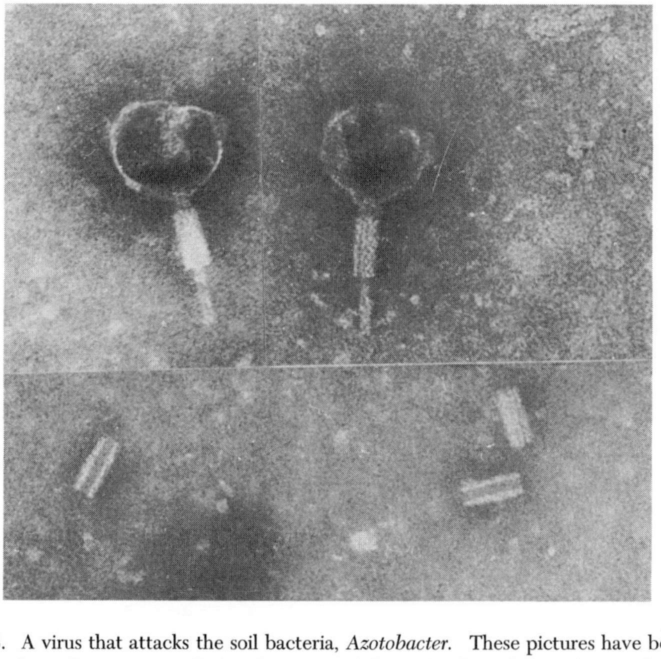

Fig. 22.3. A virus that attacks the soil bacteria, *Azotobacter*. These pictures have been prepared to show the contracted sheathes around the tail. It is believed that the sheath attaches itself to the bacterial cell wall and then contracts, pushing the central tube of the tail through the cell wall, thus creating an entrance for the phage DNA.

soluble forms of the important plant foods, potassium and phosphorus, are dissolved into the soil solution from corners of soil particles where microorganisms produce a local acid reaction.

4. The cycles of growth and death of microorganisms tie up plant nutrient materials in the bodies of microbes, conserving them against leaching from the soil.

5. Trace nutrients are released in forms that can be used for the growth of plants in the cycles of growth and death. For example, some plants can absorb nitrogen only in the form of nitrates. Microbes split ammonia from decomposing proteins, and autotrophic bacteria oxidize the ammonia to nitrate.

6. Ninety per cent of the carbon dioxide in the air (the raw material of photosynthesis) is released from organic matter through the decomposing activities of soil microorganisms.

7. The microbes also function in other cycles of the elements.

THE CARBON CYCLE

The building of organic matter from CO_2 is primarily the function of green plants and algae. A few bacteria are photosynthetic, and the chemolithotropic bacteria use CO_2 as their sole source of carbon. However, the amount of organic matter built by these two groups of bacteria is negligible. The major chemical activity of the other microbes is the release of CO_2. The amount of CO_2 produced by the respiration of animals is negligible compared to that released by respiration and fermentation of microbes. Without this return of CO_2 to the atmosphere, the carbon cycle would be interrupted and photosynthesis would cease since all carbon would be tied up as organic matter. The carbon cycle is integrated with the oxygen cycle since photosynthesis by green plants uses CO_2 and produces oxygen. Plant, microbial, and animal respiration reverse this process.

THE SULFUR CYCLE

In living material sulfur is found in the proteins. After death, putrefactive bacteria split the sulfur from the protein in the form of evil-smelling hydrogen sulfide. Hydrogen sulfide is also produced in marine environments and in the soil by the anaerobe, *Desulfovibrio,* which uses sulfate in its anaerobic metabolism as the hydrogen acceptor thus:

$$H_2SO_4 + 8H \rightarrow H_2S + 4H_2O$$

Hydrogen sulfide is oxidized to elemental sulfur (S) and to sulfate by photolithotrophic and chemolithotrophic sulfur bacteria. Sulfate is assimilated by green plants and by bacteria and built into the protein molecules.

NITROGEN TRANSFORMATIONS

The protoplasm of living cells is primarily protein, and proteins are polymers of amino acids. Some microorganisms and all plants are able to manufacture their amino acids from ammonia. All animals and many microorganisms need preformed amino acids as part of their food and secure these from those organisms having synthetic ability. Most microbial proteins are nucleoproteins, composed of protein combined with one or the other of the nucleic acids, RNA and DNA. Both of these acids contain nitrogen, which enters the molecule as ammonia or as an amino acid. When amino acids or nucleic acids are decomposed by microorganisms, ammonia is released. Ammonia plays a central role in the nitrogen conversions in nature (Fig. 22.4).

Ammonification. Most of the nitrogen in the biological world makes the circuit from ammonia to amino acids to protein and back again to amino acids and ammonia. While in protein form, it may be digested and rebuilt many times from plant to herbivorous animal to carnivorous animal proteins. A small amount is excreted by animals in the form of urea or uric acid from which microorganisms split the nitrogen as ammonia. The proteins from dead animals and plants are decomposed by microorganisms, and much is used to build the protein of microbial cells in the soil. When proteinaceous material is present in excess in the soil, ammonia is released. Ammonification, the process of splitting ammonia from proteinaceous material, is carried out by a wide variety of microorganisms.

Nitrification. When ammonia accumulates in the soil and carbohydrate material is in short supply, autotrophic microorganisms thrive and secure their energy by oxidizing ammonia to nitrite and oxidizing the nitrite to nitrate. This process of nitrification supplies nitrates for those plants which cannot assimilate ammonia through the plant roots. The chemolithotrophic *Nitrosomonas* and *Nitrobacter* are associated with this process, but other organisms may participate.

Nitrate Reduction. Any plant that secures nitrogen from the soil in the form of nitrate must be capable of reducing the nitrate to ammonia in order to utilize it in building amino acids. A wide variety of soil microorganisms also have the enzyme, nitrate reductase, which reduces nitrate to ammonia. Under anaerobic conditions when nitrate is used as the final hydrogen acceptor, much more nitrate is reduced by the microorganisms than can be built into amino acids; as a consequence

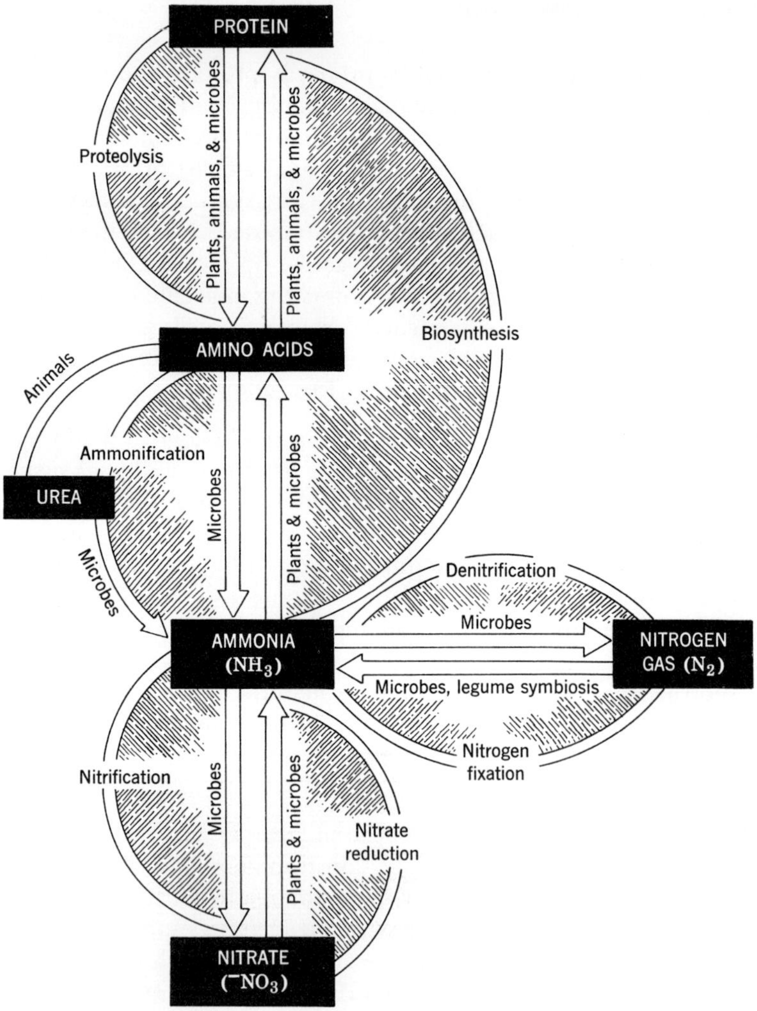

Fig. 22.4. As nitrogen metabolism is more clearly defined, it is evident that we are dealing with a series of cycles, or rather excursions, from ammonia and the amino acids. Plants may take in nitrates through their roots; this must be reduced to ammonia before building it into amino acids and proteins. Many of the processes are carried out only by microbes; plants and animals are more restricted.

ammonia is excreted into the soil. This process of anaerobic respiration is carried out by many anaerobic and facultative organisms.

Denitrification. In anaerobic soils the reduction of nitrate by some organisms is diverted at the nitrite level to release nitrogen gas (N_2) into the atmosphere. The chemistry of this reaction is not known, but many facultative anaerobes participate. This reaction is detrimental to soil fertility since nitrogen is utilized as a plant nutrient only in the form of nitrate or ammonia. Denitrification occurs to a lesser extent in well-drained, well-aerated soils. Soil chemists refer to gaseous nitrogen which escapes to the atmosphere as "free" nitrogen to differentiate it from the "fixed" nitrogen which remains in the soil. Some geologists believe that all the free nitrogen now present in air (80% of the atmosphere or 12 pounds over every square inch of the earth's surface) was released from the fixed nitrogen of the soil by denitrifying bacteria.

Nitrogen Fixation. Atmospheric nitrogen (N_2) can be fixed by chemical processes into forms such as ammonia for use as plant fertilizer. A small amount is also fixed by electrical storms. But unless some other mechanism had been available for replenishing the fixed nitrogen of the soil, life would have persisted on this earth only with great difficulty until that time when chemists learned the secret of nitrogen fixation. Biological nitrogen fixation restores to the soil a large part of that lost by denitrification; since modern agricultural practice encourages nitrogen fixation, soils actually become richer in nitrogen in spite of the removal of quantities of the element in agricultural products.

The Symbiotic System. The most important fixation of nitrogen in agricultural areas involves the use of **legume plants**, such as alfalfa, clovers, peas, beans, peanuts, and lentils. These plants cannot fix nitrogen by themselves; only when gram-negative bacteria called **rhizobia** invade their roots and form **nodules** is nitrogen fixed by the combined efforts of plant and bacteria. This is called symbiosis since both partners benefit; the bacterium secures carbohydrate, and the plant becomes independent of soil nitrogen.

When the bacterium invades a root hair of the plant, it induces the plant to produce a tumor-like swelling (the nodule) in which the bacteria multiply. The vascular system of the plant connects the nodule with the food-bearing transport system of the root and stem. While most soils contain rhizobia which would form nodules on legume plants, the modern farmer does not depend on these (wild type) strains. Instead he buys cultures of bacteria selected because of their efficiency in fixing large amounts of nitrogen when in symbiosis with legumes. Such legume inoculation consisting of the bacteria mixed with moist humus is spread over the seed to be available for invading the rootlets as soon as the seeds germinate.

Not all legume plants are susceptible to invasion and nodule formation by the same rhizobia. The genus, *Rhizobium*, has been divided into species on the basis of the legume species which are invaded; for example, one species associates with alfalfa, another with the clovers, another with soybeans, etc. The legume-rhizobium symbiosis appears to have evolved from an earlier parasitic association. Early ancestors of the bacterium may have produced a disease involving tumors of the plant roots; from this evolved a parasitic association not harmful to the plant, and finally modifications in the plant and bacterium led to the symbiosis.

Nonsymbiotic Fixation. Several types of free-living microorganisms in the soil can use gaseous nitrogen as their only nitrogen source. Where they grow vigorously they make a significant contribution to the fixed nitrogen of the soil. On the surface of the soil and in surface waters the blue-green algae and the photosynthetic bacteria make a small contribution to the total fixed nitrogen. These organisms use both CO_2 and N_2 from the air as their principal source of carbon and

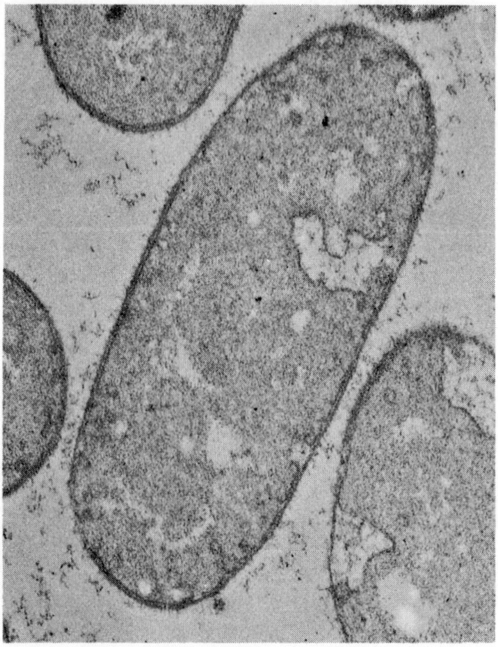

Fig. 22.5. An electron micrograph of *Azotobacter vinelandii.*

nitrogen when light is available for energy. They live essentially on air and water.

Under anaerobic conditions certain species of the genus, *Clostridium*, (gram-positive, anaerobic, sporeforming rods) fix significant amounts of nitrogen and restore at least part of that lost by denitrification. Under aerobic conditions organisms of the genus, *Azotobacter*, (gram-negative aerobic organisms with an unusually large cell of 2 to 5 microns) fix nitrogen vigorously when carbohydrate is abundant (Fig. 22.5). Several other bacterial species have been found to fix nitrogen under laboratory conditions, but whether they make any contribution to the nitrogen economy of the soil has not been assessed.

SUMMARY. Soil microbiology deals with the organisms occupying the thousands of different environments which exist on and around the soil particles. The microbe population of the soil is a dynamic system involving myriads of sequences of growth and death. With the exceptions of the algae and the autotrophic bacteria, soil microbes are involved primarily with the destruction of organic matter. This releases the elements tied up in the biological material so that they may participate further in living systems. Although the soil serves as a reservoir for plant pathogens, the overall result of the activities of soil microbes is beneficial to the growth of plants whose root systems draw nutrients from the soil.

Index